THE COMMERCIAL PILOT'S

C000302614

VOL. 2

PISTON ENGINES
GAS TURBINE ENGINES
PROPELLERS

THE COMMERCIAL PILOT'S STUDY MANUAL SERIES

Vol. 2

PISTON ENGINES GAS TURBINE ENGINES PROPELLERS

MIKE BURTON

Airlife
England

Copyright © 1997 Mike Burton

First published in the UK in 1997
by Airlife Publishing Ltd

British Library Cataloguing-in Publication Data
A catalogue record for this book
is available from the British Library

ISBN 1 85310 780 8

All rights reserved. No part of this book may be reproduced or transmitted in
any form or by any means, electronic or mechanical including photocopying,
recording or by any information storage and retrieval system, without permis-
sion from the Publisher in writing.

Typeset by Phoenix Typesetting, Ilkley, West Yorkshire.
Printed in England by Livesey Ltd, Shrewsbury.

Airlife Publishing Ltd
101 Longden Road, Shrewsbury SY3 9EB, England.

Contents

Part 1 Piston Engines

CONTENTS

Part 3 Propellers

Part 1

1

Aircraft Piston Engines

1.1 Classification.

The cylinder configuration of aircraft piston engines takes many forms. Figure 1-1 shows some of the layouts that may be used.

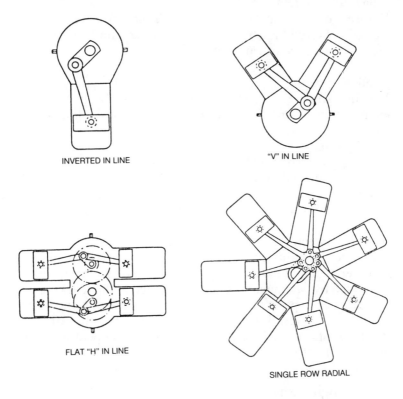

INVERTED IN LINE

"V" IN LINE

FLAT "H" IN LINE

SINGLE ROW RADIAL

Figure 1–1 Typical Cylinder Arrangements.

It is usual to classify a piston aero-engine by its method of cooling and the arrangement of its cylinders, for example, air cooled radial; liquid cooled in-line; etc. Engines may be further classified by stating the number of cylinders, whether normally aspirated, supercharged or turbocharged.

1.2 General Functional Description.

All internal combustion piston engines consist of the following systems or sub-systems:

(a) Mechanical System.
For converting the heat of combustion into power. It consists of the cylinders, valve gear, pistons, connecting rods, crankshaft, propeller shaft, etc. The pistons and crank assembly convert the combustion pressure to torque, which is transmitted to the propeller either by direct drive, or through a reduction gear.

(b) Lubrication system.
Ensures the efficient lubrication of all moving parts. The work wasted in overcoming friction is thus reduced, and the heat generated by friction kept within reasonable limits.

(c) Cooling System.
For dissipating excess heat and maintaining effective control of engine temperature. Air or liquid is used as the cooling medium.

(d) Fuel System.
To supply a correct fuel/air mixture to the cylinders. The correct mixture is ensured by metering the fuel, by means of a carburettor or injector, in proportion with the amount of air inducted into the engine. The induction system directs the mixture to the cylinders.

(e) Ignition System.
To ignite the inducted charge. The fuel/air mixture within each cylinder is ignited by two spark plugs. High tension voltage, generated by two magnetos and distributed to the sparking plugs, produces the spark at the plug points. The ignition system is controlled by ignition switches; when the switches are in the 'OFF' position, the magnetos are rendered inoperative and the engine will not run.

1.3 The Engine Structure.

All aero-engines are made up of units and sub-assemblies arranged for convenience of dismantling, rig testing, and assembling. Each unit has provision for its assembly to its parent sub-assembly, which has similar provisions for assembly to the crankcase or to another sub-assembly.

The layout of sub-assemblies making up an engine, and the number of them, varies considerably according to the engine type etc, but general layout, taken from front to rear, for a geared and supercharged engine is as follows:

(a) Propeller shaft and reduction gear assembly.

(b) Crankcase, which houses the crankshaft and connecting rods etc.

(c) Supercharger assembly.

(d) Wheelcase or rear cover assembly, on which are mounted the magnetos, various fuel and oil system components, and other accessories.

(e) The cylinders mounted on the crankcase; either individually or in blocks depending on the design of the engine. In addition to the above assemblies, a front cover is interposed between the reduction gear assembly and the crankcase to house the valve operating mechanism. The carburettor or injector is normally mounted on the rear of the engine.

1.4   Engine Mounting.

Aircraft piston engines are normally attached to the airframe via an engine bearer assembly. The engine bearer is then attached to the front bulkhead of the aircraft fuselage, in the case of a single-engined aircraft, or to engine bulkheads in the case of engines mounted on the wings.

The bulkhead not only serves as a mounting point for the engine but also provides a fire resistant wall between the engine and the cockpit or area behind the engine. Figure 1-2 shows an example of the engine bearer and firewall or bulkhead.

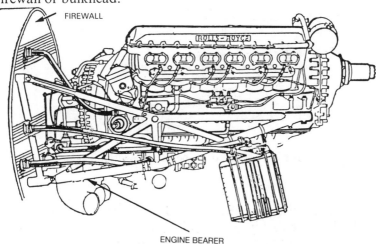

Figure 1–2 Engine Bearer and Firewall.

3

2

Four-Stroke Piston Engines
Part One: Basic Principles

2.1 Introduction.

An internal combustion engine consists basically of a cylinder closed at one end, a piston, which slides up and down inside the cylinder, a connecting rod and crank by which reciprocating movement of the piston is converted to rotary movement of the crankshaft. The closed end of the cylinder, known as the cylinder head, includes an inlet and exhaust valve, and a sparking plug. Figure 2-1 shows the basic arrangement of a single cylinder.

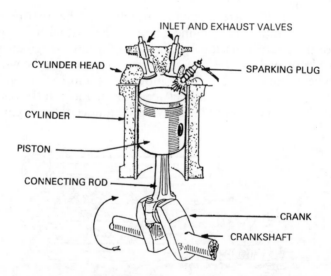

Figure 2–1 Basic Components of the Piston Engine.

The purpose of a piston engine is to convert heat energy into mechanical energy, by burning fuel in the cylinder, and utilising the resultant pressure of combustion to drive the arrangement of piston, connecting rod, and crankshaft.

2.2   The Four-Stroke Cycle.

The sequence of operations, by which the heat energy is converted into mechanical energy, is known as the four-stroke cycle. A mixture of fuel and air, known as 'the mixture', is introduced into the cylinder, the mixture is compressed, and when at maximum compression the mixture is ignited; the heat thereby generated causes a rapid and immense increase in pressure which drives the piston down the cylinder. This cyclic sequence can be divided into four separate, but mechanically related, operations normally referred to as INDUCTION, COMPRESSION, POWER and EXHAUST.

2.3   Principle of Operation.

The basic principle of operation of the four-stroke engine is as follows:

(a) Induction. (See Fig. 2-2).
At the start of the induction stroke, the inlet valve is opened, and the piston descends down the cylinder thereby causing a drop in pressure which results in the mixture being driven by atmospheric pressure into the cylinder through the inlet valve. The power output of the engine depends on the weight of mixture introduced into the cylinder or cylinders.

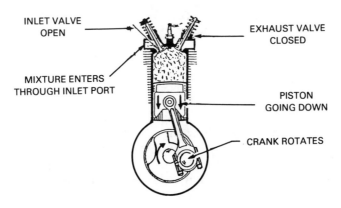

Figure 2–2 Induction Stroke.

(b) Compression. (See Fig. 2-3).
As the piston completes its induction stroke, it now starts to move up the cylinder. The inlet valve closes and the mixture is compressed. By compressing the mixture into a smaller space, the pressure it exerts when burnt is proportionally increased.

5

When the piston is at its lowest point of travel (ie maximum space in the cylinder) it is known as being at Bottom Dead Centre (BDC). When the piston is at its highest point of travel (ie minimum space in the cylinder) it is known as being at Top Dead Centre (TDC).

The ratio of the cylinder volume, when the piston is at BDC, to that when at TDC, is known as the COMPRESSION RATIO. It should be noted that this is a ratio of volumes, and not a measure of increase of pressure in the cylinder. As the mixture becomes compressed, it is heated adiabatically, as well as by conduction from hot surroundings, the pressure consequently rises to a higher value than that to be expected from volumetric reduction alone.

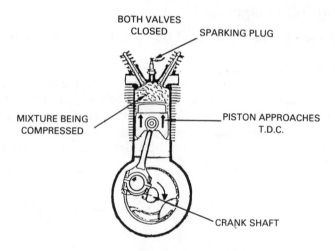

Figure 2-3 Compression Stroke.

(c) **Power or Ignition. (See Fig. 2-4).**
A spark at the sparking plug ignites the compressed mixture and combustion causes a rapid expansion of gas pressure in the combustion chamber. As both valves remain closed, the increased gas pressure forces the piston down the cylinder.

Note: As the piston is forced down the cylinder the gas temperature will reduce.

(d) **Exhaust. (See Fig. 2-5).**
The exhaust valve opens and the ascending piston forces the gases, now at a much reduced pressure, out past the open exhaust valve into the exhaust manifold and thence to atmosphere.

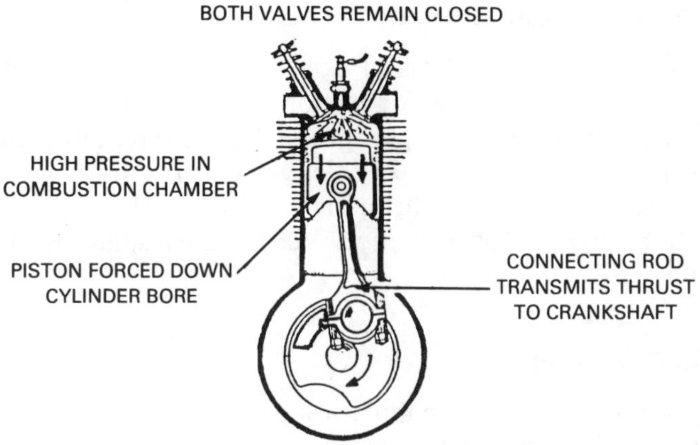

BOTH VALVES REMAIN CLOSED

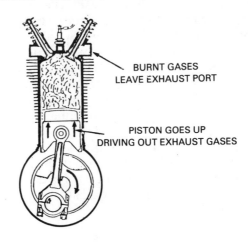

HIGH PRESSURE IN
COMBUSTION CHAMBER

PISTON FORCED DOWN
CYLINDER BORE

CONNECTING ROD
TRANSMITS THRUST
TO CRANKSHAFT

Figure 2–4   Power Stroke.

INLET VALVE CLOSED — EXHAUST VALVE OPEN

BURNT GASES
LEAVE EXHAUST PORT

PISTON GOES UP
DRIVING OUT EXHAUST GASES

Figure 2–5   Exhaust Stroke.

2.4   The 'Otto' Cycle.

The basic principle of the four-stroke cycle explained in paragraph two of this chapter is termed the 'Otto' cycle, after Dr N.A. Otto who built the first successful engine working on the four stroke cycle in 1876.

2.5   Practical Application of the 'Otto' Cycle.

It is important that the inlet and exhaust valve open and close at the correct time to ensure efficient operation of the engine. In the theoretical four stroke cycle explained in paragraph 2.2 these requirements are met by admitting mixture through the inlet valve orifice from TDC to BDC, and expelling the burnt gases through the exhaust valve orifice from BDC to TDC, but practical considerations necessitate a slight departure from this timing.

2.6   Valve Timing.

The diagrams in Figs 2-5a & b illustrating the four-stroke cycle show that the opening and closing of the inlet and exhaust valves is related to the position of the piston in the cylinder and hence the position of the engine crankshaft.

(a) Inlet Valve.
Early opening of the inlet valve ensures that the valve is fully open at the beginning of the induction stroke, there is then no time lag between the piston moving down and the mixture flowing into the cylinder as would otherwise occur due to the inertia of the mixture. The inflowing mixture is therefore able to keep up with the descending piston. The momentum of the mixture increases as the induction stroke progresses, and at the end of the stroke, is such that the gases will continue to flow into the cylinder even though the piston has passed BDC and is starting to move upwards. The closing of the valve is therefore delayed until after BDC when the gas pressure equals the gas pressure in the induction manifold. By allowing such a delay in closing the inlet valve, the maximum possible weight of charge is introduced into the cylinder.

See Figs 2-5a & b

(b) Exhaust Valve.
Towards the end of the power stroke, the temperature and pressure of the burnt gases have decreased, the crank angle becomes less effective, and little purpose would be served in keeping the exhaust valve closed until BDC. It is advantageous, however, to open the exhaust valve before BDC and use the residual gas pressure to commence the scavenging operation before the piston starts moving up the cylinder. This reduces back pressure on the piston during the exhaust stroke when it has to push the gases out. The valve will close a little after TDC because the gas will

8

continue to flow out due to its momentum – even after the upward movement of the piston has ceased.

See Figs. 2-5a & b

(c) Valve Overlap.
There is a period during which both valves are open at the same time, this is known as VALVE OVERLAP. During this overlap period, the action of the exhaust gases flowing out of the cylinder tends to reduce the gas pressure in the induction manifold. The mixture in the induction manifold commences to flow into the area of low pressure and assists in displacing the remaining burnt gases.

See Figs. 2-5a & b

(d) Effective Ignition and Valve Timing.
There are critical conditions that affect timing. They are:
(i) The limit to the speed of opening and closing of valves, beyond which excessive stresses would be imposed on the operating gear.
(ii) When a valve is almost closed mixture flow is minimal.
(iii) Time lag between ignition and the build up to maximum pressure.

There are two periods during one crankshaft revolution, when the piston movement is so small that little work is done in either induction, or exhaust. These periods occur in the top and bottom regions of the stroke, when the crank is within the range known as the INEFFECTIVE CRANK ANGLE (See Fig. 2-5a.)

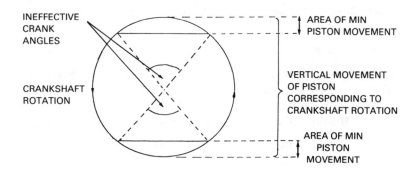

Figure 2–5a Crank Angles.

These two periods offer a suitable opportunity for the valve operation, without excessive accelerations, and following the compression stroke, the mixture may be ignited before TDC, so that the maximum pressure build up is realised at the early part of the power stroke.

The practical timing, is as shown, and can be followed using Figs. 2-5a & b.

(e) Ignition Timing.

Ignition is so regulated to advance as the engine speed increases in order to ensure that adequate burn time is provided for the mixture in the cylinder. Equally, as engine speed reduces the ignition is retarded. It must be noted that the spark, even in its fully retarded position, will occur before top dead centre. Study Fig. 2-5b.

Induction. The inlet valve opens before TDC of the exhaust stroke, and remains open during some 70° of the compression stroke. This delay, or **valve lag**, is to enable the momentum of the mixture to add to the weight of charge, thus increasing volumetric efficiency.

Compression. On the compression stroke, the spark occurs before TDC to allow the build up of pressure from the burning charge to reach its maximum early in the power stroke; this is known as **ignition advance**.

Power. Before BDC on this stroke, the exhaust valve opens (**valve lead**). This induces pressure scavenging of the combustion chamber (cylinder).

Exhaust. As can be seen, the exhaust valve remains open until some 30° into the induction stroke, this is known as **valve overlap**. The partial vacuum left in the cylinder by the rapid exit of the burnt gases, induces the fresh charge to enter.

2.7   Piston Engine Components.

Aero-engines are constructed of units and sub-assemblies arranged mainly for the convenience of dismantling when replacement and/or rectification becomes necessary. The number of units, or sub-assemblies, varies with the type of engine, but a general breakdown is as follows:

(a)   Engine block, housing the cylinders, pistons, valves and valve gear operating mechanisms.

(b)   Crankcase, housing the crankshaft and connecting rods.

Other units comprise components to be dealt with in subsequent chapters.

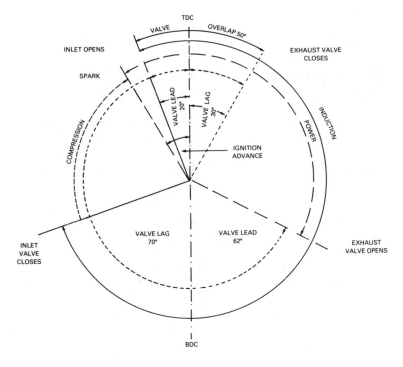

Figure 2–5b Ignition and Valve Timing.

2.8   The Cylinder.

The cylinder provides the combustion chamber and the working bore for the piston. Although considered as one unit, cylinders are in fact in two sections, the cylinder barrel, and the cylinder head, the latter being bolted and sealed gas-tight to the former. The cylinder barrels are usually made of steel, and may have a hardened bore to increase their resistance to the wear of the piston. Cylinder heads are usually made of a light alloy – aluminium – primarily for lightness of weight, and heat conductivity. The head also comprises the valve seatings, and valve guides to form a bearing for the valve stems. The seatings are made of material strong enough to withstand both the constant hammering of the valves and the corrosive action of the exhaust gases. Threaded inserts, of a more durable metal, are fitted to take the spark plugs. The cylinder head also supports valves and rocker gear, and sometimes the camshaft and its drive. To facilitate cooling the cylinder heads of air-cooled engines are finned to increase the surface area exposed to the airstream, whereas in liquid-cooled engines the heads have generous passages for the coolant fluid. Cooling is dealt with in Chapter 6.

2.9   The Piston.

The piston (Fig. 2-1) forms a gas-tight plug in the cylinder, and is made of a forged aluminium alloy to increase strength, and for lightness in weight and heat conductivity. Due to the higher linear expansion of aluminium relative to steel, pistons are tapered slightly towards the crown to enable parallel operation (to the cylinder wall) at operating temperatures. The crown of the piston may be shaped to suit the cylinder and to give valve head clearance. Pistons are fitted with piston rings (gas rings) fitted into grooves around the head to maintain a gas seal between piston and cylinder. The rings are made usually of cast-iron, which retains its springiness at high temperatures, and due to its low coefficient of linear expansion, only a relatively small 'gap' is required. The rings when new, have a slight taper of the face which contacts the cylinder, giving a rapid initial wear that allows the ring to wear to the bore quickly and does away with 'running in'. Another type of ring fitted is the scraper ring, which prevents an excessive amount of oil passing from crankcase to combustion chamber. Scraper rings are designed in various sections according to the action required – heavy or light; it is usual to have a single-action ring on the skirt allowing some oil to pass to the thrust face of the piston, and a double-action scraper above the gudgeon pin for final heavy scraping. As can be seen in Fig. 2-6 pistons are formed with bosses to accept the gudgeon pin, linking the connecting rod to the piston. Gudgeon pins 'float' inside the piston for even wear, being retained by circlips. They are made of steel, and are hollow, thus increasing rigidity and the bearing surface of the small end, without strength decrease for the same cross-sectional area. On multi-cylinder engines, pistons are of matched weight, to ensure balance, and minimise vibration.

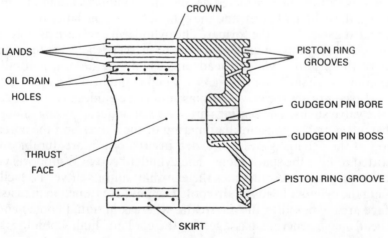

Figure 2–6   Piston Assembly.

12

2.10   Valves.

Valves (Fig. 2-7) open and close the gas ports, and are either of two types: sleeve valves, or poppet valves. Sleeve valves take the form of a ported sleeve, moving within the cylinder between piston and wall. The poppet valve is the more commonly used. It is made of special alloy steel, of great strength at high temperatures, non-scaling, and resistant to corrosion. The exhaust valve may be sodium filled, which assists in valve head cooling.

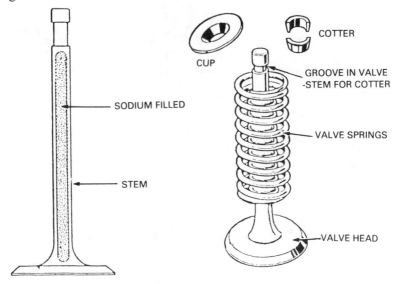

Figure 2–7 Poppet Valves.

2.11   Valve Gear Construction and Operation.

As can be seen in Fig. 2-8 the valves are operated by what is collectively termed the valve gear, a detailed drawing of which is shown in Fig. 2-9. The valve operating mechanism is driven by the engine crankshaft through a cam, push rod, and rocker arm assembly.

It should be noted at this point that as each valve opens only once during the four-stroke cycle, through gearing reduction the camshaft rotates at half the speed of the crankshaft.

The opening of the valve is carried out by the rocker forcing the valve stem down against the resistance of the valve spring. The closing of the valve is activated by the valve spring as pressure by the rocker is reduced. When the valve is fully closed and the rocker is in its fully up position there is a gap between the top of the valve spring and the rocker (Fig. 2-9). This gap allows for expansion during the full operating temperature range of the engine, and permits oil from the engine lubrication system to lubricate the two faces.

Normally valve springs are duplicated by fitting one spring inside the other. The primary purpose of this is to reduce valve bounce, but it also has a certain safety value should one spring break while the engine is running.

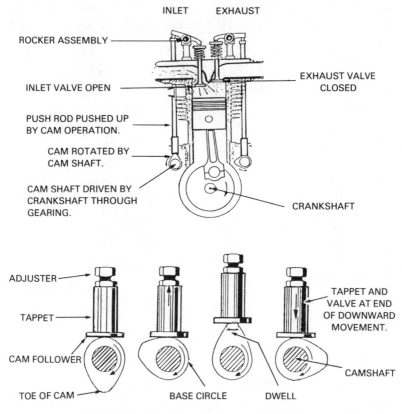

Figure 2-8 Valve and Cam Operation on
Induction Stroke.

The exhaust valve is subjected to very high temperatures and to assist in its cooling it is manufactured with a hollow stem which is partially filled with sodium.

The valve operating mechanism consists of: camshaft (or a cam drum), tappets, push rods and rocker arms. The profile of the cam lobe controls the period (in crankshaft degrees) of opening, the rate of opening and the lift of the valves. Camshafts always run at half engine speed. In direct contact with the cams are the tappets, these being kept in contact by means of the valve springs. The tappets translate the eccentricity of

14

the cam into a reciprocating motion, this motion being transferred to the valves by the push rods and rocker arms. Play is always present when the tappets are on the 'dwell' of the cam, which will ensure the valves positively close (by valve spring action). The play is known as tappet clearance. The rocker arms are pivoted on a lay shaft, one side being in contact with the push rod, the other with the valve stem base. Thus 'upward' movement of the push rod will open the valve against valve spring pressure, the downward movement allowing the valve to be closed under the same spring pressure. Valve springs are made of spring steel, and as seen above, ensure the valve remains closed unless opened by cam action. They are duplicated, and may be wound in opposite directions to reduce valve bounce. Springs are retained by tapered colletts that lock in place between cup plates and grooves in the valve stem. (Fig. 2-7).

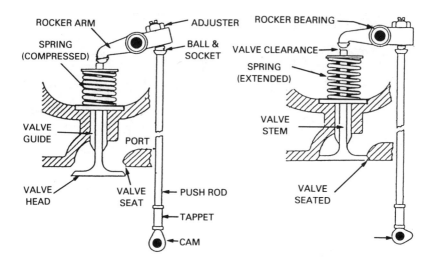

Figure 2–9 Valve Operating Mechanism.

2.12   Crankcase.

The crankcase forms the foundation of the engine. It is made of light alloy for weight and thermal conductivity, and is single or multi-section construction dependent on engine type. The crankcase houses the main bearings for crankshaft support and also provides the support for the cylinders. Main bearings vary with engine type. In-line engines have plain bearings whereas radial engines have roller bearings. The crankcase also provides support for the front and rear casings, the supercharger, sump and reduction gears etc, as required.

2.13   Crankshaft.

See Fig. 2-10. The crankshaft, via the connecting rods, changes piston reciprocating movement, into rotary motion. They are alloy steel forgings and may have hardened crankpins and journals for wear resistance. Classified according to the number of cranks it has, a shaft with one crankpin is termed a 'single throw' shaft, with six crankpins a 'six' throw. Fig. 2-10 shows a 'four' throw crankshaft. Drives at each end of the shaft transmit the rotary motion (torque) respectively to the propeller, and to the accessory drives (magnetos, oil and fuel pumps etc.). Aero-engine shafts are usually hollow, making for a stronger, lighter shaft with large bearing surfaces of long life, the bore being a convenient oil passage for lubrication purposes.

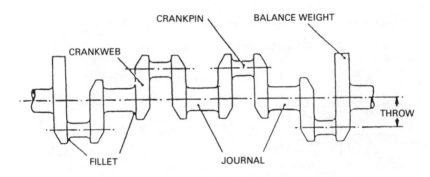

Figure 2–10 Four-Throw Crankshaft.

2.14   Connecting Rods.

See Fig. 2-11. Connecting rods are so named because they connect the pistons to the crankshaft. The small (top) end of the con rod swings on the gudgeon pin within the piston, and the big (bottom) end fits on the crankpin, thereby transmitting the force of the piston to the crankshaft. They are usually H section alloy steel forgings, the girder section increasing resistance to bending and compressive loads. The rod may be of one piece when a built up crankshaft is used, but more usually have a split big end bearing with a 'cap' secured by bolts. The big end may be lined with anti-friction metal shells forming the bearing surface on the crankpin. The small end is bushed with bronze, to provide the bearing for the gudgeon pin.

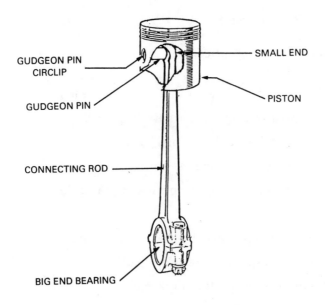

GUDGEON PIN
CIRCLIP

GUDGEON PIN

SMALL END

PISTON

CONNECTING ROD

BIG END BEARING

Figure 2–11 Connecting Rod.

2.15   Swept Volume and Clearance Volume.

The swept volume of a cylinder is that between the bottom dead centre and top dead centre positions of the piston. The clearance volume is that space above the TDC piston enclosed by the cylinder head and the closed valves. (Fig. 2-12). The difference between the swept and clearance volumes is the comparison ratio.

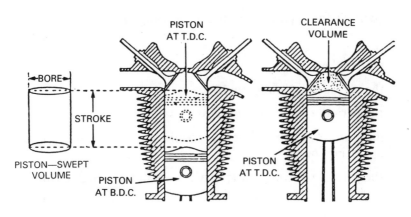

PISTON
AT T.D.C.

CLEARANCE
VOLUME

BORE

STROKE

PISTON—SWEPT
VOLUME

PISTON
AT B.D.C.

PISTON
AT T.D.C.

Figure 2–12 Swept and Clearance Volumes.

17

Section 2 Test Yourself

Four-Stroke Piston Engines

1. The valves of a four-stroke piston engine will each:

(a)   open twice during the normal 'Otto' cycle.

(b)   open once during the normal 'Otto' cycle.

(c)   open four times during the normal 'Otto' cycle.

(d)   open six times during the normal 'Otto' cycle.

Ref. 2.11.

2. The camshaft of a piston engine normally rotates:

(a)   at twice the speed of the crankshaft.

(b)   at half the speed of the crankshaft.

(c)   at the same speed as the crankshaft.

(d)   at four times the speed of the crankshaft.

Ref. 2.11.

3. Tappet and rocker arm clearance is essential:

(a)   to allow lubrication between the contact surfaces.

(b)   to allow for valve operation by the cam.

(c)   to allow for expansion throughout the working temperature range of the engine.

(d)   to allow for expansion of the lubricating oil.

Ref. 2.11.

4. Valve 'Dwell' is:

(a)   the period a valve remains open.

(b)   the period a valve remains closed.

(c)   the period taken by the rocker to take up the clearance gap before operating the valve.

(d)   the period a valve is stationary during normal engine running.

Ref. 2.11.

5. Valve overlap occurs:

(a) at the end of the power stroke.

(b) at the end of the exhaust stroke.

(c) at the end of the induction stroke.

(d) at the end of the compréssion stroke.

Ref. 2.6.

6. The weight of charge introduced into a piston engine cylinder during normal operation:

(a) is increased by closing the exhaust valve before TDC.

(b) is reduced by closing the inlet valve after BDC.

(c) is increased by delaying the closing of the inlet valve.

(d) is constant at any engine rpm.

Ref. 2.6a.

7. The exhaust valve of a piston engine:

(a) normally has a hollow stem partially filled with sodium.

(b) is normally manufactured from metallic sodium to assist with cooling.

(c) normally has a hollow head filled with sodium.

(d) is normally water filled.

Ref. 2.11.

8. Valve springs are primarily duplicated:

(a) to ensure a gas-tight seal when the valve is closed.

(b) to prevent the valve dropping into the cylinder in the event a spring breaks.

(c) to reduce valve bounce.

(d) to increase the speed of valve opening.

Ref. 2.11.

9. When the piston of a four-stroke piston engine is towards the end of the power stroke:

(a) the gas temperature will be at its highest.

(b) the gas temperature will be reducing.

(c) the gas temperature will remain constant until BDC.

(d) the gas temperature will be progressively increasing.

Ref. 2.6.

10. The compression ratio of a piston engine is the:

(a) ratio of the cylinder volume when the piston is at BDC to the cylinder volume when at TDC.

(b) difference in pressure generated when the piston is at BDC to that generated at TDC.

(c) variation between the volume of the combustion chamber and the swept volume.

(d) distance equal to the crank throw.

Ref. 2.3b

3

Piston Engine Lubrication

Introduction.

3.1 Lubrication is a means of reducing friction and wear. *Friction* is the resistance to movement when one surface slides over another. *Wear* is the loss of material resulting from the two surfaces sliding together. Solid surfaces are never smooth: the actual contact between two sliding surfaces is made at a multitude of high spots. When the high spots on a sliding surface are well spaced the material may actually be torn away. Where the body particles are very small the surface faces will become smoother but where large particles are affected the surfaces may become both rough and smooth. The purpose of a lubricant is to prevent sliding surfaces from actually touching each other and thus to eliminate friction and wear. Any substance placed between two moving surfaces to reduce friction may be termed a lubricant; mineral oil is used as the normal lubricant for piston engines. The two methods of application are:

(a)   Film Lubrication.

(b)   Boundary Lubrication.

3.2 (a) *Film Lubrication.* A thin but measurable film of oil is maintained between the two surfaces and prevents them from touching. This film works in three distinct layers, the outside layers clinging to the two separate surfaces and the central layer moving between them. The thinner the oil the easier will this movement take place, the thicker or more viscous the oil the greater the force that will be required to move one surface on the other. If the oil is squeezed from between the surfaces the cushioning function of the oil is less effective and wear will become excessive.

(b) *Boundary Lubrication.* This is the state of near breakdown of lubrication where the film thickness has, by reason of load or loss of viscosity, been reduced almost to nothing. The surfaces, while not actually touching, are very near to it, but they continue to slide until the oil disappears.

21

Lubricant Requirements.

3.3 The properties which a lubricant should possess will vary according to the particular purpose for which it is to be used. All lubricating oils for piston engines are required to:

(a) 'Wet' the surfaces to be lubricated.

(b) Possess a viscosity suitable for high loading and speeds, over a wide temperature range.

(c) Have a low evaporation rate at normal engine running temperature.

(d) Protect surfaces against corrosion.

(e) Have a low gum or sludge formation rate.

(f) Be non-injurious to materials they contact.

Lubrication System.

3.4 There are essentially two main types of lubrication systems fitted to piston aero-engines.

(a) Dry Sump Lubrication.

(b) Wet Sump Lubrication.

Both types operate in a similar manner and fulfil the same basic function. The differences will be discussed later. The majority of aircraft piston engine lubrication systems are of the dry sump type. The following text refers primarily to a dry sump lubrication system.

Principle

The internal moving parts of an aero-engine are lubricated by oil which is circulated from a tank in the airframe to the engine and back again by means of engine-driven oil pumps. Far more oil is circulated by the pumps than is needed to reduce friction alone and this excess flow is used to cool the internal components of the engine. An oil cooler fitted in the return line to the tank dissipates much of the heat absorbed by the oil in its passage through the engine. The engine pump delivers oil under pressure through internal ducts, hollow shafts and pipes to the main bearings, fitted to the engine. Oil escaping from these bearings is used to 'splash' lubricate ball and roller bearings, gears and other moving parts. Where more positive lubrication is necessary, jets of oil are directed onto the contacting faces. Oil in the engine drains into a sump where a scavenge pump passes the oil back to the tank.

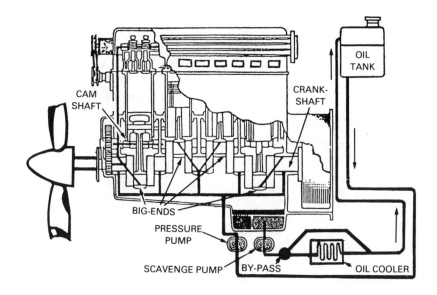

Figure 3–1 A Dry Sump System.

3.5 Most lubrication systems in engines using plain main bearings have the oil delivered at fairly high pressure (60psi to 70psi); the oil then passes into the hollow crankshafts where ducts in the crankwebs and crankpins direct it to the big-end bearings. Oil escaping from these bearings is flung onto the cylinder walls, piston and gudgeon pins to provide splash lubrication. Other plain bearings in the engine, which are not so heavily loaded, are often fed with oil from an auxiliary circuit at a much reduced pressure. This auxiliary circuit is fed from the main system, the reduced pressure being controlled by a relief valve.

Operation.

Dry Sump Type.

The system comprises:

(a) Oil tank.
This is normally a separate tank, mounted adjacent to the engine, which contains a reserve of oil to allow for minor leakage and provides an air space above the oil to allow for expansion and frothing.

23

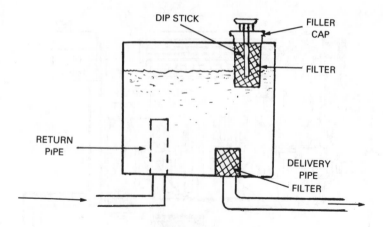

Figure 3–2 Oil Tank.

(b) Pressure Filter.
As the oil is drawn from the tank, by the suction of the pressure pump, it passes through a pressure filter to ensure that clean oil is delivered to the engine.

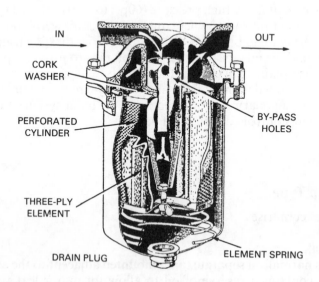

Figure 3–3 Pressure Filter.

24

(c) Pressure Pump.
The pressure pump is normally of a spur gear type and is driven by the engine. It is designed to deliver a greater quantity of oil than the system actually requires, the surplus oil being used as a cooling medium for many of the engine components. A relief valve is usually fitted adjacent to, or as an integral part of, the pump assembly to relieve excess pressure on the outlet side of the pump. The relieved oil may be directed back to the oil tank or more usually back to the inlet side of the pump.

See Fig. 3–4.

PRESSURE RELIEF
VALVE

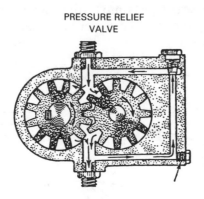

Figure 3–4 Pressure Pump.

(d) Delivery.
Oil under pressure is delivered to various orifices strategically positioned in the engine to lubricate such components as main and auxiliary bearings, rocker gear, camshaft, cylinder walls and numerous other components.

See Fig. 3-1.

Note: Aero-engines fitted with superchargers and turbochargers utilise the engine lubrication system to lubricate the main bearings of such assemblies.

(e) Sump.
Engines fitted with dry sump lubrication systems utilise the sump as a form of collector tank. As the oil is allowed to drain from the components it has lubricated, it drains into the sump where it is then collected by the scavenge pump.

See Fig. 3-1.

25

(f) Scavenge Pump.
The scavenge pump normally has a greater pumping capacity than the pressure pump, to ensure that all oil is removed or 'scavenged' from the engine. Oil collected by the scavenge pump is drawn through a scavenge filter which removes any particles of foreign matter from the oil before it passes through the pump. The scavenged oil at this stage is very hot so is passed to a cooler.

See Fig. 3-1.

(g) Oil Cooler.
Oil coolers are normally of the air cooled variety in that the oil is pumped by the scavenge pump through a matrix and is cooled by ram air passing through the cooler in a similar manner to that of a car radiator.

See Fig. 3-5.

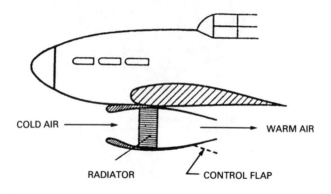

Figure 3–5 Oil Cooler.

(h) By-Pass.
Many modern piston engines are fitted with a by-pass valve which, when starting the engine (particularly at low temperatures) allows the oil cooler to be by-passed thereby allowing the oil and the engine to reach normal working temperature more quickly. The by-pass valve is usually thermostat controlled.

See Fig. 3-1.

Note: In most cases the pressure pump and scavenge pump are one assembly driven by a common drive shaft. Both pumps are of similar design but with the scavenge pump having a greater capacity than the pressure pump.

26

3.6 Wet Sump Type: Wet sump lubrication is rarely used on modern piston aero-engines. Generally, the wet sump system consists of the same components as the dry sump with one major difference: the sump of the wet system not only collects the oil as it drains from its lubrication points, but also serves as the oil tank. The major disadvantage of the wet sump system is that when the aircraft is inverted the oil tends to drain from the sump to the cylinders so reducing the efficiency of splash lubrication, and starving vital bearings of oil whilst the aircraft is in this attitude.

Section 3 Test Yourself

Piston Engine Lubrication

1. The majority of aircraft piston engine lubrication systems are of the:

   (a)   self-lubricating type.

   (b)   wet sump type.

   (c)   dry sump type.

   (d)   emulsion type.

Ref. 3.4.

2. A dry sump lubrication system:

   (a)   maintains a reserve of oil in a separate tank.

   (b)   maintains a reserve of oil in the sump.

   (c)   requires no reserve of oil.

   (d)   maintains a reserve of oil in the engine gallery.

Ref. 3.5

3. The pressure pump of a dry sump lubrication system:

   (a)   has a greater capacity than the scavenge pump.

   (b)   has less capacity than the scavenge pump.

   (c)   is driven on a common shaft and has the same capacity as the scavenge pump.

   (d)   is always electrically driven.

Ref. 3.5.

4. The pressure filter in a dry sump lubrication system is:

(a) located between the pressure pump and tank.

(b) located after the pressure pump.

(c) located between the scavenge pump and the tank.

(d) located at the base of the tank.

Ref. 3.5.

5. The by-pass valve of a dry sump lubrication system is:

(a) normally activated during low temperature engine starting.

(b) normally activated during high temperature engine starting.

(c) is a relief valve of excess oil pressure.

(d) part of the pressure assembly.

Ref. 3.5.

6. Normally on most piston engines the lubrication oil of a dry sump system is cooled:

(a) on leaving the pressure pump.

(b) before returning to the oil tank.

(c) before returning to the sump.

(d) in the tank.

Ref. 3.5.

7. The reserve of lubricating oil of a wet sump piston engine is stored in:

(a) the sump.

(b) a separate tank.

(c) the pipe system.

(d) the engine gallery.

Ref. 3.6.

8. The oil tank of a dry sump lubrication system has a space above the oil to provide for:

    (a)   jack ram displacement.

    (b)   pressurisation.

    (c)   expansion of the oil and frothing.

    (d)   cooling air.

Ref. 3.5.

9. A relief valve is provided to relieve excess pressure on:

    (a)   the outlet side of the pressure filter.

    (b)   the outlet side of the pressure pump.

    (c)   the inlet side of the scavenge pump.

    (d)   the outlet side of the scavenge pump.

Ref. 3.5.

10. The oil cooler of a dry sump lubrication system is normally cooled by:

    (a)   water.

    (b)   compressor air.

    (c)   ram air.

    (d)   engine bleed air.

Ref. 3.5.

4

Piston Engine Ignition

4.1 Introduction.

Piston engines, other than compression ignition engines, depend on electrical ignition systems to ignite the fuel/air mixture in the cylinders. The mixture is set alight by an electric spark produced at the gap between the two electrodes of a sparking plug in the cylinder head when it is desired to fire the charge. (The initial flame in a gas turbine engine is started in a similar manner.)

Two types of ignition system are in common use: coil ignition and magneto ignition. Coil ignition is used widely on motor cars and aircraft ground support equipment, its electrical supply generally being obtained from batteries or from a separate generator. The magneto, which is always used on aircraft piston engines, is a self-contained unit with its own built in generator.

4.2 Electricity.

Electricity is a form of energy and its pressure may be shown in one or more of the following ways:

(a) Heating Effect.
A flow of electricity generates heat in the conductor through which it flows. This effect can be seen in the hot element of an electric fire and in the glowing filament of an electric lamp.

(b) Chemical Effect.
A flow of electricity can cause a chemical change. For example when charging a battery the current changes the chemical composition of the plates and acid.

(c) Magnetic Effect.
A flow of electricity along a conductor causes a magnetic field to be set up around the conductor. If the conductor is wound into a coil a more powerful field is produced since the loops of the wire act together. This principle is used to form a temporary magnet which

30

may be used, for example, to attract the hammer of a bell, and for relay and solenoid switches.

4.3   The Electrical Circuit.

Study Figs. 4-1 and 4-2 in conjunction with the following text.
The conditions that exist in a simple electrical circuit can be compared with those in a water system as shown in Fig. 4-1. The pump is the source of energy to lift water from tank B to tank A so that, when the cock is open, water is directed under gravitational pressure on to the turbine, so causing it to rotate.

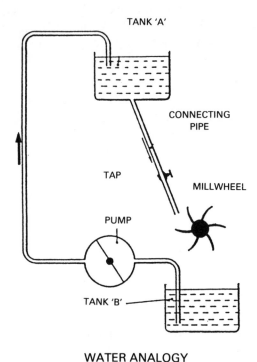

TANK 'A'

CONNECTING PIPE

TAP

MILLWHEEL

PUMP

TANK 'B'

WATER ANALOGY

Figure 4–1 Water Analogy.

A simple electrical circuit is shown in Fig. 4-2. The circuit consists of a generator connected by conductors to a switch and a lamp. Here, the source of energy is the electrical generator that produces a difference in electrical pressure (known as voltage) between the positive and negative terminals. On closing the switch, which is the counterpart of the cock in the water system, this voltage causes an electrical current to flow from the generator through the conductors and lamp back to the generator.

The heating effect of the current flow causes the lamp filament to glow and so produce light.

In the water system the resistance to the flow of water depends on the cross sectional area of the pipelines, their length, and their internal roughness. Similarly, in an electrical circuit the conductors resist the flow of electrical current. This opposition to flow (termed resistance and measured in ohms) depends on the cross sectional area of the conductors, their length, and the material from which they are manufactured.

Where the material is a good conductor (i.e. has low resistance) more current flows for the same electrical pressure. Copper is a very good conductor and is widely used for this reason. To keep the resistance in a circuit as low as possible conductors must be large in cross sectional area, short in length, and of suitable material. Materials with an exceptionally high resistance to the flow of electricity are called 'insulators'; examples are glass, porcelain, mica, rubber and some types of enamel.

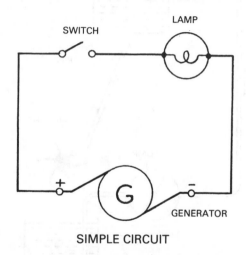

SIMPLE CIRCUIT

Figure 4–2 A Simple Electrical Circuit.

In the water system the rate of flow depends on the pressure created by the pump, i.e. the difference between pump outlet and pump inlet pressures. Similarly, in an electrical circuit the flow of current (measured in amperes) depends on the difference in electrical pressure or voltage between the positive and negative terminals of the generator.

4.4 Magnets and Lines of Force.

A magnet has an affinity for iron and this becomes apparent by the following effects:

32

(a) The ends of the magnet attract pieces of iron and steel. The ends, where the power of attraction is greatest, are known as the 'poles' of the magnet.

(b) If a bar magnet is freely suspended at its centre it comes to rest in parallel with the lines of force of the earth's magnetic field. The pole then lying nearer to the north pole is known as the north-seeking or 'north pole of the magnet' the other is the south-seeking or 'south pole'.

(c) If a second magnet is held near a pole of the suspended magnet the latter is either attracted or repelled according to the polarity of the magnet brought to it; like poles repel, unlike poles attract.

Fig. 4-3 shows the effects of the magnetic lines of force on a bar magnet.

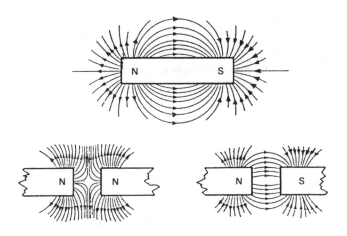

Figure 4–3 Lines of Magnetic Force.

The strength of the attraction present at the poles varies between magnets. Some indication of the area and strength of the field of attraction around a magnet can be shown by drawing lines of force. These show the direction of attraction and by their numbers, the intensity of the field. Such a field can be demonstrated by sprinkling iron filings on a sheet of paper held over a magnet. A diagrammatic representation of the magnetic field is shown in Fig. 4-3.

Lines of force tend to deflect from their normal direction to pass through any magnetic body placed within the magnetic field. Advantage is taken of this fact in the design of electric motors, generators and magnetos.

A magnet may be either a permanent or an electro-magnet. The *permanent magnet*, which is made of a special alloy or steel, retains its magnetism over a period of years provided it is carefully handled. The *electro-magnet* consists of a soft iron core with a number of turns of insulated copper wire wound around it. When an electrical current is passed through the wire the core becomes magnetised and remains so for as long as the electrical current is flowing, but, as soon as the current is switched off the core loses its magnetism.

Soft iron is used for the core because it is easily magnetised yet loses its magnetism very quickly when the magnetising force is removed.

4.5 Production of Electricity.

Electricity can be produced in a variety of ways, the more common being by expending chemicals or by converting mechanical energy.

(a) Expending Chemicals.

If two dissimilar metals are immersed in certain chemical solutions or pastes, a voltage difference occurs between the two metals and, if they are connected by an external conductor electrical current flows. Such an arrangement is known as a simple cell. A simple cell has a limited output but is of use with electric torches, door bells, and similar small units. Several cells connected together form a battery.

(b) Converting Mechanical Energy.

If an electrical conductor moves in a magnetic field so that it cuts, or is cut by, lines of magnetic force a voltage is produced across the ends of the conductor. This relative movement can be produced either by:

(i)   Moving the conductor across a stationary magnet field.

(ii) Moving the magnetic field across a stationary conductor.

(iii) Varying the strength of intensity of a stationary field about a stationary conductor. Such a variation has the same effect as the lines of force cutting across the conductor. See Fig. 4-4.

The strength of the voltage so induced into the conductor depends on the intensity of the magnetic field and the speed of the relative movement. The more intense the field and/or the faster the relative movement the greater is the amount of electricity induced.

An electrical generator, or dynamo, normally consists of a magnetic field that surrounds a rotating member, which carries the electrical conductors. Figure 4-4 shows a simple conductor moving across a magnetic field and the principle when applied to a generator.

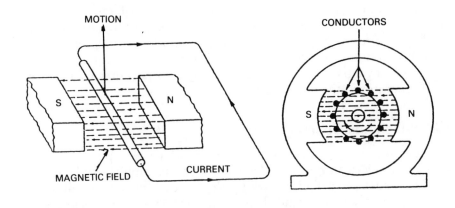

PRINCIPLE OF DYNAMO

Figure 4–4 Principle of Electricity Generation.

4.6 Electro-Magnetic Induction.

It has already been stated that when a coil wound around a soft iron core is carrying a current, then a magnetic field is formed around both the coil and the core and remains as long as a current is flowing. If the current flow is stopped however, the magnetic field collapses and the lines of force move rapidly in towards the coil causing a current to be induced in any conductor that lies within the field. Similarly, a current is induced in such a conductor during the build-up of a current in the coil.

Consider two coils wound on an iron core, one above the other and insulated from each other. If a steady current is flowing through one of the coils a steady magnetic field is formed around both coils and the core but, because there is no relative movement between the lines of force and the second coil, a current is not induced into the second coil. If, however the current in the energised coil is cut off, the magnetic field immediately collapses and, cutting across the turns of the second coil, induces a current into it. This current flows for just as long as the magnetic field takes to collapse.

The voltage so induced into the second coil depends on the ratio between the number of turns in the first and second coils, the speed at which the lines of force collapse across the second coil, and the resistance of the final circuit.

Applying this principle in order to supply a series of sparks to an engine a relatively small number of turns of stout wire, or primary winding, is wound around the core and has a secondary winding of a large number

35

of turns of thin wire superimposed upon it. A low voltage is applied to the primary winding and by starting and stopping the current in this winding a series of high voltage electrical impulses is induced into the secondary winding. The low voltage producing the primary current may be supplied by a battery (coil ignition) or by incorporating a simple electrical generator in the unit (magneto).

4.7   Magnetos General.

A magneto is a device designed to produce electrical impulses one after another at precise intervals so that each separate impulse can be used to provide a spark at a cylinder sparking plug. The magneto does this by first generating a low voltage and then collapsing the magnetic field created by the resultant current across the secondary winding to induce a high voltage impulse. A precise interval is essential to obtain correct ignition timing on all cylinders during engine running.

4.8   Description.

The essential components of a magneto are:

(a)   A permanent magnet, which provides the magnetic field necessary to generate a low voltage in the primary winding.

(b)   The Primary, and the Secondary windings mounted on a soft iron core; the complete assembly is then known as the Armature.

(c)   A rotating member that effects a change of magnetism on the armature. The particular basic principle used in the operation of the magneto is governed by this member and is indicated by the type name of the magneto, e.g. Rotating Armature Magneto, Rotating Magnet Magneto.

(d)   A contact breaker assembly which is a mechanically operated switch timed to break the primary circuit when the maximum current is flowing.

(e)   A condenser, which is connected across the contact breaker points. The action of the condenser, by reducing arcing at the contact breaker points when the points are open, stops the flow of primary current more quickly and thus brings about a faster collapse of the primary magnetic field. Further, by reducing arcing at the points, excessive burning and erosion of the points is avoided.

(f)   The distributor, which directs the high voltage impulses to the cylinders in turn as they reach their ignition point.

The internal wiring of a magneto can be conveniently divided into two, the primary or low tension circuit, and the secondary or high tension circuit.

Primary Circuit.
A simple primary circuit is shown in Fig. 4-5. It consists of a primary winding on a soft iron core, a contact breaker and a condenser. The condenser is connected across the contact breaker points.

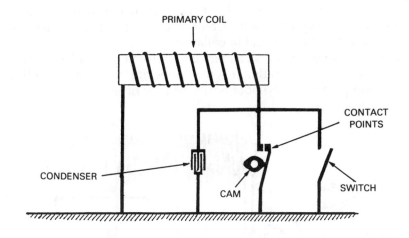

Figure 4–5 Primary Circuit.

The earthing switch shown is not a magneto component but is included to explain its action. Reference to Fig. 4-5 shows that if the switch is closed the primary circuit is completed and the contact breaker action has no effect on the circuit. The magneto is therefore 'dead' when the switch contacts are together, and 'alive' when the switch contacts are apart, that is to say, the reverse of normal switch.

Secondary Circuit.
Figure 4-6 shows the secondary circuit superimposed on the primary circuit. One end of the winding is in contact with the centre of a rotating arm, or distributor, that leads to the centre electrodes of a sparking plug. The other end of the secondary winding is connected via the primary winding to the earth electrode of the sparking plugs.

4.9   Magneto Operation.

Assuming that a current is flowing in the primary circuit when the contact breaker points are closed, then a magnetic field is also present around the primary and secondary windings, the strength of the field being dependent upon the strength of the current flow. If the cam is now operated, the contact points open, the primary circuit is broken, and primary current ceases to flow. This produces an immediate collapse of the magnetic field causing the lines of force to move across the secondary winding. Since any movement of lines of force across a conductor induces a voltage into that conductor a current will flow in the secondary circuit for the time taken for the field to collapse.

The current set up in the secondary circuit is fed to the distributor, the rotor of which is so timed that it is then opposite the segment leading to the sparking plug in the cylinder positioned for firing.

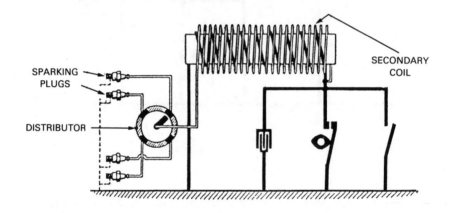

Figure 4–6 Complete Circuit with Secondary Coil
Superimposed on Primary Circuit.

4.10   Distribution.

On a four stroke engine the cylinders need to be fired once in every two revolutions of the engine in a sequence (the firing order) that produces the least vibration. To do this, high tension leads from the cylinder sparking plugs are connected in the sequence desired to segments spaced equally around the distributor block, and the distributor rotor is engine driven at half engine speed. Thus, the rotor passes each engine segment once in every two engine revolutions coupling individual cylinders to the secondary circuit in the same sequence as the firing order. (No matter how many cylinders there are on an engine the distributor rotor always rotates at half engine speed.) Therefore, provided a voltage is induced in the secondary winding whenever the rotor is opposite a segment, the secondary circuit is completed through the correct cylinder sparking plug.

Before such a voltage can be induced in the secondary windings a current must be flowing in the primary circuit. There are two basic methods of producing current in the primary circuit of a magneto: by rotating an armature within a magnetic field, or by rotating magnetic 'poles' to vary the field acting on a stationary armature (polar inductor).

4.11   Rotating Armature Magneto.

The armature of a rotating armature magneto is carried on an engine driven shaft that rotates between the poles of a permanent magnet. Figure 4-7 displays a diagrammatic representation of such an arrangement showing the flux, or lines of force changes, through the armature core during half a revolution of the shaft.

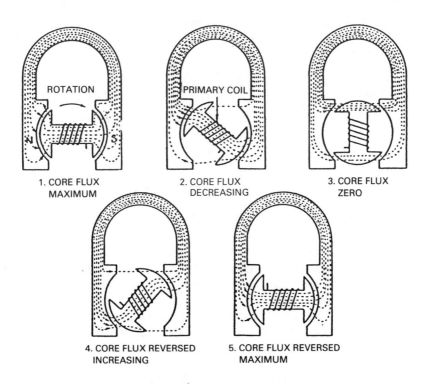

Figure 4–7 Rotating Armature Magneto.

This change of flux causes a voltage to be induced into the primary winding and primary current results. The strength of this current will be at its peak in position 3, core flux zero, when the greatest change of magnetism on the armature occurs. It is at this point that the contact breaker points are made to open, i.e. when the magnetic field created by the primary current flow will also be at its maximum. Note that this zero core flux position occurs twice only in one revolution of the armature and consequently this type of magneto supplies two sparks/rev.

The contact breaker on this type of magneto is fixed to the armature shaft, the operating cam being held in the end casing. Thus, as the armature assumes position 3, and the primary current is at its maximum, the contact breaker points are automatically opened by the cams.

The current resulting from the induced voltage in the secondary circuit is fed from the rotating armature via a carbon brush and slip ring to the centre of the distributor rotor and thence, through the distributor segments, to the sparking plugs.

This type of magneto is suitable only for light aircraft with a small number of cylinders because:

(a) Since two sparks only are supplied during each revolution the magneto speed becomes too high for engines of more than about six cylinders.

(b) Centrifugal force acting on the armature windings tend to burst the windings.

(c) A greater number of rubbing contacts are necessary inside the magneto in this type because the current has to be passed from a rotating to a stationary contact. Though the carbon brushes used at these points have a low resistance, a fixed contact is always more reliable than a rubbing contact.

4.12 Rotating Magnet Magneto.

This polar inductor type of magneto normally produces four electrical impulses in the secondary windings (or four sparks) for every revolution of the magneto shaft and is, therefore, far more suitable for engines having a large number of cylinders. Not only does a polar inductor type run at half the speed of the rotating armature type to produce the same number of sparks but the coils and switch assembly, being stationary, are free from centrifugal loading. This type of magneto has consequently largely superseded the rotating armature magneto except for those engines with fewer than six cylinders, where the speed of the magneto at low engine speeds is too slow to generate an effective primary current. Figure 4-8 shows the principle of operation of an inductor type magneto.

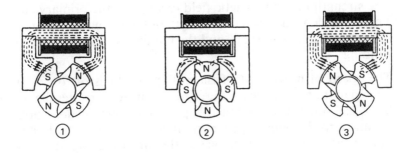

Figure 4–8 Rotating Magnet Magneto.

One form of polar inductor magneto is the rotating magnet type. The main rotating member of this type consists of a non-magnetic steel shaft on which is mounted a tubular magnet clamped between a pair of two fingered soft iron pole pieces set 90 degrees apart. One end of the tube has a north polarity, the other a south polarity and the respective polarity is imparted to the clamping pole pieces. The assembly is rotated in a tunnel formed between the iron extensions of an armature core. This arrangement is shown diagrammatically in Fig. 4-8, the three positions covering a quarter revolution of the shaft.

Flux changes through the armature core as the magnetic poles revolve produce a change of magnetism around the primary winding of the armature and the current resulting from the voltage thus induced in the primary winding reaches a maximum with the poles at position 2 (core flux zero). It is at this point that the contact breaker points are opened.

The stationary contact breaker assembly is normally housed at the non-driving end of the magneto so that a four lobed cam keyed to the end of the rotating shaft automatically opens the points when the primary current is at its peak. This arrangement does not apply to radial engines, where the operating cam and contact breaker are contained within the distributor housing.

Figure 4-9 shows an exploded view of a rotating magnet magneto.

Although the primary current is produced in a somewhat different manner to the rotating armature type the secondary current is set up by an induced voltage in precisely the same way. Thus, when the contact breaker points interrupt the primary current, causing the primary magnetic field to collapse, a voltage is induced in the secondary circuit for the period of time that the lines of force cut across the secondary winding. Similarly, the voltage of the impulse so induced is dependent upon:

(a) The strength of the magnetic field created by the primary current. This again depends upon the strength of the permanent magnet, the speed of the magneto shaft, and the number of turns in the primary winding.

(b) The speed of movement of the collapsing lines of force. This is related to the time taken for the current flow to stop after the contact breaker points have begun to open. The current does not stop instantly; as the points open, current continues to flow, though at a falling rate, until the resistance of the air at the gap at the points becomes too high. In practice this lag in current shut-off is considerably reduced by the action of the condenser.

(c) The ratio between the number of turns in the secondary windings to the number of turns in the primary winding. The greater the ratio the greater is the relative step-up in the voltage of the secondary circuit to that in the primary.

The average voltage in the primary circuit of a magneto running at normal rpm is in the region of 27 volts; that of the secondary circuit is between 5000 and 7000 volts.

On engines where it is considered that the speed of a four pole inductor would be too high, more than four poles are formed on the magneto shaft. Where this is so, more flux reversals occur per revolution of the magneto shaft and, given a suitable contact breaker, more than four sparks/rev are produced. Alternatively, two separate armatures and contact breaker assemblies may be arranged in the tunnel.

4.13   Internal Timing.

To obtain the maximum electrical output from a magneto, it is essential that the contact breaker points are opened when the primary current flow is at its peak. Further, to be sure that the resulting secondary current flows to a spark plug, the distributor rotor must be opposite a distributor segment. Normally, correct relative positioning (or internal timing) of the magnetic pole pieces, the contact breaker cam, and the distributor rotor is done during magneto assembly. In service, however, wear on the contact breaker points and cam affect the relative positioning of these components and some adjustment may be necessary to maintain full efficiency.

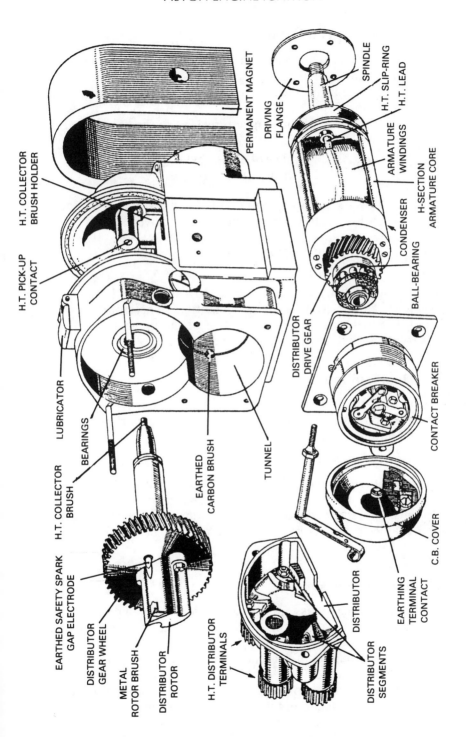

Figure 4–9 Construction of a Rotating Armature Magneto.

43

4.14 Magneto Speed Ratios.

Every cylinder of a four stroke engine requires one spark every two revolutions of the engine crankshaft. Consequently, the greater the number of engine cylinders the faster the magneto needs to be driven to provide the necessary number of sparks.

In general, the speed of the magneto relative to the engine speed may be calculated as follows:

$$\text{Magneto Speed} = \frac{\text{Number of engine cylinders}}{2 \times \text{the number of sparks/rev}}$$

Thus, for a twelve cylinder engine fitted with a rotating magnet type magneto (4 sparks/rev) the magneto needs to be driven at:

$$\frac{12}{2 \times 4} = 1\frac{1}{2} \text{ times the engine speed}$$

Each segment of a distributor is connected to a different cylinder and each requires one spark every two engine revolutions. Therefore as explained before, the distributor rotor, irrespective of the magneto shaft speed, always rotates at half engine crankshaft speed.

4.15 Dual Ignition.

All piston aero-engines are fitted with dual ignition, ie two entirely independent ignition systems. Thus each cylinder has two sparking plugs, each fed from a different magneto in order to:

(a) Reduce the possibility of engine failure because of an ignition fault.

(b) Increase the engine power output. Power output can be increased on large bore cylinders by igniting the charge at two widely spaced points: this reduces the overall time taken to burn the full charge and so enables peak gas pressure to be reached before the piston has moved very far down its stroke.

4.16 Contact Breaker.

Though contact breaker assemblies vary widely in detail design the same basic action is always retained. A typical rotating magnet type contact breaker assembly is shown in Fig. 4-10.

The assembly consists of a rocker arm that oscillates on a pivot pin secured to the base plate. One end of the rocker arm is fitted with a fibre 'heel' that bears against a four lobed cam, which is fitted to the magneto shaft. A movable contact point is mounted at the other end of the rocker, a 'fixed' point being secured to the base plate. A leaf spring attached to the rocker arm tends to hold the contacts together.

The cam is keyed to such a position on the magneto shaft that, when it strikes the fibre heel of the rocker arm thus opening the points, the primary current flow is at its maximum. The contact breaker spring closes the points when the cam has passed the fibre heel. This cycle occurs four times in every revolution of the magneto shaft and consequently both the mechanical and electrical stresses on the assembly are extensive.

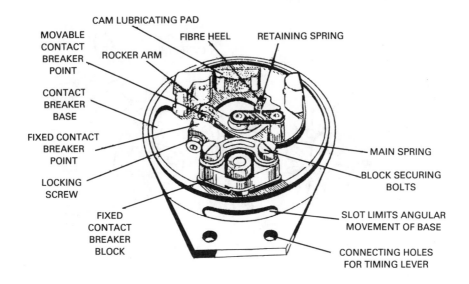

Figure 4–10 Contact Breaker Assembly.

4.17 Magneto Couplings and Ignition Timing.

To obtain the best possible engine performance the magnetos must be accurately timed to the engine. To facilitate this, some form of drive that provides an angular adjustment between the engine and the magneto is necessary. Many such magneto drive couplings are in use, some employing a vernier principle to provide a fine adjustment, others using fine pitched serrations or teeth.

4.18 Vernier Type Coupling.

The vernier coupling consists of three discs: the magneto drive, the so called flexible disc, and the magneto coupling. In the type illustrated in Fig. 4-11 the magneto drive (which is driven by the engine) has nineteen teeth; the magneto coupling, which is keyed to the magneto shaft, has twenty teeth. The intermediate flexible disc has nineteen on one side and twenty teeth on the other.

Referring to Fig. 4-11, the difference in angular movement between one tooth on the magneto drive and one tooth on the magneto coupling can be denoted A. But one tooth on the magneto drive = 1/19 part of a revolution, and one tooth on the magneto coupling = 1/20 part of a revolution.

Therefore, $A = 1/19 - 1/20 = 20/380 - 19/380 = 1/380$ rev = .95 degrees.

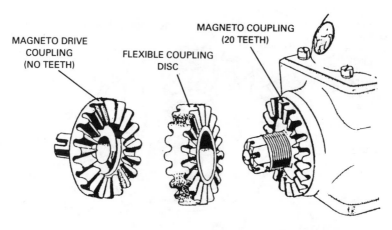

Figure 4-11 Vernier Type Magneto Coupling.

Thus, if the intermediate flexible disc is disengaged from the outer members and re-engaged in the next tooth in the same direction of rotation on each side, the shaft angularity between engine and magneto is altered by .95 degrees or approximately 1 degree. Whether this movement advances or retards the magneto depends on the direction of rotation taken by the flexible disc when making the fine adjustment.

4.19 Variable Ignition Timing.

The peak gas pressure generated within a cylinder should occur just after TDC when the piston is at the start of the power stroke. If peak pressure is reached before this point very little torque is produced and exceptionally heavy loads are placed on the crankshaft bearings because of the acute angle of the crankweb. If peak pressure is reached after this point not only has gas pressure been lost because of the increased volume above the piston but the actual working stroke has been shortened.

To ensure peak pressure always occurs at the same crankshaft position the following factors must be considered:

(a) Engine Speed.
The faster an engine runs the greater is the arc of crankpin travel during the time taken for the charge to burn. Therefore, with an increase in engine speed the timing needs to be progressively advanced, with a reduction in engine speed the ignition timing should be retarded.

(b) Manifold Pressure.
The greater the pressure of a gas, the faster the gas burns. Thus the cylinder charge of an engine running at high manifold pressure burns quicker than a charge at low manifold pressure. Therefore, to stop the peak pressure position moving as manifold pressure is increased the ignition timing should be progressively retarded.

(c) Mixture Strength.
A correct mixture burns faster than either a 'weak' or 'rich' mixture. Therefore, any variation from a correct mixture strength demands a retardation of ignition timing.
There is a tendency for these factors to cancel out, e.g. high engine speed generally means high manifold pressure and rich mixture, but the cancellation is not exact.

On low powered engines the gain to be had from making slight adjustments to the ignition timing during engine running is usually too small to be considered. On larger engines, however, where the gain can be appreciable, ignition timing may be varied to suit all three conditions. Timing variation may be made either by a flexible coupling or by a variable drive.

4.20 Ignition Cable.

The high tension leads that connect the magneto and the high energy ignition units to the plugs are made of single cored, heavily insulated cable capable both of carrying high voltages and of withstanding the ill effects of oil and fuel contamination and high engine temperatures. The single core is made of twisted strands of either tinned copper or stainless steel and rubberised insulation. The insulation is generally protected by an outer covering of varnished fabric. Low tension cable used for wiring the switch into the magneto circuit is of similar construction but not quite so robust.

4.21 Ignition Harness.

On multi-cylinder engines it is usual to enclose the HT leads, as far as possible, in a metal conduit, or 'harness'. This has the advantages of:

(a) Positive screening with less weight.

(b) Protecting the leads from damage.

(c) Sealing the leads against moisture.

In practice, an ignition harness consists of one or more rigid conduits to which are attached two large diameter flexible conduits leading to the magneto distributors, and a number of smaller flexible conduits connecting to individual sparking plugs. The complete assembly is secured to the engine by attachment lugs on the rigid conduit. Each HT lead passes from the magneto distributor block through a large bore flexible conduit, and around the inside of the rigid conduit to the small flexible conduit leading to its spark plug. Each lead has a suitable identification sleeve at each end.

4.22 Screening.

The sudden variations in current flow and the arcing that takes place in the HT windings, leads, distributors and sparking plugs during normal operation produces unwanted signals that, unless suppressed, interfere with aircraft radio reception. Radiation of such signals is prevented by enclosing all the components of the ignition system in a non-magnetic metal screen.

The magnetos are screened by the body of the magneto and the fitting of cover plates over the contact breaker and distributor block. HT leads are screened either by enclosing them in metal conduit (ignition harness) or by the use of braided cables. Screening is effective in eliminating any such interference only where all screening is electrically connected, or 'bonded', to the airframe structure.

4.23 Bonding.

All metal parts of an aircraft must be in good electrical contact one to another so that all have the same electrical charge, or potential. Unless this is done any intermittent contact that causes arcing between parts or components at different potentials produce radio interference and also increases the danger of fire. In practice pipelines, metal braided leads, metal conduit and other components that are not in constant metallic contact with the airframe are all bonded to the airframe structure with special clips or wires.

4.24   Sparking Plugs General.

Sparking plugs are the means whereby the electrical energy generated by the magneto is used to ignite the mixture in the cylinder head. The plug has two electrodes which are positioned to form a gap across which the HT current creates a spark.

An aero-engine sparking plug consists of three main parts, viz:

(a)   A hollow steel body, which screws into the cylinder head; the lower end of the body carries the earth electrodes.

(b)   A centre assembly, comprising the central electrode and its insulation. A deformable metal washer is fitted between the central electrode and the body to make the joint gas-tight.

(c)   A hollow steel gland nut which secures the centre assembly to the body.

The sparking plug is subjected to intense heat, highly corrosive gases and a high electrical voltage. Sparking plugs are designed for use in particular makes, types and marks of aero-engine and it is essential that only approved plug types for that particular engine are used.

Fig. 4-12 shows an example of a screened sparking plug.

4.25   Auxiliary Ignition Devices for Engine Starting.

When starting a piston type aero-engine it is seldom that the engine is turned over fast enough for the magnetos to operate and some other means of providing the essential spark becomes necessary. In general, the method used is decided by the size of the engine and aircraft. Low powered engines use impulse starters and larger aircraft or engines use some form of booster coil. Both methods are described below.

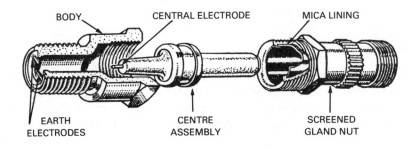

Figure 4–12 Screened Sparking Plug

49

(a) Impulse Starter.

The impulse starter is used on low powered engines and on light aircraft where the aircraft is started by hand swinging the propeller. The unit is a spring loaded coupling through which the engine drives one of the magnetos. The drive passes from the engine half of the coupling through a strong spiral spring to the magneto half of the coupling.

Operation.

When turning the engine to start, the magneto turns with the engine until just before the magneto contact breaker points are about to open. At this point the pawl falls against a stop on the magneto end plate and prevents further magneto rotation. Continued engine turning winds up the spiral spring until, just after TDC, a cam on the engine coupling releases the pawl. The spring then unwinds rapidly and flicks the magneto round fast enough to produce a spark, which is so far retarded that there is no danger of a 'kick back' of the propeller. The pawls are so mass balanced that centrifugal force holds them out of engagement during normal engine running.

4.26   High Tension Booster Coil.

High tension booster coils are used for engine starting where an electric battery is available. The unit supplies a continual stream of high tension electrical impulses each capable of producing a spark at the sparking plug. These impulses are directed to the cylinders in the correct firing order through an additional 'trailing' brush on the magneto distributor rotor.

The HT booster coil consists of an armature and an electrically operated switch. The armature, as in the magneto, has a soft iron core on which are wound primary and secondary windings. The electrically operated switch controls the primary circuit and the movable contact of the switch is secured to a leaf spring, which tends to hold the contacts closed. The hook of a flexible steel plate, upon which is mounted a soft iron pad, is caught under the leaf spring.

Operation.

When a current is fed into the primary circuit from external batteries a magnetic field is built up around the armature and the core becomes magnetised. The magnetised core immediately attracts the iron pad causing the hook to open the contact points and break the primary circuits.

This causes:

(a) The magnetic field to collapse across the secondary winding and so induce a high tension electrical impulse that is fed to the trailing brush of the magneto distributor rotor of the engine.

(b) The armature to lose its magnetism thus allowing the leaf spring to close the contact points.

The moment the contact points close the primary circuit is again energised and the cycle is repeated and continues to be repeated until the battery is switched off. Thus an endless stream of high tension impulses is fed to the distributor of the main magneto and on to its sparking plug.

As on a magneto, a condenser is fitted across the contact points both to reduce arcing at the points and to increase the speed of collapse of the primary current and magnetic field.

4.27   Low Tension Booster Coil.

This type of booster coil is used where the normal timing of the engine is retarded sufficiently for starting purposes. The operation of the unit is basically the same as the HT booster coil but a separate starter brush on the magneto distributor rotor is not required. This removes any chance of flash over at altitude and consequent engine misfiring.

Section 4 Test Yourself

Piston Engine Ignition

1. The magnetic field in a magneto is provided by:

   (a) battery current.

   (b) an excitation field circuit.

   (c) a permanent magnet.

Ref. 4.8.

2. Excessive arcing across the contact breaker points of a magneto when the points are open is prevented by:

   (a) A diode being fitted.

   (b) a condenser being fitted.

   (c) insulation of the contacts.

Ref. 4.8.

3. If the switch of a magneto becomes disconnected in flight:

   (a) the affected magneto will automatically be isolated.

   (b) the alternative magneto will maintain ignition.

   (c) the affected magneto will continue to provide a spark.

Ref. 4.8.

4. On a four stroke engine the ignition spark will occur:

   (a) once each revolution of the engine.

   (b) once every fourth revolution of the engine.

   (c) once every two revolutions of the engine.

Ref. 4.10.

5. On engine start up, the generator warning light fails to extinguish, this will result in:

   (a) the engine stopping when the battery is totally discharged.

   (b) failure of the initial excitation of the magneto.

   (c) the engine continuing to run normally.

Ref. 4.7.

6. The primary coil of a magneto consists of:

(a)   fewer windings of thicker wire than the secondary coil.

(b)   fewer windings of thin wire than the secondary coil.

(c)   fewer windings of the same thickness of wire as the secondary coil.

Ref. 4.8.

7. The distributor rotor on a four stroke engine rotates at:

(a)   the same speed as the engine.

(b)   twice the speed of the engine.

(c)   half the speed of the engine.

Ref. 4.10.

8. With increase of engine speed, ignition timing:

(a)   will advance.

(b)   will retard.

(c)   will remain constant.

Ref. 4.19.

9. A Booster Coil provides:

(a)   a continuous stream of high tension electrical impulses.

(b)   a pulsed stream of low tension electricity.

(c)   a continuous stream of low tension electrical impulses.

Ref. 4.26.

10. To assist with engine starting, some engine ignition system sparks may be:

(a)   advanced.

(b)   pulsed.

(c)   retarded.

Ref. 4.27

5

Fuel Systems

5.1   Introduction.

The aircraft fuel system consists primarily of the fuel tank in which the fuel is stored during flight, fuel pumps to supply the engine, or engines, with fuel when it is required, and filters to ensure the fuel is clean for use in the engine systems. Some engine fuel systems may be fitted with on/off cocks to isolate the fuel system or sections of it, when it is not in use.

5.2   Fuel Tanks.

Aircraft fuel tanks in civil aircraft are normally located in the wings or fuselage. In some instances additional fuel tanks have been located in such places as fins, flaps and external auxiliary tanks to increase the aircraft's total fuel capacity.

Fuel tanks may be of rigid, flexible or integral construction, and are connected by pipelines in such a way that, on larger aircraft, fuel may be transferred from one tank to another whilst in flight. In the event of engine failure on a multi-engined aircraft, fuel may thereby be transferred from one location to the other to maintain supply of fuel to the other engines. Transfer of fuel in this way is usually by cockpit switches, to control on/off cocks and transfer pumps. Figure 5-1 shows the layout of a simple fuel system.

5.3   Fuel Pumps.

Engine-driven fuel pumps in the fuel systems of piston-engined aircraft are usually either:

(a)   Gear type pumps.

(b)   Rotary vane type pumps.

(c)   Diaphragm type pumps.

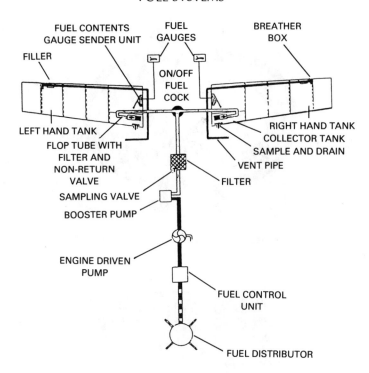

Figure 5–1 Simple Fuel System.

5.4   Gear Type Pumps.

These are similar in operation to engine oil pumps, but are not regarded as being totally satisfactory when handling high octane fuels, particularly at the high altitudes required by some modern aircraft. Positive delivery pumps of this, and rotary vane, type are usually provided with a diaphragm operated relief valve to maintain a constant delivery pressure irrespective of pump suction conditions. Fuel serving this pump acts also as a lubricant, and because of this the pump should never be allowed to run dry. (See Fig. 5-2.)

5.5   Rotary Vane Type Pumps.

In this type of pump, a number of flat vanes are arranged radially in a central rotor which is located eccentrically within the pump casing. (See Fig. 5-3). As the rotor moves round, the volumes between the vanes increase and decrease, the rotor blades sliding in and out of the slots and being kept in contact with the wall of the casing by centrifugal force. The inlet port allows fuel to enter the chamber as its volume is increasing,

Figure 5–2 Spur Gear Type Pump.

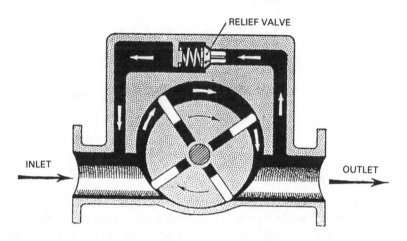

Figure 5–3 Rotary Vane Type Pump.

while the outlet allows fuel which has passed through the pump to be forced out as the crescent shaped space is decreasing. A relief valve by-passes the excess fuel as a result of excess pressure from the delivery side to the inlet side. Since the fuel acts as a lubricant to the vanes, this pump should not be run in a dry condition.

5.6 Diaphragm Type Pumps.

Fuel pumps of this category operate by the action of a reciprocating diaphragm working within a closed chamber equipped with spring loaded inlet and outlet valves. This pump is usually engine driven, the reciprocating (backwards and forwards) motion of the diaphragm being derived from a rotating cam operating direct on to a plunger connected to the centre of the diaphragm, as shown in Fig. 5-4. When cam operated, the plunger and diaphragm are pressed outwards by a spring which keeps the plunger pad in continuous contact with the contour of the cam. Sometimes the diaphragm plunger is spring loaded internally to regulate the maximum pressure of fuel which can be delivered by the pump. A separate lever is usually provided to operate the plunger and diaphragm independently of the driving cam, and thereby prime the pump and fuel lines when the engine is standing idle.

5.7   Booster Pumps, Transfer Pumps and Transfer Systems.

(a) Booster pumps.

Booster pumps are electrically operated. They may be fitted externally in the pipe leading from the tank or a group of tanks, or may be of the immersed type fitted within the tank at its outlet. When the booster pump is not switched on, a by-pass permits fuel to flow from the tank under suction from the engine-driven pump.

The purpose of the booster pump is:

(i)   To prevent any portion of the fuel system from falling below atmospheric pressure and by so doing, prevent vapour locks forming in the pipes.

(ii)   To supply adequate fuel to the engine driven pumps during take-off, landing, at high engine settings and high altitude.

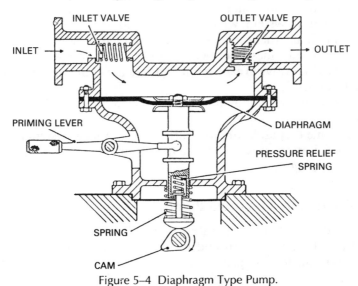

Figure 5-4 Diaphragm Type Pump.

(b) Warning Indication and Control.
In many aircraft, a fuel pressure warning light is fitted to the instrument panel to serve each engine. This lights up when the pressure at the carburettor or injector falls below a pre-determined minimum. In some systems, warning lights are fitted to the circuits of each booster and transfer pump. These lights come on when the pumps are not switched on, or are functioning incorrectly.

Booster pumps should be switched on if the fuel pressure warning light comes on or flickers when the engine is running. They should never be left on after an engine has been stopped or when the fuel tanks concerned are empty.

(c) Transfer Pumps.
The same type of pump, when fitted in a tank or system which does not feed an engine direct, is known as a fuel transfer pump, and serves to pump fuel from this tank into another tank or collector box which feeds the engine direct.

Note: A collector box or collector tank is an assembly into which fuel is fed or directed prior to being collected by the suction of the engine driven pump.

5.8 Fuel Tank Pressurisation.

Some aircraft fuel tanks, in particular auxiliary tanks, are pressurised to force fuel from them to the engine or main tanks. Fuel tanks are pressurised in a number of ways, a typical example being that where pressure is fed from the exhaust side of the vacuum pumps, and delivered to the fuel tank venting system, which is then sealed.

When auxiliary fuel tanks are used to replenish main tanks they are pressurised at all times, fuel being transferred automatically under the control of a float valve in each main tank whenever the contents fall below a predetermined level.

Pressurisation of the fuel tank or tanks also prevents cavitation at the pumps.

Note: Some fuel tanks are pressurised by a ram air system and all fuel tank pressurisation systems include the fitting of a relief valve to prevent over pressurising.

5.9 Electrically-Operated Pumps.

The type of electrically-operated pump discussed here is sometimes termed a pulsometer pump and is commonly used in external booster pumps and transfer pumps.

The pump has a centrifugal impeller, shown in Fig. 5-5, which is driven by an electric motor. Used as a booster pump the unit is normally bolted to the base of the fuel tank sump by means of a flanged mounting bracket. When the motor is energised the impeller draws fuel from the tank through the inlet in the centre of the mounting flange and delivers it through the discharge connection to the inlet side of the engine driven pump.

Note: In the event of pump failure, fuel can still be drawn through the pump by the engine-driven pump.

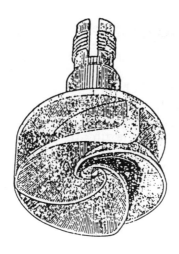

Figure 5–5   Impeller of Pulsometer Pump.

5.10   Hand-Operated Priming Pumps.

An example of a hand-operated priming pump is shown in Fig. 5-6. This type of pump is generally used for starting engines on light aircraft.

It delivers fuel to the induction manifold jets, and is sometimes used to fill the carburettor float chamber initially through a three-way cock.

When the plunger is pushed right in, it may be locked by screwing tight, so pressing a Tufnol pad against the lower end of the cylinder. This blocks the inlet and outlet ports and ensures that no fuel can be drawn through the pump by induction when the engine is running. The inlet and outlet ports are fitted with spring loaded non-return ball valves. A gland, gland nut and locking nut prevent leaks around the plunger.

Failure to depress the plunger and lock it on completion of priming will result in fuel being drawn through the pump direct into the inlet manifold by the suction of the engine's pistons, by-passing the carburettor and resulting in a rich mixture or, possibly, flooding the engine.

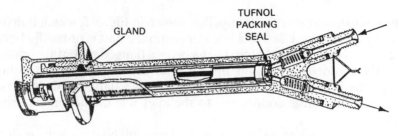

Figure 5–6 Hand-operated priming pump.

5.11 Electrically-Operated Priming Pumps.

Piston-engined aircraft fitted with fuel injection systems are normally primed by operation of an electrically operated pump, usually in the form of a booster type. It should be noted that the booster pump, on starting, is used only to prime the engine fuel system and should then be switched off before any attempt is made to start the engine. If the booster pump were to be left on during starting this could, in some cases, result in flooding the engine.

Note: Priming the engine fuel system is to fill the system with fuel and not to pressurise it.

5.12 Aviation Gasoline Fuels.

(a) **Properties.**

Gasolines, suitable for use in piston engines designed for aircraft, have high anti-knock ratings, low freezing point, high overall volatility and high stability. These together with the solvent and corrosion properties are briefly discussed below.

(i) Anti-Knock Rating.

To appreciate the need for a fuel of high anti-knock rating, the cause of detonation must be understood. Vapourised fuel mixed with air within a certain range of proportions (fuel/air ratio) forms a combustible mixture and when ignited generates heat. Provided that the combustion rate is steady, the heat generated can be efficiently converted into mechanical energy until all the charge is burnt. If a charge of mixture is ignited in a confined space (combustion chamber), the decreasing unburned portion of charge will be steadily heated by radiation, and compression due to the increase in pressure, of the burnt portion. The temperature of the unburned portion may be raised so high that it ignites spontaneously and combustion is completed in the form of an explosion. Such a condition is known as "Detonation" and, when occurring in an aircraft engine, causes serious loss of power, excessive temperature and eventual mechanical failure. Incorrect mixture strength and use of a fuel with a poor anti-knock value are two of the contributing causes of detonation in an engine.

(ii) Anti-knock Value.
The anti-knock value of fuel is defined as the resistance the fuel has to detonation. Examination of the behaviour of a range of hydrocarbon fuels in an engine shows that:
    a. Paraffins (Heptane, has pronounced tendency to detonate. Iso-octane resists detonation).
    b. Napthenes, have moderate resistance to detonation.
    c. Aromatics, have excellent anti-knock properties.

Thus the anti-knock value of a fuel is dependent on the portions of its hydrocarbon contents. By selective blending fuels of high anti-knock ratings are produced. Research has established that the anti-knock value of a fuel varies with the fuel/air ratio, the value being lower for a weak mixture and higher for a rich mixture.
Apart from the choice of hydrocarbons, the anti-knock rating of gasoline is effectively increased by the addition of metallic compounds. Tetra-ethyl lead, a chemical compound of a hydrocarbon with lead, is the most powerful and best known anti-knock compound in use.

(iii) Volatility.
The definition of a volatile liquid is one which is capable of readily changing from the liquid to the vapour state by the application of heat, or by contact with a gas into which it can evaporate. The mixture of hydrocarbon components of a gasoline boil at different temperatures, the lowest components boiling at about 100°F and the highest at about 340°F.

(iv) Solvent Properties.
Aromatic hydrocarbons, forming up to 20 per cent, by volume, of high grade aviation gasoline, are powerful solvents of rubber and some rubber like compounds. It is therefore essential that care is exercised, during handling and filling operations, to ensure that gasoline is not spilled on aircraft tyres and other rubber covered components.

(v) Corrosive Properties.
The corrosive effects of gasoline are caused by the sulphur and additive contents. Gasoline will have corrosive effects to

components it comes into contact with in both its burnt and unburnt states. New alloys and treatments to surfaces has helped to reduce the corrosive effects.

Note: The most common fuel used for piston-engined aircraft is 100 LL, which is dyed blue.

Section 5 Test Yourself

Fuel Systems

1. Fuel pumps:

   (a)   should not be run when the fuel system is dry.

   (b)   of all types are lubricated by the fuel that passes through them.

   (c)   are normally electrically operated.

Ref. 5.4.

2. Booster pumps are:

   (a)   normally driven by the engine.

   (b)   electrically operated.

   (c)   normally used for priming the engine only.

Ref. 5.7.

3. If the fuel pressure warning light comes on in flight the:

   (a)   booster pumps must be isolated.

   (b)   main fuel pump must be isolated.

   (c)   booster pumps must be switched on.

Ref. 5.7.

4. In the event of booster pump failure, the:

   (a)   fuel will continue to be drawn through the booster pump bypass by the engine driven pump.

   (b)   pump must be isolated and the remaining fuel in the tank transferred by the transfer pumps.

   (c)   fuel will be isolated in the tank.

Ref. 5.9.

5. Fuel pump delivery is normally:

   (a)   supplied at a constant flow rate to the engine.

   (b)   supplied at a constant pressure, controlled by a pressure relief valve.

   (c)   supplied at a constant volume.

Ref. 5.4.

6

Cooling Systems

6.1 Introduction.

Of the total heat produced by the burning of the fuel in the combustion chamber of a piston engine, about one-third is converted into useful energy and about two-fifths passes direct to the atmosphere with the exhaust gases. The remaining heat is absorbed by the pistons, cylinder heads, cylinders, etc, and by the lubricating oils which splash the cylinder walls and the underside of the pistons. Consequently, a cooling system becomes necessary to dissipate this heat so that the components can run at a safe working temperature. Unless the component temperature is controlled, distortion from expansion may cause seizure, or the strength of the material may drop to a degree where failure results. Excessive temperature may also cause the oil film to break down and can lead to the destruction of the lubricating properties of the oil. Conversely, to run an engine cold is to run it inefficiently, just as dissipating heat that can be turned into useful work is to waste energy. The transfer of the excess heat of the engine to the atmosphere may be either direct, as with air cooling, or by the use of a circulating liquid as in liquid cooled engines.

6.2 Air Cooling.

With air cooling all the surfaces that need to be cooled are usually extensively finned and a flow of air is directed over the exposed surfaces. The fins are kept thin and as close together as compatible with a free passage of air, thus securing a large cooling surface area in contact with the air. With fin areas that are out of the main airstream, deflectors may be used to redirect the air, or finning may be extended in that region, to maintain a uniform overall component temperature; uneven temperature will cause distortion and give rise to a high rate of wear and a general loss in efficiency. Control of the direction of air flow is effected by fixed baffles and cowlings and by movable shutters or guides. It is essential that the baffles and cowlings are close fitting and are not distorted, or disturbance from the designed flow will cause serious overheating. To maintain the efficiency of the system fins must be kept clean and free from dust or oil. A guide to the engine temperature is provided by a cylinder head temperature gauge.

6.3   Liquid Cooling.

With a liquid-cooled engine the engine temperature is controlled by circulating a cooling fluid around the space between the jackets fitted round the cylinders and the cylinder walls, and through passages drilled in the cylinder head. The basic coolant is water, but because of the low temperatures found at altitude, the addition of an anti-freeze agent is essential; thus, the coolant used in an aero-engine is a mixture of water and glycol. A simple system consists of the following:

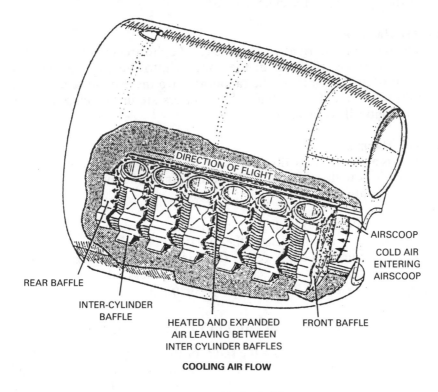

DIRECTION OF FLIGHT

AIRSCOOP

COLD AIR
ENTERING
AIRSCOOP

REAR BAFFLE

INTER-CYLINDER
BAFFLE

HEATED AND EXPANDED
AIR LEAVING BETWEEN
INTER CYLINDER BAFFLES

FRONT BAFFLE

COOLING AIR FLOW

Figure 6–1 Air-Cooled System.

(a) The Header Tank.
   This tank, positioned at the top of the system, stores the reserve of coolant and provides a head (gravity feed) of coolant to the pump.

65

(b) The Circulating Pump.
This is usually a centrifugal pump but does not produce pressure: it is fitted to increase the speed of the coolant flow through the system and so reduce the quantity of coolant required.

(c) Operation.
The coolant passes through the engine. While the main passages are centred around the cylinder heads and valves, it is sometimes found that the hot coolant is directed to jackets fitted to the induction pipe and supercharger casings. This auxiliary flow assists in vapourising the fuel/air mixture. The coolant flow through the engine is arranged to follow the normal course of the thermal current, i.e. from the base of the cylinders to the cylinder head.

(d) The Radiator.
The radiator is normally positioned in the slipstream of the propeller and dissipates the heat of the coolant into the air. Shutters are positioned at the rear of the radiator; when the coolant temperature falls below an efficient figure the shutters are inched closed, either automatically or manually.

(e) The Thermostat.
This is a thermostatically operated by-pass valve which regulates the coolant flow through the radiator and limits the minimum coolant temperature while the engine is running.

Note: Cleanliness both of the coolant and the system is imperative if the system is to remain efficient; the radiator matrix must be kept clean and free from dirt and oil. A gauge, fitted in the cockpit, gives an indication of the temperature of the coolant in the header tank.
Fig. 6-2 shows a simple liquid coolant system.

6.4 Operation of Typical Liquid Coolant System.

Coolant enters the pump from the radiator through the large inlet at the bottom. The pump is of the normal type with a sixteen-vaned rotor and a volute. Two curved outlet passages are formed on the volute, one to each side of the engine. A hand adjusted packing gland prevents coolant leakage past the pump spindle, and lubrication is by a screw down grease cup. Excessive lubrication of the spindle will result in grease entering the coolant system and possibly becoming trapped in the cylinder head, where it will cause overheating. Extra lubrication will not cure a leaking gland. The pump is fitted with a drain cock at its lowest point for use when draining the system.

From the end of each outlet passage from the pump volute a curved pipe carries the coolant to a junction box on each of the cylinder blocks, situated low down at the rear on the exhaust side. Inside the block the coolant passes around each cylinder liner, through the passages surrounding the combustion head and valve ports and thence to the outlets. A coolant manifold connects the cylinder liner jackets together on the exhaust side. There are three outlets, one at each end and one in the centre of the inlet side at the top of each block. These outlets are connected by a pipe on each block which carries the coolant towards the front of the engine. Each pipe is connected independently to the header tank, and from the header tank the coolant passes to the radiator. Each front cylinder block outlet elbow is fitted with an air vent plug to facilitate complete filling.

On the 'A' side rear outlet elbow a connection is formed from which a pipe carries a small stream of hot coolant to a union on the carburettor heating jacket. The outlet from this jacket is on the starboard side and the coolant returns to the pump through a small auxiliary inlet branch on the main inlet.

Pipe junctions on the engine are made with a large circular nut round the pipe flange and a rubber gland to make the joint coolant-tight. Pipe junctions on the remainder of the coolant system are usually made with short lengths of reinforced rubber tubing or hose secured to the pipe ends with circumferential clips.

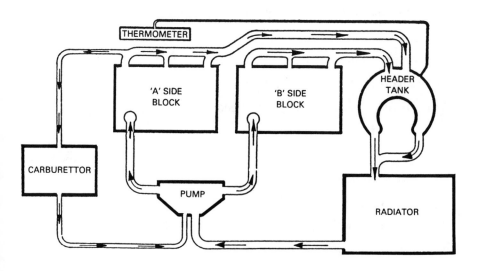

Figure 6–2 Liquid Cooled System.

Section 6 Test Yourself

Cooling Systems

1. In an aircooled piston engine:

   (a) fins are incorporated to increase the cylinder and head surface areas.

   (b) air is ducted through drillings in the cylinder head walls.

   (c) air is used to cool the cooling oil.

Ref. 6.2.

2. Air is directed over the cylinder wall fins by:

   (a) cowl gills.

   (b) baffles.

   (c) air deflection plates.

Ref. 6.2.

3. Engine temperature is normally indicated by:

   (a) cylinder head temperature gauge.

   (b) the engine master temperature gauge.

   (c) the engine lubrication system temperature gauge.

Ref. 6.2.

4. Cooling air is normally provided by:

   (a) airflow from a supercharger.

   (b) airflow from a compressor bleed.

   (c) ram air.

Ref. 6.2.

5. In a liquid-cooled engine cooling system:

   (a) temperature is controlled by a thermostat.

   (b) temperature is controlled by a master pump.

   (c) fuel is used to cool the coolant.

Ref. 6.3.

7

Float Chamber Carburettors and Fuel Injectors

7.1 Introduction.

Carburation is the process of supplying the correct amount of fuel for mixing and vapourising with the air inducted into the engine to form a suitable combustible mixture. The proportions of fuel to air in a chemically correct or normal mixture is approximately 1 to 15 by weight. This mixture is theoretically the most efficient for all engine running conditions, but in practice it is sometimes necessary or advantageous to use either a 'rich' mixture (one with a higher proportion of fuel), or a 'weak' mixture (one with a higher proportion of air). The device employed for supplying the necessary amount of fuel to form the most suitable mixture for any engine running conditions may be either a float type carburettor or some form of fuel injection unit. This chapter describes both the working principle of the simple float type carburettor, and the modifications which are embodied to adapt it for efficient operation to suit piston aero-engine requirements.

7.2 The Simple Float Type Carburettor.

(a) Description.
In its simplest form the carburettor may consist of a tube or jet mounted in a larger tube in which is arranged a throttle valve and choke tube. In addition, the jet is connected to a float chamber, vented to atmosphere, which houses a float operating a needle valve. A predetermined and constant level of fuel is maintained in the float chamber and the jet, by means of the float and needle mechanism.

(b) Operation.
Air drawn into the engine cylinder, governed by the degree of throttle opening, enters the carburettor through the air intake. At the restriction caused by the choke tube the velocity of the air is increased. The increased velocity of the air, within the choke tube and in the region

69

of the jet, is accompanied by a fall in pressure below that of the atmosphere. As the fuel in the float chamber is subject to atmospheric pressure, a higher pressure than around the jet, fuel issues from the jet and mixes with the airstream flowing to the engine cylinders. The fall in the level of the fuel in the float chamber lowers the float which lifts the needle valve off its seating, permitting more fuel to flow into the float chamber to replace that issuing from the jet. (See Fig. 7-1).

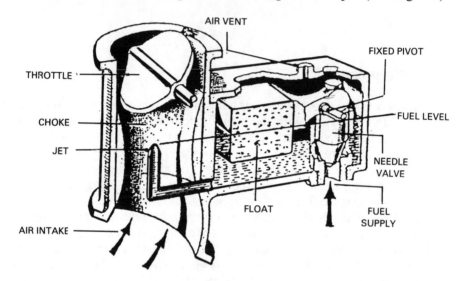

Figure 7–1 Simple Float Type Carburettor.

(c) Limitation.
Any increase in airflow will increase the pressure difference acting across the jet and consequently increase the fuel flow. The fuel flow, however, does not vary proportionately with greater airflow, and the mixture obtained from the simple carburettor becomes progressively richer as the engine speed is increased.

Note: From time to time alternative names are given to components fitted to aircraft, and the carburation system is no exception, therefore to assist in your understanding of the system as a whole alternative names are used in order to familiarise you with them. For example:

(a)   Throttle .... often called the Butterfly

(b)   Needle Valve ...... sometimes termed the Float Valve

(c)   Choke .... equally termed the venturi

(d)   Air Vent .... often called the Breather

70

7.3 Modifications to a Simple Carburettor.

The following additions and modifications have been made to the simple carburettor, to provide one more suitable for use on piston aero-engines.

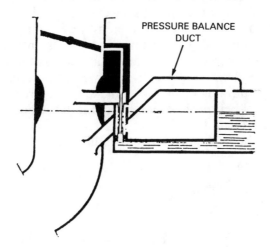

Figure 7–2 Pressure Balance Duct.

(a) Pressure Balance Air System.
To prevent upsetting the rate of discharge of fuel from the jet, the atmospheric pressure in the air intake and in the float chamber must be equal. Admitting atmospheric pressure into the float chamber through a drilling in the float chamber cover is not a satisfactory method of equalising pressures on an aero-engine carburettor because, due to manoeuvre and speed of the aircraft, the changes of pressure localised around the air intake would not be readily transmitted to the float chamber. Equalised pressure conditions are, however, obtained by admitting atmospheric pressure to the float chamber through a tube or duct opening into the air intake. This pressure balance duct also supplies air to the diffuser, and is used in some carburettors to provide altitude mixture control.
Figure 7-2 shows the position of the pressure balance duct.

(b) Diffuser.
A diffuser is fitted to prevent the main jet supplying excessive fuel as engine speed is increased; it ensures that the fuel flow is kept directly proportional to the volume of air flowing through the choke. The diffuser is basically a tube, drilled with a number of radial holes, and

positioned in the body of the carburettor above the main jet. The annular space between the diffuser and its housing is in communication with the pressure balance air system. Fuel enters the diffuser through the jet and when the engine is not running, the fuel level in the diffuser and the annular space is the same as that in the float chamber. During operation, as the engine speed is increased the fuel level in the annular space falls, thereby uncovering some of the radial holes. This allows air to flow through the holes into the diffuser, thus lessening the pressure difference acting across the jet and counteracting the tendency of the jet to supply excessive fuel. The diffuser, in addition to fulfilling its primary function, also breaks down or emulsifies the fuel before the fuel is passed into the airstream flowing to the induction manifold.

Figure 7-3 shows the position of the diffuser.

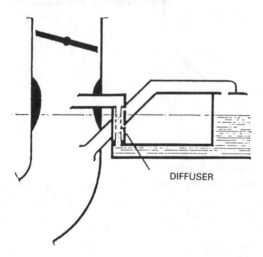

Figure 7–3 Diffuser.

(c) Slow Running Jet.

At small throttle openings the depression in the choke is practically negligible and no fuel flows from the main jet. A separate slow running jet is fitted, therefore, to supply the fuel necessary for slow running. The jet discharges near to the edge of the almost closed throttle, the strong depression at this point giving the necessary pressure difference. As the throttle is opened the depression at the throttle edge increases; the slow running jet will go out of action and the main jet will come into action. The slow running jet is arranged to give the rich mixture required over the idling range. Adjustment is usually carried out by an adjusting screw to vary the pressure difference acting across the jet.

Figure 7-4 shows the location of the slow running jet.

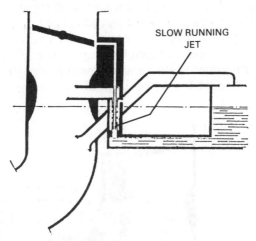

SLOW RUNNING
JET

Figure 7–4 Slow Running Jet.

(d) Power Jet.

The mixture strength supplied by the diffuser for 'cruising' condition is too weak for the engine to develop its full power output. To supply the extra fuel necessary for full power, the size or number of jets must be increased. Where a variable main jet is fitted its effective size is varied by the withdrawal of a tapered needle from the jet orifice; where a fixed main jet is fitted an additional jet is brought into action by the opening of a cam operated valve.

Figure 7-5 shows the power jet.

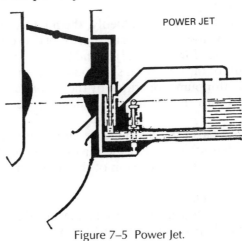

POWER JET

Figure 7–5 Power Jet.

73

(e) Enrichment Jet.

For the short period necessary during 'take-off' for an aircraft to become safely airborne, the maximum permissible engine power is required and supercharged engines are designed to develop additional power for this purpose. One method of obtaining this power increase with safety is to supply the engine with a very rich mixture. The fuel for this purpose is delivered from an enrichment jet which operates in a similar manner to the cam-operated power jet.

Figure 7-6 indicates the position of the enrichment jet.

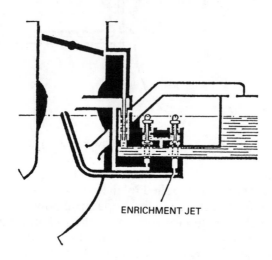

ENRICHMENT JET

Figure 7–6 Enrichment Jet.

(f) Accelerator Pump.

If the throttle is opened suddenly, the mixture supplied to the cylinders is momentarily too weak, partly because there is a lag in the increase of fuel flow from the jet, and because some of the fuel adheres to the walls of the induction system and does not reach the cylinders. An accelerator pump, operated by the movement of the throttle lever, injects fuel into the airstream to make up for this temporary deficiency.

Sometimes a spring operated delayed action pump maintains the flow for a few seconds after the throttle opening has ceased.

Figure 7-7 shows the inclusion of the accelerator pump.

(g) Mixture Control.

The density of air decreases with increasing altitude and consequently less weight of air is inducted for the same velocity of air through the

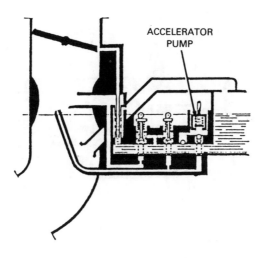

ACCELERATOR
PUMP

Figure 7–7 Accelerator.

choke. Thus a carburettor using the venturi choke as an airflow meter, delivers a progressively richer mixture as the altitude of operation increases.

Various methods are employed to correct the mixture strength at altitude. In the smaller aircraft engines this mixture control is hand operated, but on engines of medium and high power output, mixture strength is automatically controlled.

The methods employed for correcting mixture strength for altitude are as follows:

(i) Vacuum Control.

The pressure difference acting on the jet is reduced by connecting the float chamber to the choke via an orifice whose size is varied by the mixture control cock. By opening the cock the float chamber pressure can be reduced to give a pressure difference across the jet consistent with the mixture strength required.

Figure 7-8 shows the position of the mixture control.

(ii) Diffuser Air Bleed.

Air is by-passed through the mixture control cock, from the pressure balance air system to the top of the diffuser thus reducing the pressure difference across the jet.

Note: A combination of (i) and (ii) is common in some types of carburettors.

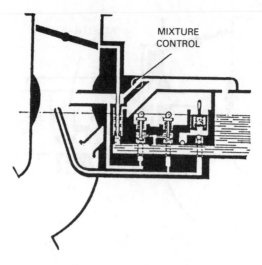

Figure 7–8 Mixture Control.

(h) Cut-Out Valve.

To stop a running engine, the ignition is switched off, but, due to the engine being hot and fuel being available at the slow running jet, the engine may continue running for a time, albeit erratically. To prevent this occurring a device is inserted into the slow running passage, which, when operated prevents any fuel from being drawn into the induction system.

Figure 7-9 shows the cut-out valve position.

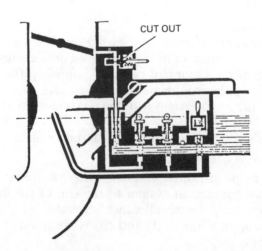

Figure 7–9 Cut-Out.

(i) 'Anti-G' Devices.
When the direction of an aircraft is suddenly changed, forces which oppose the change of direction are imposed upon the aircraft components. Fuel, being fluid, is moved in the direction of the opposing force, and in a dive at high speed the fuel may be momentarily thrown to the top of the float chamber. This interferes with the normal fuel flow with the result that the engine runs erratically or may even stop. Various 'anti-G' devices are incorporated in the carburettor design to assist in maintaining the power output of the engine while 'negative-G' conditions prevail during aerobatics; the following being typical examples of these devices.

(1) Float Needle 'Anti-G' Stop.
An adjustable stop fitted above the float needle, in conjunction with a collar on the lower end of the needle, restricts the needle movement and fuel flow during aerobatics, to allow the entry of only sufficient fuel to keep the engine running at maximum power conditions.

(2) 'Anti-G' Ball Valve.
A ball valve, fitted to the pressure balance vent in the float chamber, prevents fuel spillage into the choke during negative-G flying conditions.

(3) 'Anti-G' Stand Tube.
Engine cutting due to fuel starvation is precluded by a stand tube which feeds the metering jet from the centre of the float chamber.

Figure 7-10 shows the various 'Anti-G' devices listed above.

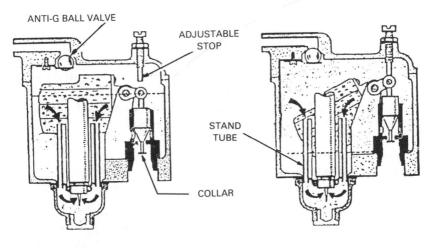

Figure 7–10 Carburettor Anti-'G' Devices.

77

7.4   Carburettor Heating.

(a) General.

To ensure satisfactory operation and efficient carburation some parts of the carburettor, in particular the throttle, choke and air intake, must be maintained at temperatures which will prevent the formation and accumulation of ice. Icing encountered by aircraft engines can be divided into two distinct types, carburettor icing and impact icing. Each is formed in a different manner and may occur either separately or together between atmospheric temperatures of -15°C and +25°C. Ice formed at temperatures below this range is of a sufficiently dry nature not to adhere and accumulate within the carburettor or around the air intake.

(i) Carburettor Icing.
The construction in the induction system caused by the choke and the throttle valve not only cause an increase in the velocity and a decrease in the pressure of the inducted air, but also lower the temperature. Furthermore, as heat is required to convert a liquid into a gas, the fuel which vaporises in the induction system absorbs heat from the inducted air and the surrounding metal, resulting in an additional drop in temperature. When the temperature of the air is reduced to below 0°C the moisture content in the air begins to precipitate and form as ice. The added constriction caused by the ice formation results in an increasing air velocity and a progressive lowering of the temperature. In these conditions ice builds up more rapidly in the system causing loss of engine power, rough running and jamming of the throttle valve.

(ii) Impact Icing.
This form of icing occurs most readily at temperatures between 0°C and –7°C and is caused by rain droplets turning into ice on striking the exposed surfaces of the carburettor. The ice adheres and builds up around the air intake so disturbing the airflow, upsetting the mixture strength and resulting in rough running and loss of power and may even stop the engine.

(b) Protection Against Ice.

The various methods and devices used to prevent or disperse ice formation in and around the carburettor are described as follows:

(i) Gapped Ice Guards.
A gapped ice guard consists of a wire screen mounted a suitable distance ahead of the air intake. Should the ice guard become blocked with snow or ice, air can continue to flow into the carbu-

rettor through the gap formed between the guard and the intake. This device gives protection against impact ice.

(ii) Sheltered Air Intake.
This device is used in conjunction with the gapless type ice guard. The sheltered air intakes, which provide an alternative entry for the air, are situated within the engine cowling and are fitted with shutters operated either automatically or by electro-pneumatic rams controlled by switches in the pilot's cockpit. The automatically operated shutters are opened by the depression created in the air intake system as the gapless ice guard becomes blocked with ice. Additionally the sheltered intake may be designed to draw its air from around heated parts of the engine or coolant radiator, thus supplying heated air to the carburettor.

(iii) Alcohol Injection System.
In some installations, an alcohol injection system is incorporated in addition to the heated air system, and is used as an emergency method of dispersing ice which may form in spite of the use of the warm air system. The system comprises an electrically-driven or hand operated pump delivering alcohol from a small supply tank to jets positioned in the carburettor air intake, which direct the spray of spirit towards the throttles. Generally the supply of de-icing spirit is sufficient for ten to fifteen minutes continuous operation at the maximum delivery rate.

(iv) Heated Throttles and Throttle Housings.
Carburettor icing is best prevented by circulating hot oil from the engine scavenge system, through jackets surrounding the throttle bores, and through the hollow spindles and throttle valves. This method, in conjunction with a controlled heated air supply for the air intake, is usually adequate and does not require the addition of a de-icing spirit injection system.

Note: The operational effects of carburettor heating are explained in Section 10.

7.5   Injection Carburettors.

The Stromberg injection carburettor differs from the previous carburettors in that it is not fitted with a float chamber nor does the choke depression act directly on the jets. The choke is known as the large venturi and inside it a small or boost venturi is fitted; this has the effect of lowering the pressure still further and this depression in the boost venturi acts upon a diaphragm which in turn regulates the flow of fuel into the carburettor by means of a poppet valve. The fuel is discharged through a spray nozzle fitted near to the eye of the supercharger. This arrangement has the following advantages:

(a)   The amount of fuel passing through the jet is dependent on the pressure inside the carburettor and is therefore almost unaffected by aerobatics and negative-G conditions.

(b)   The spray nozzle helps to atomise the fuel.

(c)   Fuel under pressure reduces the liability of vapour locks.

(d)   There is no vaporisation and consequent cold spot around the jet mouths; this helps to prevent ice formation.

Note: In this type of carburettor, the choke is retained purely as a means of measuring the airflow.

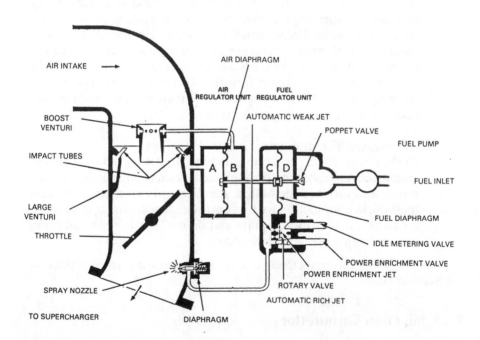

Figure 7–11 Fuel Injection Carburettor.

7.6   Fuel Injectors.

Fuel injectors differ fundamentally from float-type and injection carburettors in that the airflow to the engine is not measured by a venturi. They are thus, strictly speaking, not carburettors but engine driven pumps which supply fuel direct to the cylinders via the supercharger or turbocharger in accordance with engine requirements.

Figure 7-11 is a diagram of a fuel injector which is fitted in place of the standard engine fuel pump, and which also performs all the functions of a normal aircraft carburettor. The air supply to the engine is controlled in the usual way by a throttle valve in conjunction with a boost control unit (not shown in the diagram). Fuel is forced into the governor chamber by a vane type feed pump, which is designed to supply an excess, so that surplus fuel escapes through the relief valve and the pressure in the governor chamber remains constant.

Rotation of the governor causes the needle valve to be opened and fuel to flow, first into the governor chamber, and then through the two variable jets into the metered fuel chamber. The difference in pressure between the governed and metered fuel chambers acting on the diaphragm tends to close the needle valve in opposition to the action of the governor. Because the thrust exerted by a centrifugal governor is proportional to the square of the rpm and as the diaphragm always balances that thrust, the pressure difference across the diaphragm is also proportional to the square of the rpm. Consequently, as the flow of fuel through a jet is proportional to the square root of the pressure difference across it, for a given opening of the jets the fuel flow through them will vary directly with the engine speed.

The pressure in the governor chamber being higher than that in the governed fuel chamber, there is a small residual pressure on the needle valve tending to close it. This is balanced out by the 'idle' spring fitted against the outer surface of the diaphragm. The spring load is adjustable to provide a means of varying the fuel flow at idling conditions, when the thrust from the governor is very small.

The flow of fuel through the main jet (at a given rpm) is governed by the boost pressure and the exhaust back pressure. Ignoring the latter for the moment, the effect of an increase in boost is to compress the evacuated boost pressure capsules, thus causing the main metering needle to withdraw and the flow of fuel through the jet to increase. Control of mixture strength to suit all operating conditions is effected by variation in the taper of the main metering needle, so that the rich/weak/rich characteristic is automatically provided over the whole range of boost pressures from idling to take-off. As the flow of fuel is governed by boost and rpm, no altitude control of the kind fitted to float type carburettors is required.

It will be recalled that the fall in air pressure with altitude results in less exhaust gas remaining in the cylinders at the end of each exhaust stroke and, consequently, the volumetric efficiency improves, ie more mixture goes into each cylinder at a given induction pressure. In the float type carburettor the extra fuel is automatically drawn off by the increased depression in the choke, but in a fuel injector, compensation is necessary to avoid weakening of the mixture.

Here compensation is provided by the back pressure capsule which, although integral with the boost pressure capsule, is sealed from it and subjected to atmospheric pressure. Thus, as height is gained the back pressure capsule is compressed and the main metering needle is withdrawn sufficiently to maintain a constant mixture strength. To ensure that the main metering needle responds accurately to capsule movement, it is essential for it not to be a tight fit in its supporting bushes. Consequently, to prevent leakage between the boost and governed fuel chambers, a drainage channel is provided between the bushes.

The introduction of a temperature correction unit to the metering system is necessitated by the fact that, for a constant boost pressure and rpm, the mass airflow through the engine falls as the temperature rises, because of the reduced density of warmer air. As any decrease in airflow must be accompanied by a proportional drop in fuel consumption to maintain a constant mixture strength, a temperature controlled auxiliary jet is added in parallel with the main jet. Control is effected by the single capsule unit, which is coupled by a capillary tube to a thermometer bulb located in the induction manifold, the system normally being filled with turpentine. When the mixture temperature rises, either because of a change in outside air temperature or through a change from low to high supercharger gear, the resulting expansion of the turpentine causes the capsule to compress and the attached metering needle to reduce the fuel flow through the auxiliary jet.

From the injector the metered fuel is delivered to the injection nozzle at the supercharger inlet via the accelerator pump and flexible hose. (See Fig. 7-12).

To maintain a constant discharge pressure, irrespective of the rate of fuel flow, a needle valve, controlled by a spring loaded diaphragm, is included in the nozzle assembly. When the metered fuel pressure rises to approximately 6lb/sq in, the valve diaphragm is forced outwards, thereby opening the valve against the action of the spring. The greater the fuel flow the more the diaphragm will be deflected and the valve opened.

The diaphragm spring chamber is connected by a tube to the air intake via a slow running cut-out device which, when operated, cuts off the air balance connection and admits fuel at pump pressure to the rear of the diaphragm. As soon as the diaphragm spring chamber is filled, the diaphragm is forced inwards and the needle valve thereby closed. When

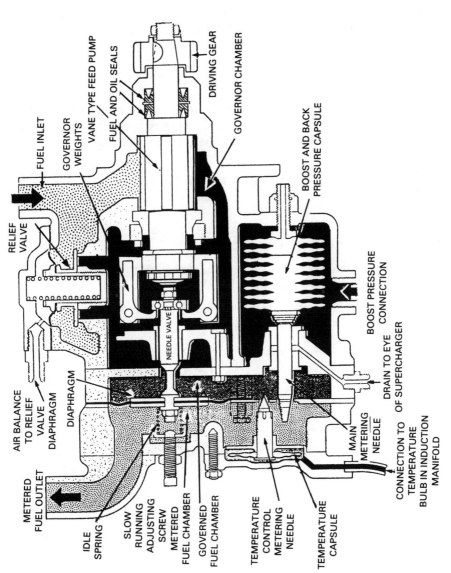

Figure 7–12 Fuel Injection Pump Unit.

the cut-off control is released the air balance connection is restored and fuel from the chamber drains to the air intake.

The accelerator pump shown in Fig. 7-12 is simply a diaphragm operated by the throttle lever. When the throttle is opened the diaphragm is forced in (to the left) and the flow of fuel to the nozzle is temporarily increased.

7.7   Fuel Cut-Off.

A pilot operated fuel cut-off is fitted to most injectors: it cuts off all fuel irrespective of the throttle setting. Some types of injector, however, have a cut-off which functions only when the throttle is closed.

Key Points – Piston Engines

Theory

1.   In a four-stroke engine, the compression stroke follows immediately after the induction stroke.

2.   The number of revolutions of the crankshaft to complete a full cycle in a multi-cylinder engine is ALWAYS two.

3.   The order in which the four strokes occur are: induction, compression, power and exhaust.

4.   A piston engine is known as a CONSTANT VOLUME ENGINE.

5.   During the four-stroke cycle, the spark is timed to occur before TDC on the compression stroke.

6.   The inlet valve closes after BDC on the induction stroke, to allow the maximum amount of mixture to enter the cylinder. (Valve lag)

7.   The exhaust valve closes after TDC on the exhaust stroke, to complete scavenging and to help overcome the inertia of the fresh mixture. (Valve lag)

8.   The inlet valve opens before TDC on the exhaust stroke, to ensure the valve is fully open at TDC. (Valve lead)

9.   The exhaust valve opens before BDC on the power stroke, to relieve the load on the bearings and to make use of the residual gas pressure to assist in the scavenging. (Valve lead)

10.   VALVE LEAD is related to the angular measurement of the crankshaft when the valves open BEFORE BDC and TDC.

11. VALVE LAG is related to the angular movement of the crankshaft when the valves shut AFTER BDC and TDC.

12. VALVE OVERLAP is when both inlet and exhaust valves are open at the same time.

13. The purpose of valve overlap is to offset the inertia of the fresh mixture and to induce it into the cylinder before the piston begins its downward movement.

14. Valve overlap increases volumetric efficiency.

15. Valve overlap will remain the same, whatever the engine rpm.

16. VOLUMETRIC EFFICIENCY is the ratio by weight of a cylinder's total capacity at Standard Atmosphere with the piston at BDC with the actual weight of mixture drawn into the cylinder during the induction stroke. It is usually expressed as a percentage.

17. Volumetric efficiency improves with increase in engine speed.

18. An increase in air temperature will decrease the weight of mixture entering the cylinder.

19. The COMPRESSION RATIO is the ratio of the volume of the cylinder when the piston is at BDC to the volume of the cylinder when the piston is at TDC.

20. The SWEPT VOLUME/STROKE is the distance travelled by a piston moving from BDC to TDC. This is equal to twice the crank throw.

21. The COMPRESSION VOLUME is the volume of the cylinder with the piston at TDC. (Combustion space)

22. The compression ratio is constant for a stated engine and all engine rpm.

23. The compression ratio equals $\dfrac{\text{Total volume}}{\text{Clearance volume}}$

24. The ratio of the power produced by an engine to the power available in the fuel is known as the THERMAL EFFICIENCY.

25. The thermal efficiency of a piston engine increases with an increase of compression ratio.

26. The SPECIFIC FUEL CONSUMPTION (SFC) is the weight of fuel required to produce 1 BHP in 1 hour.

27. INDICATED HORSE POWER (IHP) is the power developed in the cylinder during the power stroke.

28. BRAKE HORSE POWER (BHP) is the useful power developed at the propeller shaft.

29. FRICTION HORSE POWER (FHP) is the power required to overcome friction and drive the accessories.

30. MEAN EFFECTIVE PRESSURE (MEP) is the average pressure exerted on the piston during the power stroke.

31. Brake mean effective pressure is measured by a torquemeter.

32. The weight of charge on the compression stroke will remain the same.

33. The temperature of the charge on the compression stroke will increase.

34. The volume of the mixture will increase on the power stroke.

35. Engine power depends upon: the rpm, compression ratio and combustion pressure.

36. The MECHANICAL EFFICIENCY of an engine is the ratio between the power developed in the cylinders and the power arriving at the propeller shaft; it is usually expressed as a percentage.

37. Most internal combustion piston engines are roughly 90% efficient.

38. The firing order of a four-cylinder in-line engine is 1.3.4.2.

39. The firing order of a six-cylinder in-line engine is 1.5.3.6.2.4.

40. The firing order of a four-cylinder, horizontally opposed (RR Continental) is 1.3.2.4.

41. The camshaft of an engine ALWAYS rotates at ½ engine speed.

42. Volumetric efficiency increases with an increase in engine rpm. At sea level, exhaust back pressure reduces volumetric efficiency.

43. Valve overlap increases volumetric efficiency. As the aircraft climbs, volumetric efficiency will improve as the exhaust back pressure falls.

44. A normally aspirated engine is an unsupercharged engine.

45. When a sparking plug fires in an engine cylinder containing a correct air/fuel mixture, the mixture will burn and the pressure, temperature and volume will all increase.

46. Ignition is advanced as engine speed increases, to ensure that

maximum pressure is developed in the cylinder 6° to 12° after TDC on the power stroke.

Construction

1. The purpose of the crankcase breather is to prevent pressure build-up inside the engine crankcase.

2. The reason for tappet clearance is to allow for expansion due to temperature increases when the engine is running.

3. Tappet clearance is measured between the tip of the valve stem and the rocker pad.

4. Hydraulic tappets are used on some engines to reduce noise and maintenance.

5. If the inlet valve of an engine has insufficient tappet clearance, the effect on engine running will be 'popping-back' in the induction manifold.

6. The inlet and exhaust valves are closed by springs.

7. To improve safety and reduce valve bounce, two or more valve springs, usually coiled in opposite directions, are fitted to each valve.

8. The oil control rings on a piston are located below the compression rings.

Cooling and Lubrication

1. The cylinder head temperature of an air cooled engine could be controlled by cowling gills.

2. Air cooled engines are finned, to present a larger cooling surface to the airflow.

3. The assumed specific gravity of oil is 0.9 and one gallon will weigh 9 lb.

4. The scavenge pump in the oil system has a greater capacity than the pressure pump.

5. A relief valve is fitted on the outlet side of the pressure pump, to prevent excessive pressure being delivered to the engine.

6. The most probable cause of small fluctuations, or low oil pressure, would be the relief valve sticking open.

7. The oil temperature gauge records the temperature of the oil being delivered to the engine.

8. The oil control rings on a piston remove excess oil from the cylinder walls.

9. The viscosity of a lubricating oil will increase with a drop in temperature and lower the rate of flow.

10. A WET SUMP ENGINE is one where the oil is collected in the engine sump.

11. Engine oil contents should be checked a short time after the engine has stopped.

12. The cylinder head temperature measurements are taken from a thermocouple HOT junction. (Cold junction at instrument)

Carburation and Fuel Systems

1. The correct fuel for a piston engine is AVGAS.

2. The chemically correct mixture strength is 15 lb of air to 1 lb of fuel (by weight).

3. The mixture strength for piston engines varies between 8:1 (rich) and 20:1 (weak), to suit engine requirements.

4. Aviation gasolene (AVGAS) is manufactured to conform with Specification DERD 2485.

5. Shell AVGAS 100LL, coloured blue, satisfies the above specification.

6. Lead is added to aviation fuel to decrease the risk of detonation, and is essential to engines with high compression ratios.

7. The weight of 1 gallon of fuel of SG 0.72 is 7.2 lb.

8. The octane rating defines the ability of a fuel to resist detonation; the higher the number, the greater the resistance.

9. Pre-ignition is caused by the ignition of the fuel/air mixture by hot spots in the cylinder and will occur before the spark.

10. Detonation occuring after the spark is caused by unstable combustion during the power stroke.

11. The purpose of the choke tube (venturi) in a carburettor is to create a depression at the fuel jet.

12. The pressure in the carburettor choke tube will decrease with an increase in engine speed.

13. The position of the throttle valve (butterfly) in a carburettor depends on the direction of the airflow through the choke.

14. The mixture control on a carburettor varies the flow of fuel to the main jet.

15. The fuel flow to the engine will be affected by: the rpm, throttle position and mixture setting.

16. The effect of a punctured float would be flooding of the carburettor.

17. The slow running jet is located in the choke tube, where the throttle valve closes and the depression is greatest.

18. The purpose of a diffuser is to meter the fuel correctly for all engine speeds and to improve its vapourisation.

19. To compensate for poor scavenging of the exhaust gases at slow running, the mixture is enriched.

20. At full power, the mixture is enriched to ensure satisfactory cylinder cooling, to prevent detonation.

21. The purpose of an altitude mixture control is to correct the mixture strength for the decreasing density of the air as altitude is increased.

22. An accelerator pump is fitted to compensate for a 'weak cut' on rapid opening of the throttle.

23. The 'back-suction economiser' reduces pressure in the float chamber to reduce the differential pressure, thus weakening the mixture for economical cruising.

24. A weak mixture decreases the specific fuel consumption.

25. The fuel pump in the fuel system ensures a positive flow to the float chamber.

26. When fuel priming is used to assist engine starting, a quantity of fuel is supplied directly into the induction manifold.

27. A booster pump prevents vapour locks which occur due to the decrease in pressure with increasing altitude.

28. Should the priming pump not be locked in after start-up, a rich mixture will result.

29. The vent pipe of an aircraft's fuel tank must not become blocked, because, as the fuel level drops, the pressure will fall and the flow will be restricted.

30. Water in a fuel tank will sink to the bottom of the tank.

31. When the aircraft is on the ground, the correct action to reduce the possibility of water entering the fuel system, due to condensation, is to keep the fuel tanks full.

32. In a direct fuel injection system, the mixture control is manually controlled and a manual priming pump is unnecessary.

33. In a direct fuel injection system, the fuel enters the inlet manifold continuously.

Ignition Systems

1. The primary circuit of a magneto receives its initial current from a magnetic field build-up across the primary coil.

2. The electrical current flowing in a magneto is transformed from low to high tension by the rapid collapse of the magnetic field across the secondary windings.

3. To assist in the rapid breakdown of the magnetic field across the secondary windings, a capacitor (condenser) is fitted.

4. A capacitor is also fitted to prevent arcing across the contact breaker points.

5. The spark in the combustion chamber occurs when the contact breaker points are JUST opening.

6. The distributor of a magneto distributes the secondary current to the correct sparking plug at the correct time.

7. The engine speed falls when one magneto is switched off, due to the flame rate of the burning mixture being reduced.

8. To stop an engine, the magneto switch is switched 'OFF'; this earths the primary circuit.

9. If a magneto becomes disconnected from its ignition switch, the switch will fail to stop the engine when switched 'OFF'.

10. The effect of a magneto switch lead shorting to the aircraft structure in flight would be to cause the engine speed to fall.

11. An ignition switch which becomes 'shorted out' on one magneto would cause a dead cut when the other magneto switch was switched 'OFF'.

12. The impulse coupling in a magneto flicks over the armature when starting, to increase the HT current and give a better spark.

13. The impulse coupling operates as a solid magneto drive coupling after the engine has started up.

14. To assist in the starting of a piston engine, a high tension booster coil is used. This supplies HT current directly to the sparking plugs through a retarded electrode on the rotor arm. It is sometimes known as the 'shower of sparks' system.

15. What happens if vent becomes blocked in a magneto. Answer = Corrosion takes place.

Ground Handling

1. Before starting an engine, the propeller should be rotated slowly by hand for a few revolutions, to relieve any 'hydraulicing'.

2. Hydraulicing refers to an accumulation of liquid in a cylinder which could cause damage to the engine on start-up.

3. When starting an engine, it is dangerous to pump the throttle lever, because there could be a risk of fire in the carburettor air intake.

4. Prolonged idling may cause fouling of the spark plugs.

5. Carbon deposits on a spark plug electrode may cause misfiring.

6. Black smoke from the exhaust would indicate a too-rich mixture.

7. Magnetos should be checked at slow running, to ensure that the ignition system is serviceable, before a check is made at a higher rpm.

8. The engine is checked for 'dead-cut' at slow running.

9. Excessive engine vibration may be caused if the propeller blades are out of track.

10. A weak mixture could be detected by a large drop in rpm when a single ignition check is carried out.

11. The engine power required to rotate a fixed pitch propeller will increase as air temperature falls.

12. The rpm of an engine on the approach must be at a specific limit, so that it will be able to accelerate when necessary.

13. The ratio of power required to power available affects the fuel consumption.

14. During take-off, an increase in rpm at a fixed throttle setting is caused by a more efficient angle of attack of the propeller blades.

15. For an aircraft with a fixed pitch propeller, when taking off from an airfield with a higher ambient temperature, the rpm would be less than normal.

16. On a normally aspirated engine fitted with a fixed pitch propeller, the manifold pressure decreases as the aircraft climbs at a fixed throttle setting.

17. Excessive cylinder head temperatures could be caused by prolonged use of a weak mixture, especially at high altitude.

18. Lower barometric pressure on a power check will mean less engine power.

19. Weak mixture gives a reduction in power and also decreases the specific fuel consumption.

20. Prolonged operation of an aero-engine at high rpm, in conditions where the atmospheric temperature is high, could result in the possibility of overheating and detonation.

21. Carburettor heat during ground run and take-off must be OFF, as the hot air is unfiltered and may cause engine wear.

22. Carburettor hot air is used in flight to overcome carburettor icing.

23. On a normally aspirated engine fitted with a fixed pitch propeller, carburettor icing may be indicated by a fall in rpm for no apparent reason.

24. On selection of carburettor heat to HOT during a ground run, a fall in rpm should be observed.

25. An engine should be run at low rpm after flight, to allow engine components to cool to a more uniform temperature.

26. Upon starting, if the 'STARTER ENGAGED' light stays on, it means that power is still connected to the starter and, if it is still on after 30 seconds, the cause must be investigated.

Section 7 Test Yourself
Carburettors and Injectors

1. An alternative name sometimes given to the choke is the:

    (a)   butterfly.

    (b)   venturi.

    (c)   intake controller.

Ref. 7.2. Fig. 7-1.

2. As engine speed is increased:

    (a)   excessive fuel is prevented from passing through the main jet by the diffuser.

    (b)   excessive fuel is prevented from passing through the main jet by the pressure duct.

    (c)   the variable jet increases fuel supply with altitude.

Ref. 7.3(b). Fig. 7-3.

3. During take-off, to assist in achieving maximum permissible engine power:

    (a)   the accelerator pump is operated continuously.

    (b)   the diffuser is fully open.

    (c)   the enrichment jet supplies a very rich mixture.

Ref. 7.3(e). Fig. 7-6.

4. When some types of aircraft are in inverted flight, fuel starvation of the engine is avoided by:

    (a)   the enrichment jet.

    (b)   the fitting of a stand tube to the float chamber.

    (c)   the diffuser.

Ref. 7.3(i) Fig. 7-10.

5. The carburettor cut-out, if fitted, is normally:

    (a)   attached to the diffuser.

    (b)   located in the slow running jet line.

    (c)   connected to pressure balance duct.

Ref. 7.3(h). Fig. 7-9.

6. To prevent fuel starvation due to sudden opening of the throttle:

(a) the enrichment jet is fitted.

(b) the pressure balance duct is fitted.

(c) the accelerator pump is fitted.

Ref. 7.3(f). Fig. 7-7.

7. To ensure a smooth rate of discharge of fuel from the carburettor jet:

(a) a balance duct is fitted.

(b) a twin jet is fitted.

(c) the float chamber is subjected to boost pressure.

Ref. 7.3(a). Fig. 7-2.

8. When an aircraft is inverted in flight, fuel starvation of the engine may be prevented by:

(a) the carburettor balance duct.

(b) the power jet.

(c) a stand tube.

Ref. 7.3(h). Fig 7-10.

9. Carburettor anti-icing is normally provided by:

(a) hot air from the cooling system.

(b) hot oil from the engine lubrication system.

(c) spray mat heater elements.

Ref. 7.4(b).

10. In an injection carburettor, the:

(a) fuel flow is measured by the choke.

(b) airflow is measured by the choke.

(c) air and fuel are mixed in the choke.

Ref. 7.5.

8

Supercharging

8.1 Introduction.

The amount of power developed by a piston aero-engine is dependent upon the weight of fuel/air mixture burnt in the cylinders in a given time. As each piston descends on the induction stroke it creates a depression, and the weight of mixture, usually referred to as the charge, that enters the cylinder is dependent on the pressure in the induction manifold. In a normally aspirated engine (ie one which breathes at atmospheric pressure unaided) manifold pressure is governed by the pressure of the atmosphere and the amount by which the throttle is opened. Consequently, as the atmospheric pressure progressively decreases as the aircraft gains altitude, the weight of charge entering the cylinders slowly decreases for a given throttle setting. To prevent a loss of power as altitude is increased it is necessary to maintain the inlet manifold pressure at sea level conditions. This is achieved by supercharging.

8.2 Supercharger.

(a) Location and drive.

A supercharger, sometimes termed a blower, is basically an engine driven fan or impeller which is normally positioned between the carburettor and the induction manifold. The supercharger is normally mounted on the rear face of the engine as shown in Fig. 8-1, and is driven through gearing from the engine crankshaft. It may be single or multi-staged.

The impeller, or fan, of the supercharger normally revolves nine to ten times faster than the engine rpm. The impeller drive absorbs an appreciable amount of horsepower and to reduce the impeller bearing loads it is common practice to have a three-fold drive to the impeller drive shaft, i.e. three trains of gears.

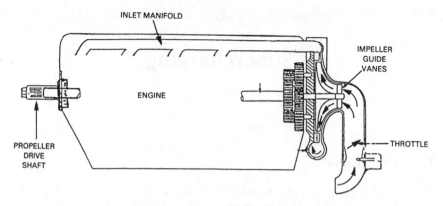

Figure 8–1 Location of Supercharger on Rear Face of Engine.

An intermediate clutch that equalises the load and relieves the gearing from shock loads during sudden changes in engine speed is usually fitted with the gear trains. To smooth the drive further and so reduce vibration of the impeller, some form of spring drive is normally fitted and used as the initial drive from the crankshaft. Supercharger bearing lubrication is provided by the engine lubrication system.

Figure 8-2 shows the friction clutch mechanism used to reduce shock loads on the gearing.

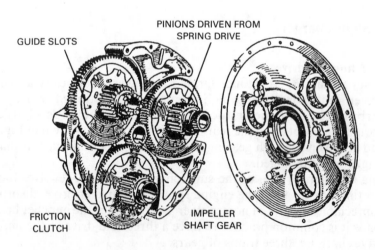

Figure 8–2 Friction Clutch
Mechanism.

Figure 8-3 shows the spring drive mechanism which may be used to smooth the drive transmission, and so reduce vibration.

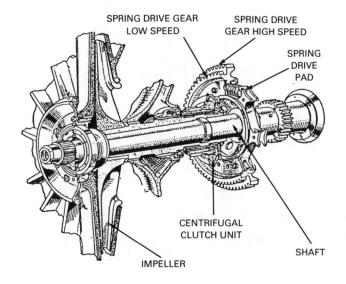

Figure 8–3 Spring Drive Mechanism.

(b) Mixture Flow.

The fuel/air mixture is drawn through the carburettor by the supercharger and enters the eye of the impeller; the rotational speed of the impeller then throws the mixture outwards with increasing velocity. Surrounding the impeller is a system of divergent passages, collectively known as a diffuser, the function of which is smoothly to decelerate the flow of the mixture from the impeller to give an increase in pressure as it enters the inlet manifold. Once it has entered the inlet manifold under pressure the mixture is normally referred to as manifold pressure.

A pressure gauge situated in the cockpit, usually graduated in pounds per square inch, or inches of mercury, indicates the pressure above or below standard sea level atmospheric pressure.

This manifold pressure gauge is often called a Boost Gauge. (See Fig. 8-4.)

Note: Standard atmosphere pressure is indicated as zero on the boost gauge.

Figure 8–4 Boost Gauge.

8.3   Automatic Boost Control.

Pressure above normal atmospheric pressure is referred to as 'Boost Pressure' or sometimes as 'Positive Boost' and below atmospheric pressure as 'Negative Boost'.

A boost control unit, more commonly called the automatic boost control unit, is fitted to most supercharged engines to maintain sea level atmospheric pressure in the inlet manifold as the aircraft climbs. The automatic boost control unit serves a variety of purposes, viz:

(a)   to maintain sea level atmospheric pressure in the inlet manifold by automatically controlling the throttle.

(b)   to relieve the pilot of constant boost setting adjustment for a given rpm as the aircraft climbs or descends.

(c)   to prevent the supercharger overboosting the manifold at low altitude, which could result in overstressing and damage to the engine.

(d)   to control the boost pressure within certain limits to avoid mixture detonation.

(e)   to prevent excessive combustion pressures at any altitude, which could lead to mechanical strain or failure.

The automatic boost control unit operates by opening and closing the throttle to adjust engine rpm, thereby supercharger rpm, and hence manifold pressure. The net result is control of the weight of charge entering the cylinders.

Figure 8-5 shows an automatic boost control unit with its relative position and linkage to the carburettor, throttle and supercharger.

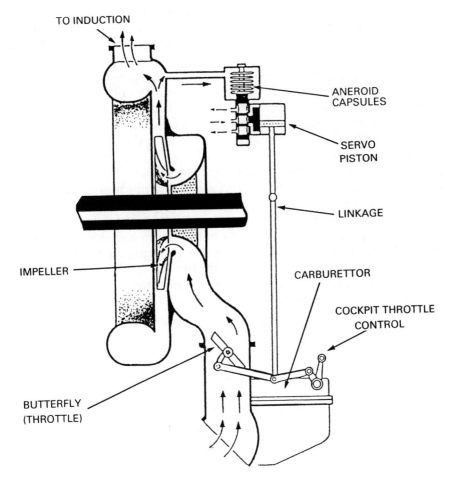

Figure 8–5 Automatic Boost Control.

8.4   Supercharger Automatic Boost Control Operation.

The aneroid capsule assembly is exposed only to inlet manifold or boost pressure in the induction system: it is in turn coupled to the throttle linkage via an oil operated servo piston in such a way that when the capsule is compressed the throttle or butterfly is partly closed, and when the aneroid capsule expands the throttle valve will be partly opened. The oil which operates the servo piston is supplied under pressure by the engine lubrication system.

When the engine is started the induction manifold pressure will fall to a low value, because of the increase in velocity of the mixture flow from

99

the supercharger. This reduction of pressure in the inlet manifold will be sensed by the aneroid capsule assembly and result in the capsules expanding. The expansion of the aneroid capsule will then cause oil to be directed below the servo piston, which thereupon moves to the top of its stroke. Subsequent throttle opening is accompanied by an increase in induction manifold pressure, causing the aneroid capsule to compress and the valve to rise until the supply of oil to the underside of the piston is cut off. Any further opening of the throttle will now cause oil to be directed above the piston, which will descend and close the throttle valve until the induction pressure falls sufficiently to cut off the servo oil supply. Therefore whatever the position of the throttle lever, the induction pressure or boost, cannot rise above a certain value, known as 'Rated Boost'.

With the valve in the equilibrium position, any tendency for the induction pressure to fall as height is gained will be counteracted by a progressive opening of the throttle or butterfly through the admission of more oil beneath the servo piston, until that altitude is reached where, with the throttle lever fully advanced, the throttle is fully open. This situation, Rated Altitude, is the point above which the induction manifold pressure will fall in the same manner as an unsupercharged or normally aspirated engine.

8.5   Operational Example.

For the purpose of a better understanding of the relationship between the supercharger, throttle and engine rpm, consider a supercharger that is capable of a pressure ratio of 2:1. Assume:

(a)   The engine speed to be 2600 rpm.

(b)   The impeller speed to be at a ratio of 9:1 and therefore to be 23,400 rpm.

(c)   Maximum take-off boost not to exceed +6 lb sq in.

With these conditions the manifold will have an absolute pressure of 20.7 lb sq inch. This is 14.7 lb sq inch, an assumed atmospheric pressure plus 6 lb sq inch boost providing 20.7 lb sq inch. Such figures relate to an example of a maximum of 6 lb sq inch boost.

In reality at 6 lb sq inch boost pressure the throttle will be only partially open. If the throttle is fully open at sea level, with a supercharger ratio of 2:1 then the manifold pressure will be 14.7 x 2 = 29.4 lb sq inch. This will exceed the maximum take-off boost by 8.7 lb sq inch. i.e. 29.4 lb sq inch minus 20.7 lb sq inch = 8.7 lb sq inch.

It is evident that the throttle valve must be partially closed to restrict the amount of mixture going into the manifold to keep the absolute pressure within the limitations of 6 lb sq inch boost.

For the sake of simplicity at this stage it is assumed that there is neither ram air effect on the air intake as a result of forward speed, nor pressure reduction due to the restriction of the carburettor. As the aircraft climbs, so the density of the air progressively reduces and the automatic boost control unit will progressively open the throttle valve to compensate for the reduction in the air density, thereby maintaining 20.7 lb sq inch absolute or +6 lb sq inch boost in the induction manifold. This is assuming no alteration is made to the cockpit throttle setting.

When the aircraft reaches 9000ft the atmospheric pressure will have dropped to 10.35 lb sq inch and with a compression ratio of 2:1 the supercharger will therefore maintain a manifold absolute pressure of 20.7 lb sq inch. The automatic boost control has compensated by progressively opening the throttle up to this altitude and has now reached a position where the throttle is fully open.

As the example engine has now been maintaining constant rpm and a constant boost of +6 lb sq inch then:

(a)   With the engine set at constant rpm and constant boost with the throttle fully open it is at 9000ft or full throttle height.

(b)   With the throttle fully advanced and the throttle valve fully open, the aircraft can also be said to have reached its rated altitude. If the aircraft now continues to climb above the 9000ft example altitude no further compensation is available and so the manifold pressure will start to fall as it would with a normal aspirated engine.

Note: In the example given any further movement of the throttle in the cockpit, if any is still available, will in effect be lost motion as the throttle is fully open, this situation can only be changed by the installation of a further device known as a variable datum cam.

8.6   Variable Datum Cam.

At low altitudes, the action of the automatic boost control unit, as described so far, would be such that 'rated boost', i.e. the value for that particular boost setting, would be reached with the throttle partly open, beyond which point there would be lost motion on the throttle in the cockpit. Furthermore, although the aneroid capsule and unit would prevent a fall in boost pressure during a climb at full throttle, it would not be able to do so at a pressure lower than the rated boost, and it would be necessary for the pilot to be continually advancing the throttle. These disadvantages are overcome by the use of a variable datum cam which is normally fitted to the top of the aneroid chamber of the automatic boost control unit and is interconnected with the throttle lever. (See Fig. 8-6.)

FIXED BOOST ADJUSTMENT

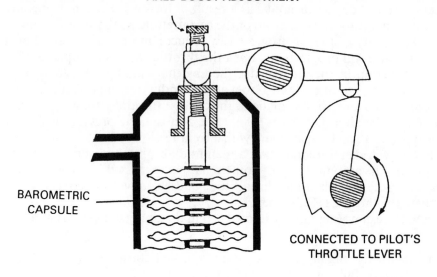

BAROMETRIC
CAPSULE

CONNECTED TO PILOT'S
THROTTLE LEVER

Figure 8–6 Variable Datum Cam Assembly.

Note: Barometric capsules are sometimes prone to sticking to the walls of the cylinders in which they are housed. To prevent this a coil spring is usually fitted between the capsule and the cylinder wall. Such springs may also be fitted to the Automatic Mixture Control Capsule for the same reason.

8.7   Variable Datum Cam Operation.

This cam permits the aneroid unit to rise as the throttle is closed; thus, with the aneroid unit adjusted to give the rated pressure with the throttle lever fully advanced, the valve will be progressively re-set as the throttle is closed so that the equilibrium position will occur at lower boost pressures. For a given position of throttle lever, a corresponding degree of boost will be obtained.

8.8   Full Throttle Height.

The full throttle height is the altitude up to which a given boost setting can be maintained at a given rpm.

The lower the boost pressure selected by the pilot the greater is the altitude to which it can be maintained by the automatic boost control unit. For example, in an aircraft at its rated altitude and still climbing, the butterfly will be fully open at its rated boost, which will then begin to fall; but at a lower boost the butterfly will still be opening through the action of the aneroid capsule, and the pressure will be maintained until the butterfly can open no further. This is known as 'Full Throttle Height' for that particular boost and rpm. The speed of the engine is a qualifying factor because it controls the speed of the supercharger impeller; at higher than normal rpm the full throttle height will be raised.

Note: The rated altitude is the full throttle height at rated boost and normal rpm for that boost. Fig. 8-7 shows examples of power curves for a supercharged engine.

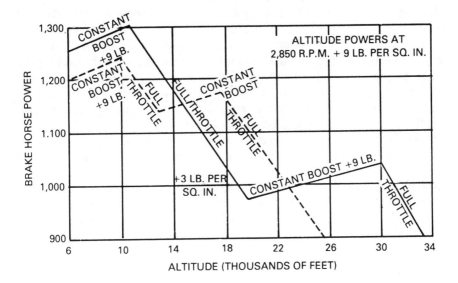

Figure 8–7 Two Examples of Power Curves.

8.9 Automatic Boost Control Override.

So that the maximum possible power is available for take-off and emergencies, provision is made for the rated boost to be exceeded under these circumstances. This may be done either by arranging for the pressure in the aneroid capsule chamber to be reduced through a controlled leak, or by lowering the aneroid unit beyond the rated boost position. In one installation, when the throttle lever is advanced beyond a gated position on the quadrant, an extension to the variable datum cam gives the required depression and at the same time brings the enrichment jet into operation.

8.10   Supercharger Losses.

From Fig. 8-7 it will be seen that, for a constant boost and rpm setting, engine power increases up to the full throttle height. As an aircraft climbs, the fall in temperature of the air is accompanied by a corresponding drop in the charge temperature. Consequently the density of the mixture increases and a greater weight of charge is burnt per power stroke. Furthermore, the decreasing atmospheric pressure offers less resistance to the expulsion of the exhaust gases and less impulsion to the downward movement of the pistons, in the former case improving the volumetric efficiency and the latter raising the mean effective pressure.

Of the total power absorbed by the supercharger, a proportion is wasted in overcoming friction and in heating the mixture adiabatically. The rise in mixture charge temperature, unavoidable though it is, must be kept as low as possible because the higher the temperature the greater the loss in engine power due to reduced charge density, and the greater the risk of detonation. Both frictional losses and supercharger heating increase with increase of impeller rpm; consequently for efficient operation the engine speed should be as low as possible.

It is clear that a supercharged engine is comparatively inefficient at or near sea level; much of the power absorbed by the supercharger goes to restoring the drop in induction pressure necessarily created by the butterfly to prevent over-boosting; the power developed at a given boost and rpm setting is lower than at altitude because of the higher temperature and pressure; and, although considerable power can be obtained by using high boost pressures and rpm, it involves the supply of a very rich mixture to counteract the combined effects of high air temperature and adiabatic heating.

8.11   Control Settings for Maximum Efficiency.

Maximum efficiency, or minimum specific fuel consumption, is obtained when the butterfly is fully open and the rpm is as low as can be obtained without detonation. In practice this is at the full throttle height for the power setting in use. The power is obtained by using the highest possible weak mixture boost in conjunction with the lowest practicable rpm to give the required air speed.

8.12   Two-Speed Superchargers.

When a high rated altitude is required, it is necessary to step up the supercharger gear ratio so that the impeller can be driven at a sufficiently high speed. With such an arrangement, however, the power losses at low altitudes are considerable for the reasons already given. To avoid such losses, superchargers with two impeller gear ratios are used, the change from one to the other being made either manually or automatically at a certain height. (See Fig. 8-8).

Note: Superchargers with two gear ratios are normally termed two-speed superchargers.

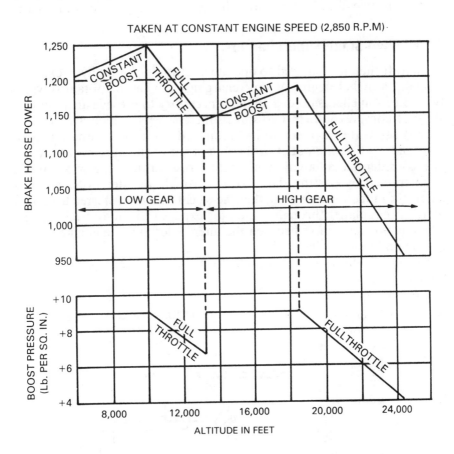

Figure 8–8 Typical Two-Speed Supercharger
Power Curves.

In Fig. 8-8 which shows how the power output varies with altitude at rated boost and normal rpm, the loss of power at low altitudes in high gear is immediately evident. Furthermore it can be seen that it is pointless to change from low gear to high gear at the low gear rated altitude for, although the rated boost pressure would be maintained, the power output would immediately fall, in this case by about 190 bhp.

105

The change should be delayed until the boost pressure has fallen by about 2 lb sq inch, when the altitude is reached at which the low and high power curves intersect. The rated power in high gear, obtained at 13,000ft, is well below that in low gear because of the extra power needed to drive the supercharger at the higher speed.

On some two-speed installations the selection of high gear is automatic.

8.13   Two-Stage Superchargers.

In aircraft that are required to operate at altitudes normally in excess of 30,000ft, a higher degree of supercharging than can be obtained with a two-speed impeller is needed, and it is necessary to provide an additional stage of compression. In two-stage superchargers (which are also two speed) separate impeller units, mounted on a common shaft, are arranged, so that the outlet of the first is fed to the inlet of the second. The considerable adiabatic temperature rise through the two stages is counteracted by passing the mixture through an intercooler before it enters the induction manifold, the excess heat being transferred to coolant which is circulated through a radiator exposed to the outside airflow. There is no connection between the intercooler and the engine coolant system on liquid-cooled engines.

Figure 8-9 shows a diagram of a two-stage supercharger with inter-cooler.

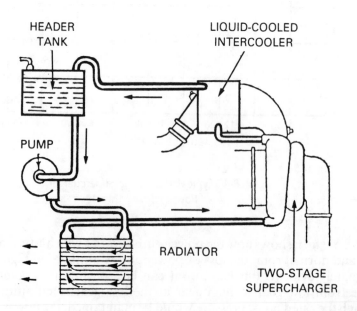

Figure 8–9 Supercharger Intercooler.

Section 8 Test Yourself

Supercharging

1. The supercharger is normally positioned:

    (a)   in the exhaust manifold.

    (b)   before the carburettor.

    (c)   between the carburettor and the inlet manifold.

Ref. 8.2

2. The impeller of a supercharger rotates:

    (a)   twice the speed of the engine.

    (b)   half the speed of the engine crankshaft.

    (c)   nine to ten times the speed of the engine crankshaft.

Ref. 8.2

3. Supercharger impeller vibration may be reduced by:

    (a)   a spring drive on the impeller drive shaft.

    (b)   a spring drive on the turbine drive shaft.

    (c)   a hydro/mechanical clutch.

Ref. 8.2

4. The supercharger is normally located:

    (a)   at the side of the engine.

    (b)   at the rear of the engine.

    (c)   at the front of the engine.

Ref. 8.2

5. Manifold boost pressure is:

    (a)   the indicated pressure in the inlet manifold between the impeller and the inlet valves.

    (b)   the indicated pressure in the inlet prior to the carburettor.

    (c)   the pressure indicated in the supercharger.

Ref. 8.2

9

Turbocharging

9.1   Introduction.

The primary disadvantage of the supercharger is its lack of an infinitely variable drive. Much research has led in more recent years to the development and production of the turbocharger. The supercharger relies on a gear drive from the crankshaft of the engine, the turbocharger however, utilises the exhaust gases of the engine to drive a compressor, the product of which is used to pressurise the inlet manifold in a similar manner as the supercharger. The use of exhaust gases from the engine has provided a useful source of energy in providing boost to the inlet manifold. As more than one-third of the energy that should be derived from the combustion of the fuel in the cylinders is lost through the exhaust gases, any useful work obtained from them is an asset to the performance of the engine.

9.2   Turbocharger Location and Drive.

The turbocharger consists primarily of a fan or compressor which is driven by a turbine which in turn is driven by the exhaust gases of the engine. (See Fig. 9-1.)

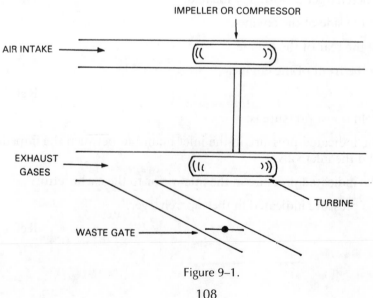

Figure 9–1.

108

Just as with the supercharger, the turbocharger compressor increases the pressure in the inlet manifold to increase the weight of charge of the mixture entering the cylinders. The turbocharger turbine is located in the exhaust system and the compressor element is situated between the air intake and the carburettor or injector, unlike the supercharger which is normally positioned between the carburettor and the inlet manifold.

9.3   The Turbocharger.

A turbocharger consists of a turbine wheel and an impeller (sometimes termed the compressor, fan or blower), mounted on a common shaft, the bearings for which are contained within a bearing housing and are lubricated by oil from the engine lubrication system. The turbine and compressor casings are attached to the bearing housing and are connected to the exhaust and intake systems respectively. The compressor is shielded from the heat of the turbine, and an intake of external air is ducted between the two casings to remove excess heat. The turbocharger is not necessarily an integral part of the engine, on most engines it is not, but may be mounted on the engine or on the fireproof bulkhead, and shielded from combustible fluid lines in the engine bay.

Figure 9-2 shows an operational diagram of a turbocharger.

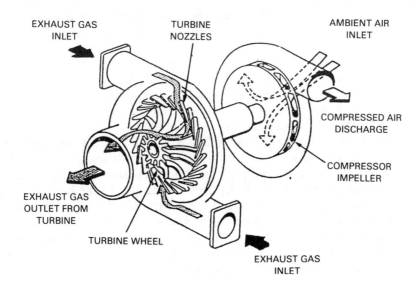

Figure 9–2 Turbocharger.

Engine exhaust gases are ducted to the turbine casing, where they pass through nozzles and impinge on vanes on the turbine wheel causing it to rotate; the gases then pass between the vanes and are exhausted overboard. As the impeller is attached to the same shaft as the turbine wheel it also rotates, drawing in air from the intake duct and throwing it outwards at high velocity through diffuser vanes in the compressor casing; these vanes convert the velocity energy into pressure energy, and the compressed air is delivered to the engine.

9.4   Turbocharger Operation.

For any particular power output the turbocharger delivers a fixed weight of air to the engine in a given time, and, since the density of air decreases with altitude, a greater volume of air is compressed and the impeller rotates faster at high altitude than it does at low altitude. Therefore, some form of control over compressor output must be provided, and this is achieved by varying the quantity of exhaust gas passing to the turbine. A turbine by-pass, in the form of an alternative exhaust duct, is fitted with a valve, known as the waste gate, which regulates the degree of opening of the by-pass. When the waste gate is fully open nearly all the exhaust gases pass to atmosphere, but as the waste gate closes gases are directed to the turbine, and the maximum turbine speed is reached when the waste gate is fully closed. The waste gate may be manually controlled by the pilot, or more usually on modern turbochargers be controlled automatically to prevent over-boosting the engine. Figure 9-3 is a diagram of a turbocharger system.

In an automatic control system, the waste gate is mechanically connected to an actuator, the position of which depends on the opposing forces of a spring and engine oil pressure. The spring tends to open the waste gate and engine oil pressure tends to close it. Engine oil pressure is fed to the actuator through a restrictor, and the waste gate controllers are placed in the return line as shown in Fig. 9-3. When a controller opens the return line, oil flows from the actuator and then through the controller back to the engine sump, and pressure in the actuator falls. The extent to which the oil pressure will fall depends on the size of the bleed through the controllers; the larger the bleed the lower the oil pressure will drop. Therefore oil pressure in the actuator is controlled to regulate the position of the waste gate according to engine requirements. Various types of controllers may be used to vary the waste gate actuator pressure, and these will be discussed in later paragraphs.

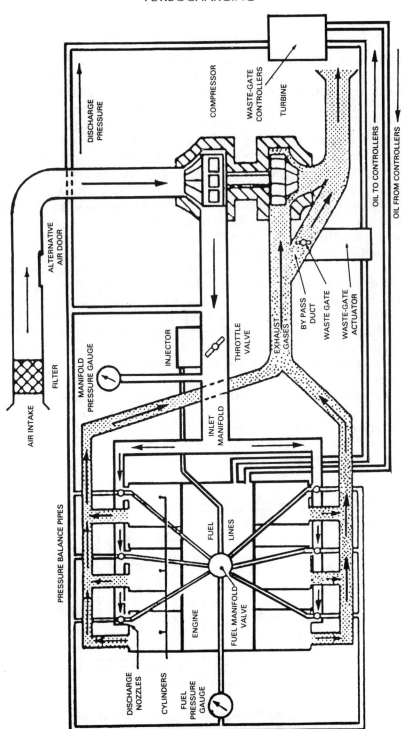

Figure 9–3 Turbocharger System.

9.5 Operation of the Waste Gate.

Some simple turbocharger systems use a single controller, called an Absolute Pressure Controller, which is designed to prevent the turbocharger outlet pressure from exceeding a specified maximum; this type of controller is shown in Fig. 9-4. At low power settings full oil pressure is applied to the waste gate actuator, which closes the waste gate and diverts all exhaust gases through the turbine. As the throttle is opened, engine speed increases, and more exhaust gas passes through the turbine; this results in an increase in the speed of rotation of the turbine and impeller, and produces a higher turbocharger outlet pressure which is communicated to the capsule chamber in the Absolute Pressure Controller. When the controlled outlet pressure is reached, the capsule is compressed sufficiently to open its bleed valve and thus bleed off oil pressure from below the waste gate actuator piston. The piston moves down under spring pressure and starts to open the waste gate, diverting exhaust gas from the turbine and reducing its speed. Thus at high power settings at low altitude the waste gate is almost fully open, but as the aircraft climbs and more air has to be compressed it is gradually closed until, at critical altitude (equivalent to Rated Altitude on an internally driven supercharger) it is fully closed. Above this height both manifold pressure and power output will decrease, even though the turbocharger is operating at its maximum speed.

It should be noted that, since the speed of the impeller increases with altitude, the temperature of the charge will also increase, and this will reduce power output for a given manifold pressure and engine speed. Engine oil and cylinder temperatures will also increase as a result of the higher combustion temperatures.

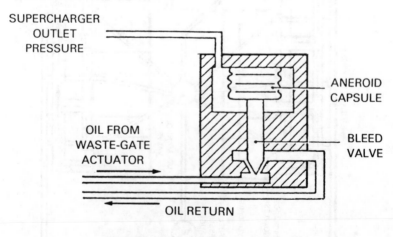

Figure 9–4 Absolute Pressure Controller.

9.6   Variable Pressure Controller.

A variation of the single controller is the Variable Pressure Controller (see Fig. 9-5) which is similar to the variable datum control for internally driven superchargers. A cam, operated by a linkage from the throttle control lever, adjusts the datum of the valve in the Variable Pressure Controller, so controlling the degree of opening of the waste gate and producing a manifold pressure which is related to the power setting of the throttle lever. Operation of this system is otherwise similar to the operation of the Absolute Pressure Controller.

Figure 9-5 is an operational diagram of a Variable Pressure Controller.

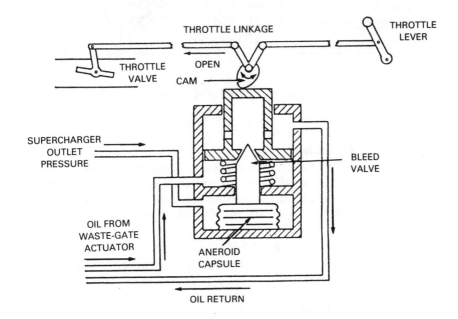

Figure 9–5 Variable Pressure Controller.

9.7   Dual Control Unit System.

On some ground boosted turbochargers a dual unit control system is used to adjust waste gate actuator oil pressure; the units are the Density Controller and the Differential Pressure Controller, which are installed as shown in Fig. 9-6.

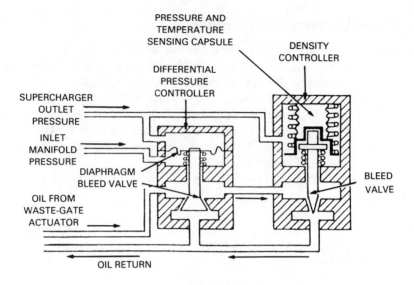

Figure 9–6 Dual Unit Controller.

(a) The Density Controller.
The Density Controller is designed to prevent the turbocharger output from exceeding the limiting pressure; it regulates oil pressure only at full throttle and up to the turbocharger's critical altitude. The capsule is normally filled with dry nitrogen and is sensitive both to temperature and to pressure changes. Contraction or expansion of the capsule varies the quantity of oil bled from the waste gate actuator and repositions the waste gate, thus maintaining a constant density at full throttle.

(b) The Differential Pressure Controller.
This component controls the waste gate at all positions of the throttle other than fully open. A diaphragm divides a chamber which has the turbocharger outlet pressure on one side and inlet manifold pressure on the other, therefore responding to the pressure drop across the throttle valve. The bleed valve is fully closed at full throttle, when the pressure drop is least, and gradually opens as the throttle is closed and the pressure drop increases. The controller therefore opens the waste gate as the throttle is closed, and reduces turbocharger outlet pressure in accordance with the power selected.
Figure 9-7 shows the waste gate and its basic operation.

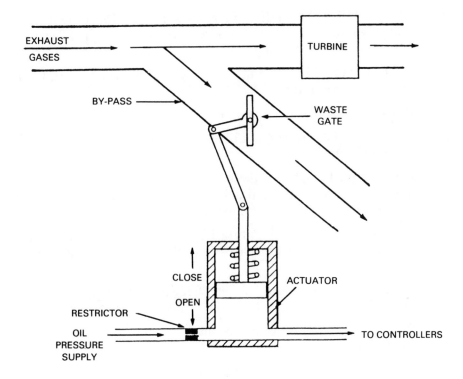

Figure 9–7 Basic Control and Operation of Waste Gate.

Key Points – Superchargers and Turbochargers

Theory

1. BOOST PRESSURE is the pressure in the induction manifold, measured in lb per square inch above or below ISA.

2. MANIFOLD PRESSURE is the absolute pressure in the induction manifold expressed in inches of mercury.

3. STATIC BOOST is the manifold pressure indicated on the boost gauge when the engine is stationary and will be 0 lb/sq in, or 29.92 inches of mercury.

4. Manifold and boost pressure are both measured between the throttle valve and engine inlet valve.

5. FULL THROTTLE HEIGHT is the height at which the throttle butterfly is fully open for any pre-selected boost or rpm. (There are many full throttle heights)

6. RATED POWER is the maximum power at which continuous operation is permitted.

7. Rated power is less than take-off boost.

8. RATED BOOST is the manifold pressure permitted at rated power and rated rpm.

9. RATED ALTITUDE is the altitude at which maximum continuous rpm can be maintained on a supercharged engine. For turbocharged engines it is known as CRITICAL ALTITUDE.

10. A decrease in air temperature has the effect of increasing the density, therefore the greater weight, of mixture pumped into the cylinders.

11. High manifold pressure has the effect of increasing power and manifold temperatures, which could cause detonation.

12. With an increase in compressor discharge pressure, the fuel flow will increase.

13. The primary purpose of the supercharger/turbocharger is to increase the mass charge entering the cylinder.

14. The function of the supercharger/turbocharger is to increase power output and maintain sea level conditions at altitude.

15. Diffuser vanes are fitted to the outlet side of the compressor, to form divergent passages, to convert kinetic energy to pressure energy.

16. The temperature of the mixture/air passing through the supercharger/turbocharger will increase.

17. A normally aspirated engine climbing from sea level to 20,000 ft altitude, at constant rpm, will lose approximately 50% of the maximum power available.

18. The supercharger/turbochargers are lubricated by the engine lubrication system and both use AVGAS as fuel.

Superchargers

1. An internally-driven supercharger is driven by the engine crankshaft and rotates at approximately six to twelve times crankshaft speed.

2.   The normal position of a supercharger is between the carburettor and the engine inlet manifold.

3.   One of the effects of supercharging an engine is that power is lost at the crankshaft.

4.   A limit is imposed on the amount of supercharging which can be tolerated by an engine; this occurs at maximum boost on the take-off (maximum rpm).

5.   The fuel and air are mixed before passing into the supercharger and enter the eye of the impeller, leaving at the periphery.

6.   During climb at constant manifold pressure, the power due to supercharging will increase.

7.   Up to rated altitude, the power output of a supercharged engine will increase, due to improved volumetric efficiency through a decrease both in temperature and in exhaust back pressure; above this altitude, power will decrease.

8.   At full power on the runway at take-off, the throttle butterfly is only partially open.

9.   A two-stage supercharger has two rotating impellers, with the outlet from the first delivering to the inlet of the second.

10.   A two-speed supercharger rotates at low speed at low altitude, high speed at high altitude and increases the boost available under all flight conditions.

11.   When increasing altitude, the two-speed supercharger high speed gear is selected at an altitude slightly in excess of the low speed gear full throttle height.

12.   As a supercharged engine climbs, the power available and power required tend to move together.

13.   An automatic boost control unit is a device which maintains rated boost by progressively opening the throttle butterfly as the aircraft climbs and vice versa when descending.

14.   The automatic boost control capsule is made sensitive to manifold boost pressure.

15.   A variable datum cam on top of the automatic boost control capsule chamber allows the boost pressure datum to be varied with throttle lever movement.

16. If the capsule of the automatic boost control unit were to be punctured in normal cruise flight, then the manifold boost pressure would rise.

17. A leak in the capsule chamber would cause a higher boost setting than selected.

18. If there is a fault in the automatic boost control unit which allows the throttle to progressively open above that selected, the throttle must be retarded manually.

19. To reduce the risk of detonation, an intercooler may be fitted between the two compressors of the two-stage supercharger.

20. The intercooler is cooled by ram air.

Turbochargers

1. A TURBOCHARGER consists of a compressor driven by a turbine, which, in turn, is driven by exhaust gases.

2. A turbocharger designed to maintain sea level pressure at altitude is called an ALTITUDE TURBOCHARGER.

3. A turbocharger designed to maintain a higher than sea level pressure at all altitudes is known as a GROUND BOOSTED TURBOCHARGER.

4. The manifold pressure of a turbocharged engine is determined by the throttle butterfly position.

5. The waste gate of a turbocharger is fitted in the exhaust manifold; it regulates the quantity of exhaust gases bypassing the turbine.

6. The waste gate position is determined by a controller that is sensitive to turbocharger discharge pressure or density.

7. The ABSOLUTE PRESSURE CONTROLLER is designed to prevent turbocharger output exceeding the design maximum pressure under any conditions.

8. A VARIABLE PRESSURE CONTROLLER adjusts the position of the waste gate in relation to throttle position.

9. At idle or low manifold pressure conditions, the turbocharger waste gate is normally closed.

10. In a turbocharged engine, opening the throttle below maximum manifold pressure will increase the boost pressure.

11. With a turbocharger and at a constant throttle setting, the manifold pressure remains constant as the aircraft climbs.

12. The position of the throttle for take-off is determined by the overboosting warning light.

13. If the waste gate were to seize before the throttle was fully open during a continuous climb, engine power would decrease.

14. In the event of an engine shut-down in flight, restarting a turbocharged engine, compared to a normally aspirated engine, is more difficult.

15. An exhaust manifold leak upstream of the turbocharger will cause a loss of engine power at altitude.

16. On the descent, with low power set, the turbocharger waste gate is fully closed.

17. If the turbocharger fails, the relief doors will open and supply air to the manifold.

18. BOOTSTRAPPING is a term used to describe unstable conditions of the inlet manifold pressure, caused by changes in gas flow or gas temperature.

19. When increasing power with a turbocharger, care must be taken to prevent bootstrapping.

20. As a turbocharged engine climbs, the cylinder head temperature will increase, due to maintaining manifold pressure as the aircraft climbs.

Section 9 Test Yourself

Turbocharging

1. The waste gate of a turbocharger is normally operated, when being closed by:

    (a)   spring pressure.

    (b)   engine lubrication system oil pressure.

    (c)   engine hydraulic system oil pressure.

Ref. 9.4.

2. The impeller of a turbocharger of an aircraft in a climb at constant engine rpm, will:

    (a)   increase with altitude.

    (b)   reduce with increase of altitude.

    (c)   remain constant until full throttle height is reached.

Ref. 9.5.

3. On an aircraft flying at a specific height and constant rpm, as the throttle is then slowly closed:

    (a)   the waste gate will fully close.

    (b)   the waste gate will slowly open.

    (c)   the waste gate will remain in the same position.

Ref. 9.7.

4. The turbocharger impeller is situated:

    (a)   prior to the fuel injector.

    (b)   after the carburettor.

    (c)   in the exhaust system.

Ref. 9.2.

5. Turbocharger main bearings are lubricated by:

    (a)   the engine hydraulic system.

    (b)   the engine lubrication system.

    (c)   grease packs.

Ref. 9.3.

6. The turbocharger impeller is:

    (a)   driven by intake ram air.

    (b)   driven by exhaust gases.

    (c)   mounted on the same shaft as the turbine.

Ref. 9.3.

7. The impeller of a turbocharger:

    (a)   draws air through the intake air duct.

    (b)   draws air through the carburettor intake duct.

    (c)   draws air through the turbine guide nozzles.

Ref. 9.3.

8. The waste gate is:

    (a)   hydraulically operated when being opened.

    (b)   mechanically connected to the actuator.

    (c)   electrically trimmed.

Ref. 9.4.

9. The degree of opening of the waste gate is controlled by:

    (a)   the actuator and spring.

    (b)   the engine lubrication system.

    (c)   the Variable Pressure Controller.

Ref. 9.6.

10. If a leak occurs in the exhaust system prior to the turbocharger turbine, the:

    (a)   waste gate will fail to operate.

    (b)   boost pressure will be reduced.

    (c)   the waste gate will open.

Ref. 9.4.

10

Piston Aero-Engine Operation and Performance

10.1   Introduction.

This chapter is primarily devoted to a supercharged engine driving a propeller fitted with a constant speed unit.

10.2   Precautions Before Engine Starting.

Before starting a supercharged piston engine, the following points should be noted.

(a) Cooling.
If practicable the aircraft should be positioned facing into wind to achieve the best possible cooling from the air when the engine is running.

(b) Hydraulicing.
If the engine has been standing without being run for some time, the engine should be turned over, preferably by hand, for at least two revolutions of the propeller in order to break down the film of oil which will have formed on the cylinder walls of the engine.

   If the engine is of inverted or radial type, it is possible that oil may drain past the piston rings and collect in the combustion chambers of the inverted cylinders. Attempting to start an engine in this condition may create hydraulic shocks, known as hydraulicing, of a magnitude sufficient to cause serious damage to the engine. To avoid hydraulicing the propeller should be turned through two complete revolutions in order to eject the collection of oil from the combustion chambers through the exhaust manifold. If resistance is felt to turning the propeller it may be necessary to remove the sparking plugs to drain the offending oil before the propeller can be turned.

(c) Static Boost.
While the engine is static, with the aircraft on the ground, the boost gauge should be read prior to starting the engine. The indicated boost in this situation is termed 'STATIC BOOST'. It is important that the indicated static boost reading be noted and remembered.

The boost gauge will read the pressure that exists in the inlet manifold with the engine stationary. If the pressure in the manifold is mean sea level atmospheric pressure of 14.7 lb/sq inch or 1013 millibars, then the boost gauge will read 'zero'. As atmospheric pressure varies, so the gauge will read above or below zero. Whatever the indicated reading in these static conditions, it is termed 'STATIC BOOST'.

Static boost should be studied in conjunction with 'Reference Revolutions'. (f overleaf)

(d) Engine Priming (Manually).
The fuel lines to the engine should be fully primed, that is to say filled with fuel, prior to engine starting. On engines fitted with conventional carburettors, priming is normally carried out by operation, in the cockpit, of a manual fuel priming pump, usually of a plunger type. (See Fig. 10-1.) The pump simply draws fuel from the fuel system and sprays it direct, through small jets, into the inlet manifold, by-passing the carburettor.

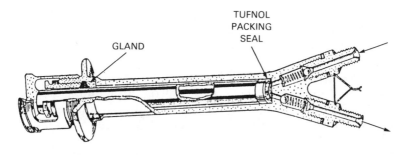

TUFNOL
PACKING
SEAL

GLAND

Figure 10–1 Hand-operated Priming Pump.

The plunger of such pumps, must not be left extended when the engine is being started. On completion of priming the plunger must be pushed fully in and secured. Failure to secure the plunger can result in fuel being drawn through the pump when the engine is started, and supplied direct to the inlet manifold. This action, coupled with the fuel/air mixture being drawn through the carburettor, will result in a very rich mixture at the cylinder inlet valves and will probably result in the engine stalling. Hand-operated priming pumps should be operated in accordance with the aircraft manual, normally however, the pump is operated until resistance is felt.

(e) **Engine Priming (Electrically).**
The fuel lines to the engine should be fully primed in the same way as in the manually-primed system. In the electrically-primed system the manually-operated pump is replaced by an electrically-driven pump operated by a switch or push button in the cockpit. On engines fitted with fuel injection systems priming is carried out electrically, the booster pump being switched on in the cockpit, the system being primed with fuel and the booster pump then switched off before any attempt is made to start the engine.

(f) **Reference Revolutions.**
On starting the engine the indicated boost will fall, this is primarily due to the increased velocity of the mixture in the inlet manifold causing a decrease in pressure. To restore the manifold pressure to that indicated at static boost, the throttle must be opened further. When the indicated boost reading is the same as at static boost, the indicated rpm is reference revolutions.

10.3   Take-off.

The boost required is normally set or selected prior to take-off. Carburettor heating must also be switched off during the take-off run unless it is absolutely essential. Failure to switch off carburettor heating will result in a loss of power.

The loss of power as a result of carburettor heating being selected is due to the reduction in air density at the carburettor intake as a result of increased temperature by the anti-icing heater. A considerable loss of power is incurred during the initial take-off run due to loss of ram air effect.

Prior to take-off, the engine should be run up to at least the static boost reading (ref-revs), or to the highest boost that can be held on the brakes. The purpose of this is to clear the plugs and also clear the supercharger of any residual fuel sticking to the casing.

10.4   Engine Temperatures.

It is important to watch the engine cylinder head temperature and/or coolant and oil temperatures, and to keep them within the limitations. The cooling of air-cooled cylinders is controlled by the setting of gills which in general should be:

(i) Fully open for all ground operations, or running, provided the engine has reached normal operating temperature or +100 degrees centigrade.

(ii) Closed or part open for take-off.

(iii) Adjusted in flight as required.

If the gills or cooling ducts are closed, drag is minimised and during take-off safety speed is reached earlier. On the majority of aircraft the cowling gills are controlled by switches marked 'Open', 'Off' and 'Closed'. To operate the gill motor, the switch is depressed and the gills set as required; when the desired position is reached, as shown by the gill position indicator, the switch should be turned off.

The cooling of liquid-cooled engines is almost always regulated automatically, but the pilot may have control of the air through the radiator. Radiator shutters should be open only as much as required for adequate cooling, in order not to increase drag.

Temperatures of all types of engines can be reduced by climbing the aircraft some 10 to 15 knots faster than the recommended climbing IAS without seriously affecting the rate of climb. Climbing with weak mixtures may lead to high temperatures.

On liquid-cooled engines the oil cooler is normally incorporated in the coolant radiator assembly and control is automatic.

10.5 Mixture Setting (Manual Mixture Control).

On engines with manual mixture controls, the mixture must be set to rich before the boost is raised to a value greater than that specified for the maximum weak mixture.

10.6 Automatic Mixture Control.

There are two main methods of automatic mixture regulation:

(a) The throttle lever is set to give not more than the maximum weak mixture boost, therefore ensuring that the mixture is correctly set.

(b) The throttle is set at or behind the economical cruise position marked on the quadrant.

With engines using method (a) some care is necessary, particularly when flying at or near full throttle height, to ensure that rich mixture is not being used inadvertently. To ensure that weak mixture is in use under these conditions, the throttle should be opened fully and then slowly closed until the boost starts to fall; this position will then give the required weak mixture setting. If at any time the fuel consumption becomes high, a check should be made to see that weak mixture is in fact being used.

10.7 Climbing.

On most aircraft the rpm and boost are automatically maintained at the values set by the pilot until the full throttle height for that power is reached. If the climb is continued above this height the boost then falls progressively.

10.8 Some Common Faults.

(a) On engine starting, black smoke is seen coming from the exhaust manifold:

Mixture too rich.

(b) On engine starting, blue smoke is seen coming from the exhaust manifold:

Oil leaking into the combustion chamber past the piston rings.

(c) On engine starting, black smoke is seen coming from the exhaust manifold, mixture setting is correct, throttle setting is correct:

Engine is overprimed.

Manual priming pump has not been locked and is allowing additional fuel into the inlet manifold.

(d) Engine idle rpm is difficult to maintain for the correct throttle setting:

VP Prop ground fine, or extra fine has not been selected.

(e) During ground running, engine temperature rises above normal:

Engine cooling gills or shutters are fully closed or not in the recommended position.

(f) During taxying the engine tends to overheat:

Engine cooling gills or shutters in closed position; normally, should be kept in fully open position during taxying.

(g) During take-off, a loss of power is experienced for a given rpm and boost.

Carburettor warm air is selected. During take-off this should be selected only if it is absolutely necessary.

(h) A backfire occurs during starting on an aircraft with an updraught carburettor.

Warm air is selected, this must be avoided or it may result in priming fuel igniting and causing a serious fire.

(i) When throttling back (closing throttle), for example on final approach, engine "backfires" coupled with a rapid rise in inlet manifold pressure.

Throttle is closed too quickly causing boost reversal.

(j) When descending from altitude, in an aircraft fitted with automatic boost control, boost pressure rises excessively.

Waste gate is possibly seized in the closed position. Engine must be controlled on the throttle to reduce the overboosting.

Practice Paper 1

1. The 'Otto' cycle is:

(a) induction, power, compression, exhaust.

(b) compression, induction, power, exhaust.

(c) exhaust, induction, power, compression.

(d) compression, power, exhaust, induction.

Ref. 2.2

2. The compression ratio of a piston engine is:

(a) a ratio of volumes.

(b) a ratio of areas.

(c) a ratio of pressures.

(d) a ratio of area and volume.

Ref. 2.3

3. The inlet valve of a piston engine:

(a) opens after top dead centre to ensure maximum weight of charge is induced.

(b) opens before top dead centre to ensure maximum weight of charge is induced.

(c) opens after the exhaust valve to ensure fire in the inlet manifold is avoided.

(d) opens before the exhaust valve closes to reduce the temperature in the exhaust manifold.

Ref. 2.6a

4. The primary function of duplicated valve springs is to:

(a) provide a back up spring if one should break.

(b) ensure a gas tight seal is made between valve and valve seat.

(c) minimise valve bounce.

(d) increase cooling surfaces.

Ref. 2.10

5. The camshaft of a piston engine rotates:

   (a)   at the same speed as the crankshaft.

   (b)   at twice the speed of the crankshaft.

   (c)   at four times the speed of the crankshaft.

   (d)   at half the speed of the crankshaft.

Ref. 2.11

6. As the piston is forced down the cylinder on the power stroke:

   (a)   the gas temperature will increase.

   (b)   the gas pressure will progressively increase.

   (c)   the gas temperature will reduce.

   (d)   the gas temperature and pressure will remain constant.

Ref. 2.3c

7. The space above the oil in a dry sump lubrication system oil tank:

   (a)   is to allow for oil displacement by the pressure pump control piston.

   (b)   is to allow for oil expansion and frothing.

   (c)   provides for tank pressurisation.

   (d)   allows for scavenge pump ram displacement.

Ref. 3.5

8. The output pressure of the pressure pump of a dry sump lubrication system is controlled by:

   (a)   a relief valve.

   (b)   the movement of the swash plate.

   (c)   the operation of the scavenge pump.

   (d)   the pressure plate displacement piston.

Ref. 3.5c

9. In a dry sump lubrication system:
   (a) return oil is collected direct from the oilways by the scavenge pump.
   (b) return oil drains into the sump and is then scavenged.
   (c) the engine sump is eliminated to save weight.
   (d) oil is fed direct to the bearings and returned direct to the tank.

Ref. 3.5h

10. The scavenge pump:
   (a) has a lower pumping capacity than the pressure pump.
   (b) normally is of a swashplate design.
   (c) scavenges at the same rate as oil is pumped into the system.
   (d) has a greater pumping capacity than the pressure pump.

Ref. 3.5h

11. Aircraft piston engine lubrication systems:
   (a) are normally of the wet sump type.
   (b) are normally of the dry sump type.
   (c) are of a sumpless type.
   (d) are of a compound lubrication type.

Ref. 3.5

12. The by-pass valve in a dry sump lubrication system is:
   (a) to allow oil to by-pass the sump when maximum pressure is reached.
   (b) to allow oil to by-pass the filter when the element is blocked.
   (c) to allow oil to by-pass the auxiliary system until normal operating temperature is reached.
   (d) to allow oil to by-pass the cooler.

Ref. 3.5

13. A condenser is fitted to the distributor to:

   (a)   minimise arcing at the points.

   (b)   reduce the speed of collapse of the magnetic field.

   (c)   intensify arcing at the points.

   (d)   control and direct the high tension impulses.

Ref. 4.7e

14. On a four-stroke engine the spark will occur:

   (a)   once each revolution.

   (b)   twice each revolution.

   (c)   once every two revolutions.

   (d)   four times each revolution.

Ref. 4.10

15. In flight, if the mixture weakens, for efficiency, the ignition timing should be:

   (a)   advanced.

   (b)   retarded to TDC.

   (c)   retarded to before TDC.

   (d)   unaltered.

Ref. 4.19c

16. Vapour locks are prevented from forming in fuel system pipelines by:

   (a)   the main fuel pump.

   (b)   ram air fuel tank pressurisation.

   (c)   the fitting of booster pumps.

   (d)   swash plate pumps.

Ref. 5.7a

17. Booster pumps are:

   (a)   mechanically driven and electrically selected.

   (b)   electrically driven.

   (c)   air driven for safety.

   (d)   driven by the hydraulic system.

Ref. 5.7a

18. The engine fuel pressure warning light flickers in flight:

(a)   the booster pump should be switched on.

(b)   the collector pump should be switched on.

(c)   the main fuel pump should be switched on.

(d)   the booster pump should be switched off.

Ref. 5.7

19. The pressure balance duct of a basic carburettor is:

(a)   connected between the carburettor intake and the float chamber.

(b)   providing a pressurised (above atmospheric) space above the fuel in the float chamber.

(c)   connected between the diffuser and the float chamber.

(d)   connected between the choke and the float chamber.

Ref. 7.3a

20. When the throttle is opened rapidly, additional fuel is supplied to the engine by:

(a)   the choke jet.

(b)   the enrichment jet.

(c)   the accelerator pump.

(d)   the power jet.

Ref. 7.3f

21. A supercharger is normally located:

(a)   prior to the carburettor.

(b)   between the carburettor and the inlet manifold.

(c)   in the exhaust manifold.

(d)   in the exhaust manifold by-pass duct.

Ref. 8.2

22. Vibration in a supercharger may be reduced by:

(a)   a spring drive mechanism.

(b)   a friction clutch.

(c)   hydraulic drive.

(d)   mechanical overload diffusers.

Ref. 8.2

23. When the engine is started on a supercharged engine, manifold pressure will:

(a) rapidly rise.

(b) slowly rise.

(c) remain constant.

(d) fall.

Ref. 8.4

24. A given boost, can be maintained at a given rpm up to an altitude which is known as:

(a) critical height.

(b) rated boost altitude.

(c) rated throttle height.

(d) full throttle height.

Ref. 8.8.

25. An intercooler is sometimes fitted between the supercharger and inlet manifold:

(a) to reduce pre-ignition.

(b) to minimise detonation.

(c) to reduce the weight of charge.

(d) to increase the combustion temperature.

Ref. 8.13

26. The impeller of a supercharger rotates at:

(a) twice the speed of the crankshaft.

(b) four times the speed of the crankshaft.

(c) twenty times the speed of the crankshaft.

(d) nine to ten times the speed of the crankshaft.

Ref. 8.2

27. The impeller of a turbocharger:

(a)   reduces rpm with increase of altitude.

(b)   rotates at a constant rpm with variations of altitude controlled by the waste gate.

(c)   increases rpm with increase of altitude for a given waste gate setting.

(d)   will reduce rpm with increase of altitude as the waste gate closes.

Ref. 9. 4

28. A turbocharger's rpm is regulated by:

(a)   the waste gate.

(b)   the impeller rpm.

(c)   hydraulic system oil pressure.

(d)   spring pressure.

Ref. 9.4

29. As the throttle is being closed, when the aircraft is flying straight and level at altitude, the waste gate will:

(a)   remain fully open.

(b)   move to the fully closed position.

(c)   move towards the open position.

(d)   remain in the same position.

Ref. 9.7

30. On engine starting, the waste gate will:

(a)   move towards the closed position.

(b)   remain fully open.

(c)   remain in the same position as that prior to starting.

(d)   move to the fully closed position.

Ref. 9.10

Part 2

Gas Turbine Engines

1

Basic Theory, Principles and Intakes

1.1 Introduction.

Gas turbine engines at present used in aircraft are divided into two main classes:

(a) The turbojet engine, which derives its power from the reaction of exhaust gas expelled rearwards.

(b) The turboprop engine, which utilises the greater part of its power output to drive a propeller, the residue augmenting the thrust by jet reaction.

1.2 Basic Principle.

An aircraft that is propelled by an air-breathing engine (as distinct from a rocket) obtains its forward motion in exchange for accelerating a mass of air rearward. The difference between propeller and jet propulsion is that the propeller accelerates a relatively large mass of air rearward at relatively low speed, whereas the jet accelerates a much smaller mass of air but at a much greater speed. In each case it is the reaction to the rate of change of momentum of the mass of air that propels the aircraft.

1.3 Principle of Operation.

The principle of operation of the gas turbine engine is similar to the piston engine in that there are induction, compression, ignition and expansion, and exhaust. However in the gas turbine these are continuous processes and not intermittent as in the piston engine. Figure 1-1 illustrates the principle of operation from which it will be seen:

(a) that air is drawn in through the intake 'A' by a compressor 'B' which is mounted on the main shaft 'C'.

(b) The turbine 'D' is mounted on the other end of the shaft.

(c)   air drawn through the intake by the compressor will increase in pressure, temperature and velocity as it passes through the compressor stages of the engine.

(d)   air leaves the compressor and passes to the diffuser 'E', which converts the velocity energy to pressure energy.

(e)   on leaving the diffuser the air passes into the combustion chambers 'H'. Of the total mass of air entering the combustion chambers approximately 25 per cent, known as primary air, enters the flame tubes through the flame tube orifice 'G'.

(f)   the remainder of the air, passes along the outside of the flame tubes, entering through dilution holes 'J' in the side of the tubes.

(g)   each combustion chamber is provided with a burner containing a swirl type atomiser through which fuel is injected under pressure by the fuel pump into the combustion chamber, where it mixes as fine droplets with the incoming primary air.

(h)   the combustible mixture so formed is ignited (on start-up) by igniters in two or three of the combustion chambers. On completion of the starting cycle the igniters are cut off. At this stage the engine is said to 'light up' and from this point combustion is continuous and the pressure in the combustion chamber for a given fuel flow is constant.

(i)   the remaining secondary air, which passes through the dilution holes into the flame tube, mixes with the main mass of burning gas and cools it sufficiently to allow it to pass through the turbine at a temperature within the safe limits of the turbine material.

(j)   within the combustion chamber, owing to the added heat energy of the fuel, the gas not only rises in temperature but also increases in volume.

(k)   after passing through the combustion chambers the hot gases enter the nozzle guide vanes 'K' which direct them at increased velocity on to the turbine blades, causing the turbine disc 'D' to rotate and so drive the compressor.

(l)   of the total energy generated approximately 60 per cent is used to drive the compressor, so that there is a considerable drop in gas pressure and temperature across the turbine.

(m)   the 40 per cent of energy remaining after driving the turbine and compressor is used to form a high speed jet, which has a substantial residual pressure; this jet passes into the exhaust cone 'L' to emerge at atmospheric pressure at orifice 'M'.

(n)   the jet not only has kinetic energy owing to its velocity but also has considerable heat energy. The heat energy is released to atmosphere, however, and is consequently wasted.

1.4   Thrust and Propulsive Efficiency.

An aircraft is propelled by a force known as 'thrust', this force being necessary to accelerate the aircraft and balance the drag. Piston engines are rated in horse power and turbojet engines are rated by the amount of static thrust they produce. An aircraft that flies and is self propelled acquires propulsion by displacing something – usually a mass of the supporting medium – in the opposite direction. To make this mass move backwards it is necessary to exert a rearwards acting push on it, consequently, in accordance with Newton's third law, an equal and opposite forward reaction is set up. This forward acting force is 'thrust'.

The simple relationship between the force applied to a body, its mass, and the resulting acceleration that it experiences can be stated as:

Force Mass × Acceleration

Consequently the thrust experienced by an aircraft depends on the mass of air passing through the propeller disc or jet pipe in unit time and the rate at which its velocity is changed.

It is also essential to remember:

MASS

is usually defined as the quantity of matter contained in a body and is constant.

WEIGHT

is the gravitational force attracting a body towards the earth, and is not constant, decreasing as distance from the earth's centre increases. Therefore the weight of a body is slightly less at the equator than at the poles.

Where the force of gravity is less, the acceleration due to gravity must also be proportionately less: i.e. the body will not gain speed so rapidly if allowed to fall freely. Thus the weight of a body divided by the acceleration due to gravity (W/g) will always be constant, regardless of its position on earth or in space. This is the mass, and for all normal purposes is obtained by dividing the weight by 32.2 when working in ft lb/sec^2 units. Returning to Force Mass × Acceleration, and applying it to a stationary aircraft with its engine running at high power, assume that in one second W lb of air are accelerated from rest to V_2 ft/sec. The mass of air handled by the propeller or jet in that time (i.e. the mass flow) will be $\frac{W}{g}$

Consequently the thrust acting on the aircraft will be $\dfrac{WV_2 \text{ lb.}}{g}$

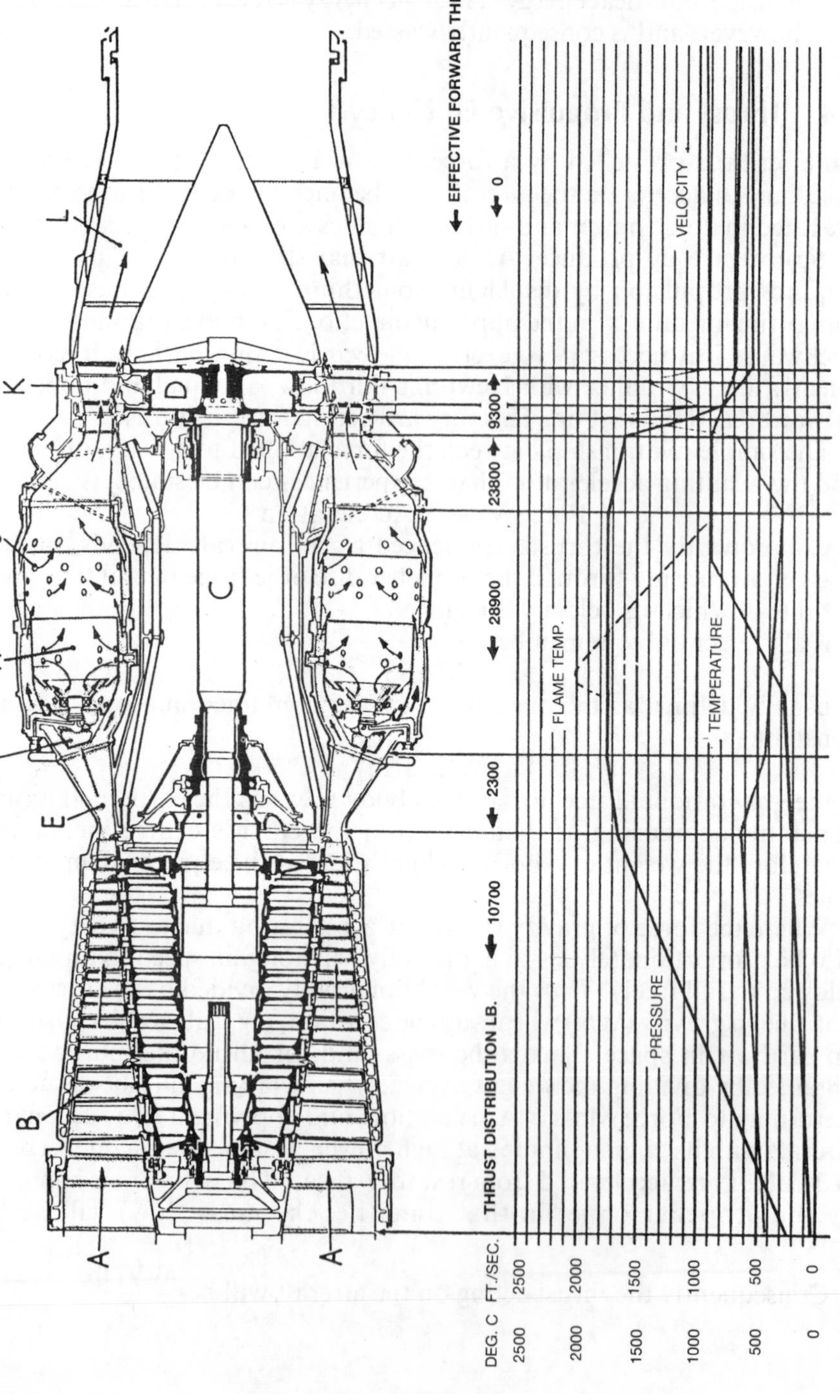

Figure 1-1   The Gas Turbine.

140

But as the aircraft cannot move, all the energy given to the slipstream or jet is wasted and the propulsive efficiency is zero.

If the aircraft is now permitted to move, it will take off and attain a certain velocity, V_1ft/sec, i.e. the air about to pass through the propeller disc or turbine has a velocity towards the aircraft of V_1ft/sec. Assuming that the resultant velocity of this air relative to the aircraft is still V_2ft/sec, the acceleration is only (V_2-V_1) ft/sec and if the mass flow remains the same the thrust will be $\frac{W (V_2-V_1) \text{ lb}}{g}$.

In other words, thrust falls off as speed increases.

At this stage a factor which favours the turbine engine makes itself evident; air pressure tends to build up in front of any object moving through it, an effect hardly noticeable at low speeds but considerable pressure will build up in front of the object as speed is increased. This increase in pressure becomes pronounced at speeds above about 250 knots, and increases the mass flow through the engine. This is known as ram effect. The result is shown in Fig. 1-2 where it can be seen that up to about 250 knots thrust falls steadily, as would be expected from the decreasing acceleration given to the air. Above this speed, however, the ram effect is sufficient not only to half the fall but to reverse the trend, until at 500 knots the static value has been regained. The rate of rise of thrust decreases beyond Mach One as a result of the formation of shock waves in the entry duct unless measures are taken to counter the effect of shock waves on or in the intake.

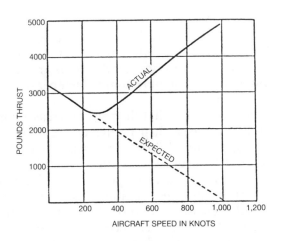

Figure 1-2 How Ram Air Affects the Thrust.

1.5 The Effects of Ram, Density and Temperature.

As altitude is increased, atmospheric pressure, density and temperature decrease, and coupled with ram air effects, these variations have a considerable effect on the performance of the gas turbine engine. At constant rpm the pressure ratio of the compressor (the difference of pressure between the inlet and outlet of the compressor) and the temperature rise across the compressor remain constant irrespective of height; however, due to the drop in density, it is necessary to reduce the fuel supply to prevent high combustion temperatures as a result of the excess fuel to air mixture. As well as the drop in density there is also a drop in air temperature, and consequently the temperature of the air entering the compressor inlet will also be lower, and therefore the air entering the combustion chambers will also be cooler. This reduced temperature will allow a slightly greater quantity of fuel to be used than would be possible if a constant temperature were maintained.

The increase in temperature results from an increase in change of momentum of the gas passing through the engine, so that one pound of air now produces more thrust than at sea level, this is because there is an improved expansion ratio across the turbine, which increases the efficiency. The total mass of air passing through the engine reduces with increased altitude owing to the reduction in air density, and therefore if the total mass airflow is less then the total mass weight will also be less. It has been shown, however, that one pound of air produces more power at height, so the power decreases at a lower rate than the air density.

The power available from one pound of air is increased if the air enters the compressor at a lower temperature. If the air at sea level is cold the density is higher. The thrust obtainable from a gas turbine engine is therefore greater on a cold day, not only due to the extra power obtained from each pound of air passing through the engine, but also because the total weight of a given volume of air is greater due to its greater density.

Figure 1-3 shows the effect of intake or inlet temperature on the power delivered by a gas turbine.

It can be seen from the curve that the power increases considerably as the temperature falls: as much as 50 per cent increase in the sea level power is obtained at a temperature of 0 degrees F compared with the output design temperature at 60 degrees F. With increased height and lower temperature therefore, a considerable proportion of the power will be regained by virtue of the lower temperature. As the aircraft gains height the compressor load decreases due to the lower density and, unless the fuel flow is reduced, the turbine overspeeds. This contingency is covered by the use of a barometric unit which monitors the output of the fuel pump and adjusts it accordingly. As altitude is increased the fuel output for a given power setting will progressively reduce, and so fuel consump-

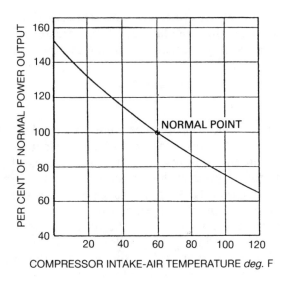

Figure 1–3 Effects of Air Temperature on
Power Output.

tion progressively decreases. It shculd be noted therefore that an increase in temperature causes a loss of power, since an increase in temperature results in reduced air density and, therefore, the weight of the volume of air flowing through the engine reduces.

So far there has been a gain due to increased density at low temperature and a loss due to the lower density at high temperatures. At altitude the overall thrust is less, due to the reduced density, but also due to the reduced density the total drag of the aircraft is less than at sea level, consequently less power is required to propel the aircraft at a given true airspeed. The reduction in drag however, is not proportional to the reduction in air density because, at altitude, the angle of attack of the wing must be increased to provide the same amount of lift, and this results in an increase in induced drag, so raising the total drag. Drag therefore decreases with increased altitude at a lower rate than the density. If the Thrust Horse Power of a jet aircraft decreases with increased altitude at the same rate as the decrease in total drag, then the True Air Speed is constant at all heights, but at height the drag is less and therefore the thrust required from the engine is proportionally less; this reduction in the required thrust is accompanied by a reduction in fuel consumption. If, however, power from the turbine decreases at a lower rate than the reduction in drag, then the speed increases with height. This gives a further increase in efficiency as a result of the increase in speed, resulting

143

in an increase in propulsive efficiency. This increase in speed also results in greater ram effect, thus increasing the compressor efficiency which therefore absorbs less power from the turbine to do the same amount of work on the air.

1.6 Intake Design.

The ideal subsonic aircraft gas turbine engine air intake, for air to flow smoothly through the compressor, should have a velocity of about Mach 0.4 at the inlet, and an even pressure distribution across the compressor face; these conditions, however, hold good not only for aircraft flying at subsonic speeds, but aircraft which fly at speeds in excess of Mach 1.0. To achieve this the intake must be designed to decelerate the free stream airflow to the correct inlet velocity over the designed aircraft speed range, and convert the kinetic energy of the flow into static pressure with a minimum of shock or functional losses, that is to say, the compressor inlet pressure should be as near as possible to the total head pressure. Total head pressure is the pressure of the air when it is decelerated or brought to rest in front of a wing or engine intake, it increases as the aircraft speed increases. As the air accelerates away from the deceleration (or stagnation) point, the pressure decreases. Intakes are designed to avoid this pressure loss and the efficiency of an intake is measured by its ability to maintain compressor inlet pressure at or near its total head pressure.

1.7 Intakes for Supersonic Flight.

Downstream of the normal shock wave the flow is always subsonic and, as the supersonic Mach Number increases upstream, the subsonic Mach Number following the normal shock wave decreases. The pressure recovery across a normal shock wave is near unity up to approximately Mach 1.4 and so a simple fixed intake design is satisfactory.

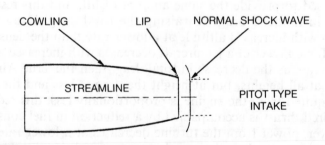

Figure 1–4 Pitot or Simple Cowl Intake.

144

An example of a fixed or pitot type, intake is shown in Fig. 1-4. This type of intake is satisfactory at subsonic, transonic and low supersonic speeds. At higher speeds the recovery across the normal shock wave drops off rapidly and it becomes necessary to find a more efficient design of intake to capture the airflow and regain the total head of pressure.

The Mach Number downstream of an oblique shockwave is supersonic at nearly all the possible combinations of upstream Mach Number and shock angle, and the pressure recovery is close to unity for all upstream Mach Numbers less than about mach 2.5. The deceleration of a supersonic free stream flow is thus most efficiently achieved by a sequence of shock waves, one or two obliques followed by one normal shock. For flight conditions above Mach 1.4 the intake must be designed to produce oblique shock waves and this function may be achieved by use of a centre body intake or a wedge type. See Fig. 1-5.

CONICAL OR CENTRE BODY INTAKE

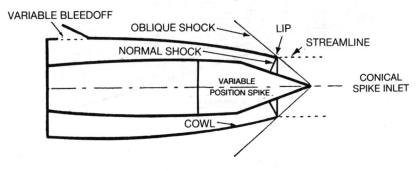

WEDGE TYPE INTAKE, MAY BE FIXED OR VARIABLE

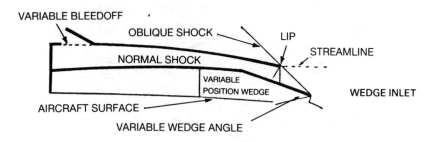

Figure 1–5 Centre Body and Wedge
Type Intakes.

1.8   Intake Shapes.

At subsonic speeds a divergent intake duct is required to decelerate the free stream flow and increase the pressure. See Fig. 1-6.

At supersonic speeds a converging intake duct is required to achieve the same objectives. For aircraft which fly at high supersonic speeds the converging duct is usually followed by a diverging duct and the intersection between these two ducts forms the diffuser 'throat' where the cross section is at its minimum. See Figs. 1-7 (a) and 1-7 (b).

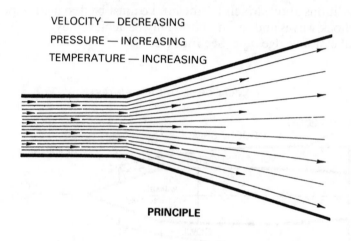

VELOCITY — DECREASING

PRESSURE — INCREASING

TEMPERATURE — INCREASING

PRINCIPLE

Figure 1–6   A Divergent Duct.

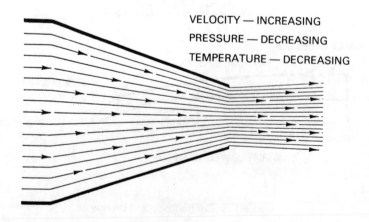

VELOCITY — INCREASING

PRESSURE — DECREASING

TEMPERATURE — DECREASING

Figure 1–7 (a)   A Convergent Duct.

146

Maximum pressure recovery, which is the product of the individual shock wave recoveries, is achieved when each of the oblique shock wave pressure losses approximately equals the remaining shock pressure loss. The balancing of shock wave losses is not possible in a centre body, or spike inlet because the actual contour of the spike tip cannot be varied.

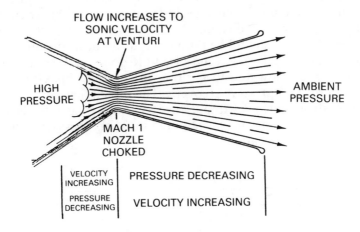

Figure 1–7 (b).

1.9   Critical Conditions.

Three general types of gas turbine intake operation are employed and though they can be considered as being independent of the location of the oblique shock are dependent on the position of the normal shock wave relative to the intake lip:

(a)   Critical operation occurs when the normal shock wave is near the intake lip. This is the most desirable condition because maximum pressure recovery exists. There are no instabilities in the entering flow and maximum mass flow is captured.

(b)   If a normal shock wave occurs outside the intake, sub-critical operation exists with the shock system completely expelled upstream of the intake lip. The intake pressure recovery is less than in the critical condition due to the changes in the shock location which may cause 'buzz' and result in mass spillage of flow. High drag is caused by the air spilling around the intake lip but this can be reduced if the spillage air is exhausted through a bleed-off behind the intake lip.

(c) If a normal shock wave occurs inside the intake it is said to be operating supercritically. Although near maximum flow is captured, pressure recovery is less than during critical operation.

1.10 Variable Intakes.

Critical operation can only be achieved by continuously varying the shape of the intake to allow for changes in temperature (as experienced with variations in altitude) and engine airflow as well as by flight speed. The oblique shock wave should be positioned to occur at the intake lip just like the normal shock wave, and bleed-off doors may be used both to divert any excess flow and to position the normal shock for optimum shock patterns and pressure recovery. The intake therefore takes in the full free airstream airflow without any streamline drag at the head of the lip. A variable geometry inlet is required to satisfy these desirable conditions of shockwave location.

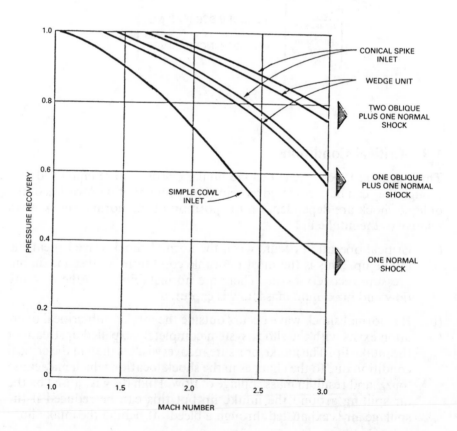

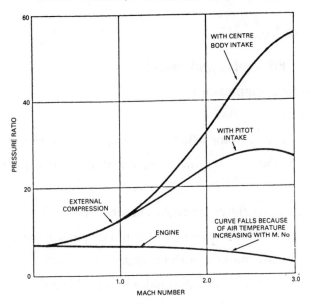

Pressure Ratio of a Jet Engine Varying with Mach. No., and with Differing Types of Intakes.

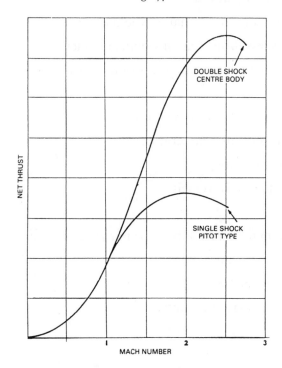

Shows how Thrust is Affected by Intake Design.

GENERAL INFORMATION FACTS

Section 1 Test Yourself

Basic Theory, Principles and Intakes

1. The gas turbine compressor is:

(a) driven by the airflow.

(b) driven by the turbine which is connected to a common shaft.

(c) driven by the turbine which is mounted on a separate drive shaft.

Ref. 1.3.

2. After the gas leaves the combustion chambers it:

(a) is directed onto the turbine by the nozzle guide vanes.

(b) flows directly onto the turbine blades.

(c) is directed onto the turbine blades by variable guide vanes.

Ref. 1.3.

3. One pound of air at altitude:

(a) produces more thrust than it would at sea level.

(b) produces less thrust than it would at sea level.

(c) produces the same thrust as it would at sea level.

Ref. 1.5.

4. Air drawn through the compressor will:

(a) maintain constant temperature.

(b) reduce in pressure.

(c) slightly increase in velocity.

Ref. 1.3.

5. Within the combustion chambers the burned fuel/air mixture:

(a) increases in volume.

(b) reduces in volume.

(c) maintains a constant volume.

Ref. 1.3.

6. Some secondary air is directed through the dilution holes in the combustion chambers to:

    (a)   atomise the fuel prior to combustion.

    (b)   create a swirl effect of the mixture.

    (c)   cool the gas before it reaches the turbine.

Ref. 1.3.

7. Igniters are fitted:

    (a)   in each combustion chamber.

    (b)   immediately aft of the combustion chambers.

    (c)   to just two or three combustion chambers.

Ref. 1.3.

8. As altitude is increased, compressor load:

    (a)   remains constant.

    (b)   decreases.

    (c)   increases.

Ref. 1.5.

9. At supersonic speeds, the airflow at the gas turbine inlet:

    (a)   will be reduced to subsonic speed.

    (b)   is increased to Mach 1.4

    (c)   will be maintained at the same speed.

Ref. 1.6.

10. An intake designed for transonic speeds will be:

    (a)   a converging duct.

    (b)   a diverging duct.

    (c)   a convergent/divergent duct.

Ref. 1.8.

2

Compressors

2.1 Introduction.

Two basic types of compressors are used in modern gas turbine engines, they are the:

(a) Centrifugal type.

(b) Axial Flow type.

The centrifugal compressor is similar in appearance and principle of operation to the supercharger impeller of a piston engine. The airflow is radial (outwards from the centre), and currently the centrifugal type is most commonly used on gas turbines for helicopters.

The axial flow type has an airflow path that flows parallel to the compressor shaft. Axial compressors are the most widely used type. A few engine designs also use a combination of centrifugal and axial flow compressors.

Each type has its advantages and disadvantages.

2.2 Design.

Compressor design is mainly concerned with aerodynamics, some principle factors affecting the performance being the aerofoil section of the blades, the blade pitch angles, and the length/chord ratio of the blades. Another important detail is the clearance between the blade tips and the shroud around them. Compressibility effects within the compressor can have a marked effect on the performance.

To achieve maximum efficiency a compressor must satisfy a number of requirements:

(a) It must provide the required pressure rise.

(b) Compression must be effected with the least possible loss, as the greater the loss the greater the power absorbed by the turbine.

(c) It must be aerodynamically stable over the operating range of rpm.

152

(d)   The tip speed of the impeller, or rotors, should not approach too closely to sonic speed, a maximum speed of .9M at any point on the radius being preferable.

Compressor design in most engines is a compromise between high performance over a narrow band of rpm or moderate performance over a wide band of rpm. Consequently, although it is possible for the compressor to be designed so that very high efficiency is obtained at the highest power, any deviation from the design conditions may cause serious changes in the aerodynamic flow conditions and so a loss of efficiency and unstable conditions within the engine. As the flow varies with operating conditions it is usual to compromise and design for lower efficiency, giving greater flexibility of performance and the retention of the highest possible performance over a wider range of rpm.

2.3   Centrifugal Compressors.

The single stage centrifugal compressor consists of three primary components: the compressor casing, which embodies the air inlet guide vanes and outlet ports, the compressor (sometimes termed the impeller), and the diffuser.

The main features of this unit are:

(a)   For a given useful capacity and pressure ratio it can be made comparatively small in size and weight.

(b)   As motion is purely rotary, the impeller can be accurately balanced.

(c)   A reasonable efficiency can be maintained over a substantial range of operating conditions.

(d)   It is very robust.

(e)   It is relatively simple to manufacture.

Figure 2-1 shows the impeller of a single entry compressor. Figure 2-2 shows the essential component parts of a single entry impeller or compressor assembly.

2.4   Centrifugal Compressor Airflow.

Air enters the air intake at atmospheric pressure and temperature passing into the eye (centre) of the impeller, which is designed to admit the air without excessive velocity. The air is picked up by the rotating vanes of the impeller and, due to the centrifugal force and the rotational speed, leaves the periphery of the impeller at approximately right angles to its entry at an increased velocity. On leaving the impeller vane passages, the

Figure 2–1 Single Entry Impeller.

air acquires in addition to its radial velocity, a tangential velocity which represents approximately half the total energy acquired during its passage through the impeller.

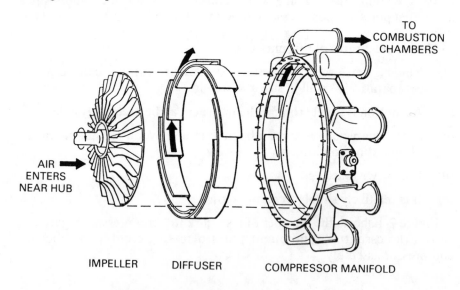

Figure 2–2 Single Entry Centrifugal Compressor.

The air then passes through the diffuser where the velocity energy is converted into pressure energy, so that the velocity is reduced and the pressure increased. Work is done by the compressor in compressing the air, and, since the process of compression involves adiabatic heating, a rise in temperature results.

154

Figure 2-3 shows the passage of air through a single entry centrifugal compressor.

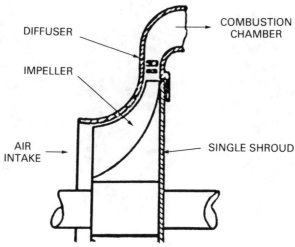

Figure 2–3 Passage of Air Through Centrifugal
Compressor.

Apart from the losses, the temperature rise across the compressor depends on the work done, and this in return depends broadly on the tip velocity of the impeller and the total air inlet temperature. The common types of centrifugal compressors in use today have a pressure ratio of approximately 4.5 to 1 with an adiabatic efficiency in the region of 80 per cent.

It must be appreciated that with ideal compression there are no losses but, as with most other types of practical machines, there are losses due to friction, turbulence, and shock, and these increase with the rate of flow through the impeller. Consequently the effective pressure rise is reduced, and a constant pressure ratio with varying flow is not obtained for a given tip speed. Therefore it follows:

(a)   The pressure obtained from an impeller is less than the theoretical value, and depends on rpm and diameter, and varies with the mass of air flowing through it.

(b)   The work capacity of an impeller at a given speed is less than the theoretical value.

(c)   The temperature rise depends mainly on the work capacity of the impeller and on frictional losses, but is independent of the pressure rise.

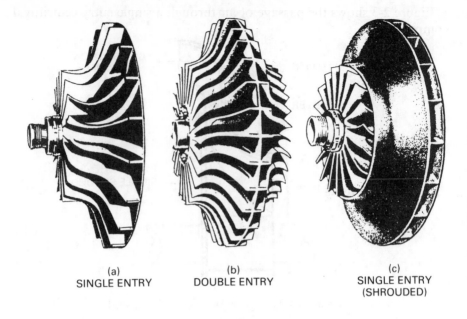

(a)
SINGLE ENTRY

(b)
DOUBLE ENTRY

(c)
SINGLE ENTRY
(SHROUDED)

Figure 2–4 Types of Centrifugal Compressor Impeller.

2.5   Compressor Design Variations.

There are two main types of centrifugal compressors in use today, the single entry, shown in Fig. 2-4(a) and the double entry shown in Fig. 2-4(b).

A third basic type has been used in the past but is rarely seen today, this being the shrouded impeller, a sketch of which is shown in Fig. 2-4(c) for information only.

(a) Single Entry Compressor.
  The single entry compressor consists of a disc having integral radially disposed vanes. When the compressor is assembled in its casing (Fig. 2-5) these vanes form divergent passages, which turn the incoming air so that it is discharged radially from the compressor tip into the diffuser vanes. At high tip speeds the velocity of the air relative to the vane at entry approaches the speed of sound, and it is essential for maximum efficiency that there is the minimum shock (compressibility effects) at entry. On most compressors therefore, the pick up (air entry) portions of the vanes are curved and then blended into the radial portions of the tip, the curvature being so adjusted that the sections of the vanes in planes normal to the axis of rotation are

truly radial. There are consequently no secondary bending stresses in the vanes from the effects of rotation alone and, from the stress point of view, the loads that arise from imparting angular motion to the air are negligible.

The centrifugal compressor is a highly stressed component. A major problem that arises is vibration. Vibration primarily occurs due to the pressure concentration around the leading edge of the vanes. As each vane passes a diffuser tip it receives an impulse, the frequency of which is a product of the number of vanes and the rpm. If this frequency should coincide with the natural frequency of a part of the compressor, resonance occurs and vibration develops. Therefore a process, which begins with the failure of the internal structure of the material, may spread until centrifugal stresses are high enough to tear the material, causing structural failure.

Note: Early type centrifugal compressors generally produced 20 per cent of the compression within the impeller, and 80 per cent within the diffuser. With more recent designs the compression of the air is approximately 50/50 between the impeller and the diffuser.

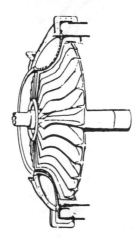

Figure 2–5 Impeller in
its Casing.

(b) Double Entry Compressor.

The double entry compressor, see Fig. 2-6, is similar to the single entry type, but has radial vanes on both sides of the disc. Air enters at each side, and is delivered radially to a common diffuser. Balance is an important operation in compressor manufacture, and any out of balance forces must be eliminated to prevent the serious vibration that might otherwise develop at high speeds.

Whilst a single entry centrifugal compressor would require to be larger in diameter to produce the same volume of airflow as the double sided, double entry compressor, the double sided impeller suffers a loss of efficiency due to heat transfer through the dividing disc or shroud. This primarily reduces the compression efficiency within the impeller on the second side of the double sided impeller.

Figure 2–6 Double Entry Impeller.

2.6   Diffuser System.

The object of the diffuser is to convert the velocity energy of the air leaving the compressor to pressure energy before it passes into the combustion chambers. The diffuser may be formed as an integral part of the compressor casing, or be bolted to it. It consists of a number of tangential vanes, the inner edges of which are parallel to the direction of the resultant airflow from the rotating compressor, the passages between the vanes being so proportioned that the air pressure attains the requisite value on entry to the combustion chambers. (See Fig. 2-7.)

The passages formed by the diffuser vanes are divergent, so that the velocity decreases and the pressure increases in the direction of the flow. These passages or ducts require very careful designing, as an excessive angle of divergence may lead to a breakaway of the boundary layer, causing general turbulence and loss of pressure energy. The outside diameter of the tangential portion of the diffuser varies considerably, depending on whether it completes the diffusion process or not. In some engines further diffusion takes place in the elbow leading to the combustion chambers. The usual design of the diffuser passages is such that the area increases very gradually for the first 5 to 10cm from the throat, the rate of increase being stepped up during the latter stages of expansion. The clearance between the tips of the diffuser vanes and the compressor tips is an important factor, because if placed too close together, the tips may set up aerodynamic buffeting impulses which are communicated to the compressor, causing unsteady flow and possibly initiating dangerous vibration. The usual clearance is about 5cm.

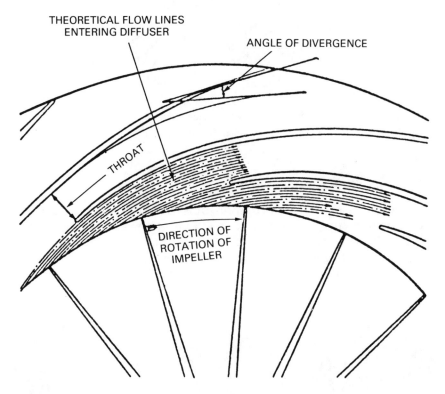

Figure 2–7 Diffuser.

2.7 Multi-Stage Centrifugal Compressors.

This type consists of two or more, single compressors mounted in tandem on the same shaft. (See Fig. 2-8.) The air compressed by the first stage, is passed onto the second stage at its point of entry near the hub. The second stage provides further compression before the air is diffused and passed to the combustion chambers.

This type of arrangement is commonly used on modern helicopter free turbine engines.

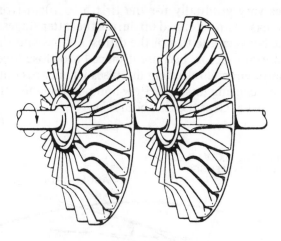

Figure 2–8 Multi-Stage Compressor
Impeller Assembly.

2.8   Axial Flow Compressors.

The function of an axial flow compressor is to convert kinetic energy into static pressure energy through the medium of rows of rotating blades (rotors) which change the whirl velocity of the air, and alternate rows of stationary diffusing vanes (stators) which convert the kinetic energy into pressure energy. Figure 2-9 illustrates an example compressor unit.

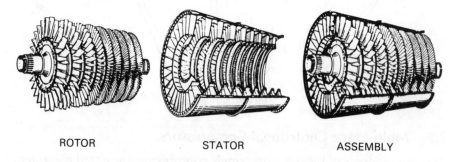

ROTOR   STATOR   ASSEMBLY

Figure 2–9 Axial Flow Compressor Rotor and Stator Assembly.

The entry section of the compressor contains one or more inlet guide vanes. These may be fixed or adjustable, and if the latter are normally termed variable inlet guide vanes. The inlet guide vanes may also be called swirl vanes. After the guide or swirl vanes there are several rows of vanes

160

of aerofoil shape which are alternately moving and fixed. The moving vanes are attached to one or more discs mounted on the compressor shaft, and the fixed vanes are attached to the compressor casing. At the rear of the compressor there is an exit section which houses a final row of stator vanes and air straightener vanes. One or two additional sets of stator vanes may be fitted before the first row of compressor vanes to improve entry conditions and so raise the compressor efficiency. The above is purely a general description and may vary according to individual engine type design requirements.

2.9 Compressor Rotor.

The rotor and stator vanes vary in length according to the pressure stage, the longest being at the low pressure or entry stage. To compress and transfer the large amount of air required, and to obtain a smooth flow with the minimum of turbulence and harmful characteristics, the vanes are of aerofoil section.

(a) Vane Twist.
The necessity for twist in the vane can be more readily appreciated if two points on an untwisted vane are considered, one near the tip of the vane and the other near the root. In an untwisted vane the section at both points has the same angle relative to a plane through the axis of rotation, but the root point has a lower rotational speed and therefore a different angle of attack. To obtain the optimum angle of attack at each point over the whole length of the vane, the angle of the tip section must be reduced and that of the root section increased. The vane must therefore be twisted so that the angle of incidence of all sections decreases from root to tip giving a constant angle of attack during rotation, as with a propeller.

(b) Vane Research.
Many years of research and testing have revealed the critical features of compressor design as:

    (i)   Surface eddies which appear as trailing edge vortices at the root and the tip of the vanes, caused by boundary-layer effects through the stages.

    (ii)   Radial clearances between the vane tips and the compressor casing.

    (iii) Axial clearance between rows of vanes.

    (iv) Turbulence of the wakes from preceding vane rows.

2.10   Airflow Through an Axial Compressor.

Air enters the compressor through guide vanes which ensure a correct angle of entry to the first row of rotating vanes, where it is picked up and accelerated during its passage across the moving vanes, leaving at a greater velocity than at entry. Owing to the angle of incidence and the rotation of the vanes the air leaves the vanes at some new angle. The air then flows over the first row of stator vanes, and is again changed in direction and velocity, ready for the next stage of rotating vanes. There is now a fixed lift and drag force for each row of vanes. Increasing the lift is the equivalent to turning the air through a greater angle and consequently achieving greater changes of velocity, and thus greater pressure changes. The increase of lift is accompanied by an increase in drag, which reduces the velocity increase, and also the pressure at delivery. As the turning angle of the air is limited by the maximum lift coefficient of the aerofoil section used, it follows that the maximum compression ratio is also a function of the lift coefficient.

Each row of stators acts as a diffuser for converting into pressure the kinetic energy of the air leaving the preceding rotating row of vanes, and also as nozzles for guiding the air into the next row of rotating vanes. There is a limit to the amount of diffusion and the angle through which the air can be turned, if this is exceeded, high losses result due to blade stalling.

After passing through the final row of rotating vanes, the air passes through a final stage of stator vanes and, in some engines, a row of straightener vanes. These provide any further diffusion necessary and give the best conditions for entry of the air into the combustion chambers.

Note: The compression ratio is the ratio between the inlet and outlet pressure of the compressor.

2.11   Reverse Flow Compressors.

Some axial flow gas turbines have been designed and produced with the airflow through the compressor in a forward direction (towards the front), parallel to the axis of the rotor. Figure 2-10 illustrates an example airflow diagram of such an engine.

2.12   The Main Features of the Axial Flow Compressor.

The main features of the axial compressor are:

(a)   High efficiency and therefore a lower fuel consumption at a given power. A compression ratio of up to 7 to 1 without serious loss of

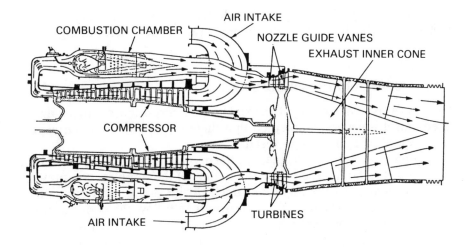

Figure 2–10 Reverse Flow Compressor Design.

efficiency is possible with this type of compressor. This compares with a compression ratio of only 4.5 to 1 with a centrifugal compressor.

(b)   A smooth airflow into the combustion chambers is assured.

(c)   As the motion is purely rotary, the rotor can be accurately balanced.

(d)   As large mass airflows can be catered for, an axial compressor is more suitable for use in high powered engines.

2.13   Compressor Surging.

Surging is instability of flow through the compressor. For the purpose of a simplified explanation of surge assume that a compressor is pumping air into a container, and as a result of some outside force there is a reduction of mass flow into the inlet side of the compressor. This causes the local pressure in the compressor to fall, and the air or gas in the container tends to blow back into the compressor. When this happens, the flow is reduced and the pressure therefore tends to rise. When or soon after maximum pressure has been reached a surge may begin, the air surging to and fro through the passages of the compressor instead of supplying the container with a steady flow of air in one direction. The surging can become strong enough to produce a vibration, which is transmitted to the aircraft. Surge is evident by rapid oscillation of delivery, accompanied by audible indications of instability, varying from a muffled rumbling noise to an abrupt loud bang or cough and vibration.

As has been stated, a compressor is designed for a certain range of flows which may be fairly broad at low pressure ratios but reduced at high pressures.

2.14 Axial Compressor Surging.

The mechanisms of surging of an axial flow compressor are rather complicated, but it is generally accepted that there are two kinds of surge, one at low speed and one at high speed.

Surging is caused by a decrease in the mass airflow, accompanied by a decrease in the axial velocity and the stalling of the complete compressor. With an increase in the angle of attack of the vanes, the flow pattern changes and becomes more difficult for air to follow the contour of the vane, the air then breaks away from the surface behind the leading edge and the vane stalls with a sudden deterioration in compressor efficiency.

With a reduction in mass flow at low rpm, the angle of attack of the first low pressure stages is greater than that of the high pressure stages, so that the low pressure stages are the first to stall, the succeeding stages not necessarily being affected. This is often indicated by an audible rumbling and a higher than normal jet pipe temperature. With a further reduction in mass flow, caused by either a reduction in indicated air speed or an attempt to accelerate the engine, the remaining stages stall in succession, unless the first stage stall so disturbs the airflow that a general breakdown and surge will occur. At high speed the angle of attack of all stages is about the same, so that at stalling conditions all stages are affected simultaneously and the engine surges without any warning. The vanes may be unstalled by throttling back fully and slowly, and on some occasions it may be necessary to stop the engine and then re-start it.

As surging is caused by a reduction in mass flow from the optimum figure, similar effects and subsequent stall may be caused by a limitation of mass flow through the combustion chambers or turbine. This may be a problem during starting as the sudden ignition of fuel tends to cause a choking effect, which momentarily reduces the mass flow and consequently sets up stalled conditions.

Similar conditions may arise following a sudden acceleration from idling speed. The tendency to surge is in general overcome by paying careful attention to the compressor vane design, and by incorporating devices such as variable incidence inlet guide vanes, sometimes known as swirl vanes, and pressure operated air release valves, or bleed valves, situated in the compressor at certain stages to bleed off excess air. On most modern gas turbines a set of release valves or bleed valves, are situated after the compressor stages but before the combustion chambers.

Figure 2-11 shows the location of the release valves in a typical compressor assembly.

AIR RELEASE OR BLEED VALVES

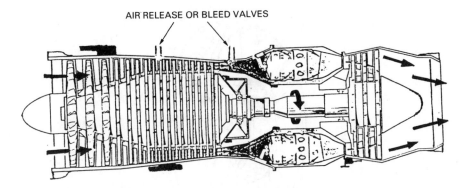

Figure 2–11 Air Release or Bleed Valve Location.

2.15 Effects of Compressor Surge.

The surging of the compressor imposes severe vibrations and excessive temperatures on the engine and should be avoided or minimised. A surge condition is also accompanied by a falling off of thrust (reducing rpm), and an increase in fuel consumption. The surge condition can be readily identified by the severe vibrations associated with it; the more violent conditions of surge are accompanied by a loud cough or bang.

2.16 Variable Position Guide Vanes.

Many modern gas turbine engines are fitted with variable position guide vanes, more commonly referred to as variable inlet guide vanes, and usually operated automatically. During engine starting and low rpm the guide vanes move to the fully closed position, but as rpm is increased they either progressively or completely move to the fully open position.

In the closed position the inlet guide vanes give a swirl to the incoming air so that the angle of attack of the low pressure blades is kept moderate and stalling is therefore avoided. In the open position they admit the maximum quantity of air. Figure 2-12 shows an example of a variable inlet guide vane assembly.

2.17 Air Release Valves (Bleed Valves).

The air release valves automatically permit air to be bled from critical points in the compressor and immediately after the compressor when pressures are at a particular level, thus allowing a higher mass flow

Figure 2–12 Variable Inlet Guide Vanes.

through the compressor, and reducing the mass flow through the combustion chambers and turbine. This action will minimise the tendency to stall or surge.

In some engines the air release valves or bleed valves operate in conjunction with the variable inlet guide vanes.

Note: Some engines are fitted with bleed valves to supply compressed air from the compressor to the air conditioning and pressurisation systems. Figure 2-13 shows the location of the bleed supply points.

BLEED SUPPLY

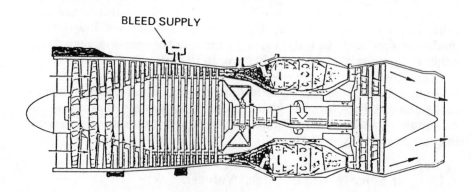

Figure 2–13 Main Bleed Supply.

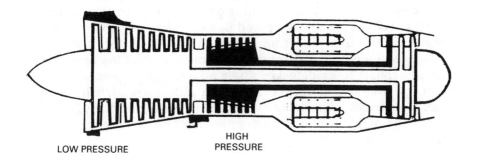

LOW PRESSURE   HIGH PRESSURE

Figure 2–14 Twin Spool Compressor.

2.18 Multi-Spool Engines.

Many modern gas turbine engines are fitted with multi-spool compressors, that is to say, a single spool comprising perhaps fourteen stages, is replaced with two or three spools or compressor assemblies. Usually each compressor spool is driven by a separate turbine.

Figure 2-14 shows a simple diagram of a twin or two spool compressor engine.

Such a twin spool compressor is a further method of avoiding flow troubles at high pressure ratios. The low pressure spool runs at a lower rpm than the high pressure spool and so the onset of compressor stalling at low rpm is avoided. Further, the high pressure spool running at higher rpm prevents the last stages operating at large negative angles of attack. Although the low pressure compressor runs at lower rpm than the high pressure unit its speed increases with the reduction of density with increased altitude. As a result, the rate of decrease in thrust with increase in altitude is less than that of a single spool engine with the same sea level output.

To further reduce the tendency to stall, in particular at engine starting, the engine is started by rotating the high pressure spool thus drawing air through the low pressure spool and causing it to rotate. Intermediate bleed valves are usually fitted between the spools to further reduce the tendency to stall or surge.

2.19 Compressor Icing.

Because of the high working rpm of the centrifugal type compressor and related high working temperatures, ice will not usually adhere to the impeller in a quantity sufficient to affect the efficiency to any great extent, and any large pieces of ice that may form will normally pass through the compressor without causing serious damage. Any ice that forms on the intake will usually break up and dissolve when passing through the compressor. For axial flow compressors, however, the formation of ice can be a serious problem, because the delicate nature of the vanes makes them susceptible to ice damage and, in addition, an appreciable loss of power and overheating will occur when the intakes are partially blocked by ice. To prevent such damaging results intakes are normally heated to prevent the build up of ice. Such anti-icing and de-icing systems are discussed in detail later.

2.20 Comparison of Axial Flow and Centrifugal Flow Compressor Engines.

(a) Power.
For a given temperature of the air entering the turbine, the power output of a gas turbine engine is a function of the quantity of air handled. The axial flow engine can handle a greater mass of air per unit of frontal area than can the centrifugal type.

(b) Weight.
In terms of unit weight of structure for unit thrust, axial flow gas turbines in general deliver a given thrust for a lower weight than does the centrifugal type, that is to say, the axial has a better power/weight ratio.

(c) Efficiency.
The efficiency of each component of a gas turbine engine is displayed in the fuel consumption. The centrifugal compressor may reach an efficiency of 75 to 80 per cent up to pressure ratios as high as 4:1. Above this, efficiency drops off at a rate which is prohibitive. The axial flow compressor, by contrast, can have an efficiency of 80 to 90 per cent over a wide range of compression ratios. The centrifugal compressor is therefore not as economic as the axial flow type in terms of fuel used per pound of thrust generated (specific fuel consumption).

(d) Design.
As the centrifugal compressor is of considerably simpler structure than the axial flow type, this factor dictated its use in the early history of the gas turbine engine. Equally important, much more was known at that time about the mathematics of the centrifugal impeller as a result of its long use in supercharged piston engines.

168

In small units where high efficiency is not so critical, the centrifugal type is still commonly used. It is simple and therefore cheaper to manufacture, is less susceptible to stall and/or compressor surge, and as a result is ideal for use on helicopters where turbulent airflow is sometimes a problem across engine intakes.

(e) High Altitude Operation.
Satisfactory combustion at altitudes of 50,000 to 70,000 feet is normally only practicable with the high compression ratios only available from axial flow engines.

(f) Application.
Increasing the power of the centrifugal engine is primarily confined to increasing the diameter of the impeller, or fitting a number of impellers in tandem on the drive shaft. Increasing the diameter will result in an increase of drag due to the larger frontal area. Increasing the number of impellers mounted in tandem on the drive shaft will increase the length of the engine and therefore nullify one of the major advantages of the centrifugal type: the compactness of the engine. As a result, few centrifugal compressor types have been fitted with more than two impellers in tandem.

The power of the axial flow gas turbine, on the other hand, can be increased by using more stages in the compressor without a marked increase in diameter. For performance increase in modern high speed aircraft, without incurring drag penalty, the axial type has major advantages.

There are, however, limitations: the greater the number of stages the greater the airflow problems incurred, hence the increasing use of multi-spooled compressors.

Irrespective of the type of compressor, about 100bhp is required to deliver one lb of air to the combustion chambers. Since this rate of flow provides approximately 50 lb of thrust, the compressor of an engine developing a thrust of 5000 lb requires in the region of 10,000 bhp to drive it.

Section 2 Test Yourself

Compressors

1. In a centrifugal compressor, air enters:

(a)   the centre of the impeller.

(b)   the outer rim of the impeller.

(c)   the diffuser.

Ref. 2.4.

2. As air passes through the impeller of a centrifugal compressor:

(a)   velocity remains constant.

(b)   velocity increases.

(c)   velocity reduces.

Ref. 2.4.

3. The compression ratio is the:

(a)   ratio between the inlet to the engine and the exhaust outlet pressure.

(b)   ratio between the pressure at the inlet to the compressor and the outlet of the compressor.

(c)   ratio between the entrance to the engine intake and compressor outlet pressure.

Ref. 2.10.

4. Compressor surge may be indicated by:

(a)   a reduction in engine gas temperature.

(b)   an increase in jet pipe temperature.

(c)   a rapid increase of power.

Ref. 2.14.

5. Intermediate bleed valves are fitted:

(a)   immediately after the compressor.

(b)   at the compressor inlet.

(c)   at an intermediate stage within the compressor.

Ref. 2.14.

6. During compressor surge, thrust will:

   (a)   increase.

   (b)   remain constant.

   (c)   reduce.

Ref. 2.15.

7. During engine starting, variable inlet guide vanes will be:

   (a)   fully closed.

   (b)   fully open.

   (c)   partially open.

Ref. 2.16.

8. Air release valves, or bleed valves:

   (a)   have no effect on mass flow.

   (b)   increase mass flow.

   (c)   reduce mass flow.

Ref. 2.17

9. Compressor surge may be identified by:

   (a)   increased engine rpm.

   (b)   a fall in engine gas temperature.

   (c)   an indication of vibration.

Ref. 2.13.

10. The rate of decrease of thrust from a twin spool compressor engine compared with a single spool engine as altitude increases:

   (a)   is greater.

   (b)   is the same.

   (c)   is less.

Ref. 2.18.

3

Combustion Systems

3.1 Introduction.

The purpose of the combustion chamber is to burn a mixture of air and fuel at a steady rate and thereby produce a continuous steady stream of gas at a uniform temperature. The primary requirements of the combustion chamber are:

(a) high combustion efficiency.

(b) reliability.

(c) low pressure loss.

(d) low sensitivity to variations within a grade of fuel.

(e) ability to operate efficiently over the range of pressures, inlet temperatures, and air/fuel ratios required.

(f) simplicity of control.

(g) ease and cheapness of manufacture.

3.2

Figure 3-1 illustrates the location of the combustion chambers within a simple axial flow gas turbine engine.

3.3 Basic Types of Combustion Chambers.

There are three primary types of combustion chamber (sometimes called combustion cans) used in current types of gas turbine engines:

(a) Multiple chambers arranged around the circumference of the engine body and sometimes called 'cannular' combustion chambers.

(b) The single annular chamber.

(c) Can-Annular or Tubo-Annular.

COMBUSTION CHAMBERS

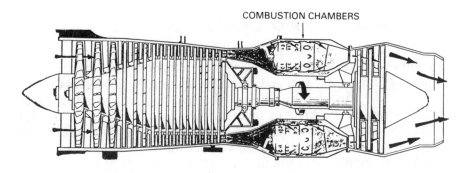

Figure 3–1 Location of Combustion Chambers.

Figures 3-2 and 3-4 show the basic configuration of the three main types of combustion chamber. Different manufacturers tend to call the types by different names, some alternative names are listed with the illustrations.

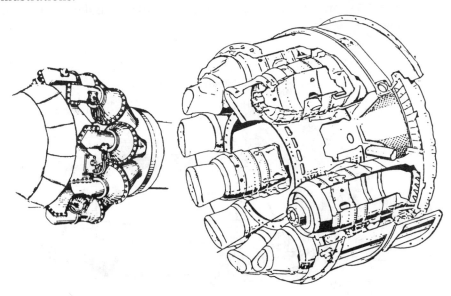

Figure 3–2 Shows a simple cannular arrangement on the left and a canannular arrangement on the right.

Alternatively they may be called a multi-chambered burner and a tubo-annular arrangement respectively.

3.4   Multiple Combustion Chambers.

Although multiple chambers, as fitted to numerous engine types, are basically similar, there are considerable variations in detail, particularly in the methods of mixing the fuel and air and obtaining the desired amount of turbulence. Multiple combustion chambers, sometimes 6 to 14 in number, may be arranged for direct or reverse flow according to design requirements. The principal advantage of the reverse flow type is the total engine length is reduced; this is sometimes very useful when applied to an axial compressor engine. An example of a reverse flow system is shown in Chapter Two.

3.5   The Cannular Type Combustion Chamber.

The Cannular combustion chamber used in older but current combustion chamber systems consists of an air casing carrying a torch igniter used for starting, (normally fitted only to two of the cans), an inter-connector and a fuel drain.

Figure 3-3 shows the arrangement and detail of a cannular combustion chamber.

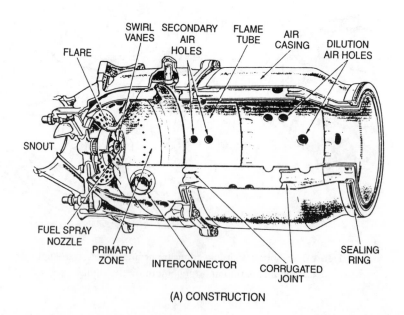

(A) CONSTRUCTION

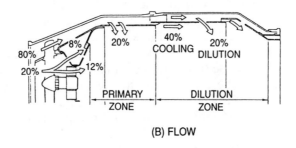

(B) FLOW

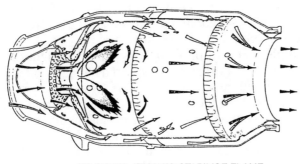

(C) CIRCULATION TO STABILISE FLAME

Figure 3–3 The Cannular Combustion Chamber.

In the air casing is a flame tube, located concentrically and consisting of two parts: the primary portion and the main tube. The primary portion, at the front end of the tube, is composed of an outer cap and a double end plate (sometimes called the colander), to which is fitted the swirl assembly. The airflow from the compressor is separated at the outer cap into primary and secondary airflows, the primary flow being concerned with combustion and the secondary flow with cooling. Approximately 80 per cent of the primary air flows over the outer cap and through the annular space between the flame tube and outer casing. The remaining 20 per cent flows through the central orifice of the outer cap, (known as the snout), a small amount passes through the holes in the colander and then helps to create a circulation effect to assist in stabilising the flame in conjunction with the swirl vanes which generate a toroidal vortex. This combined action produces a flow of low velocity to reduce any tendency of Flame Out or Blow Out, ie the extinguishing of the flame.

Combustion is completed within the first one-third of the length of the combustion chamber, known as the Primary Zone, the remainder of the volume constituting a dilution and mixing chamber. The annular space between the flame tube and air casing maintains an insulating layer of cool air between the flame tube and the air casing.

Figure 3-3b shows the flow of air through the various parts of the combustion chamber. Key points are: 20% of the air enters the snout. At the Fuel Spray Nozzle the mixture ratio of air to fuel is 15:1, 20% of the total air enters the Secondary Air Holes helping to create the circulating effect within the chamber and increasing the overall air to fuel ratio from 45 to 1 to 130 to 1.

A further 20% air enters the dilution holes to start the cooling of the flame leaving 40% solely for cooling. Overall, therefore, 40% is used for combustion and 60% for cooling purposes. At the centre of the flame the temperature is in the order of 2000 degrees C.

With multiple combustion chambers, only two igniters are usually fitted since the chambers are inter-connected and ignition in one chamber is propagated instantaneously to the others. The inter-connectors join the adjacent air casings and flame tubes so that in addition to propagating the flame they also equalise the pressure in all chambers.

Figure 3-4 shows the general arrangement of the inter-connectors, or as they are sometimes known, pressure balance tubes.

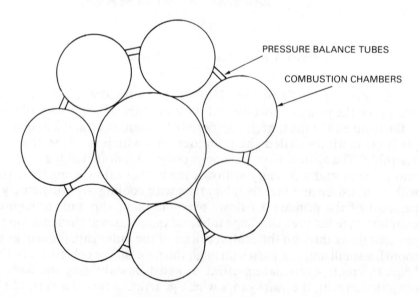

PRESSURE BALANCE TUBES

COMBUSTION CHAMBERS

Figure 3–4 Pressure Balance Tubes.

3.6   The Annular Combustion Chamber.

The annular combustion chamber (Fig. 3-5) surrounds the main body of the engine and is open at the forward end to the compressor and at the rearward end to the turbine. Within the annular chamber is an annular flame tube, similar in section to the multiple tube type. At the compressor end is a supporting plate for a series of burners, sometimes as many as twenty, which inject the fuel downstream into the flame tube. In some designs the burners are arranged to inject the fuel up-stream; in these types the spray from the burners is not diffused in a wide angle as with the down-stream type, since some degree of penetration of the incoming air is required. The air is metered and made to swirl by suitable arranged holes in the front plate.

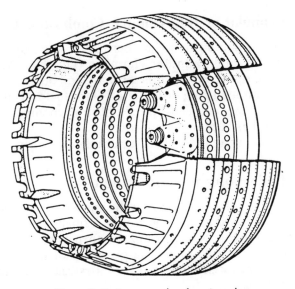

Figure 3–5   An example of an Annular
Combustion Chamber.

The annular chamber forms a continuous sheet of hot gas which flows from the primary zone to the turbine; the design is similar to the multiple chamber system in that the primary air supports combustion in the high temperature turbulent zone, and the secondary air and tertiary air cool the flow of gas before entry into the turbine. The main advantages of this system are:

(a)   The total chamber area exposed to the gas is reduced, resulting in reduced pressure loss.

(b)   Instead of a series of outlets to the nozzle guide vanes, a continuous sheet of gas at uniform temperature over the whole area is obtained, resulting in better pressure and flow distribution into the nozzles.

(c)   Ease of servicing.

(d)   Simplicity of manufacture.

(e)   Smaller overall diameter when used with an axial flow compressor, and because the combustion chamber is also much shorter therefore allows a shorter engine to be manufactured.

(f)   As the total surface area of the annular combustion chamber is smaller, less cooling air is required and, therefore, more air is available for burning.

3.7   Can-annular or Tubo-annular Combustion Chamber.

The can-annular combustion chamber uses a series of individual flame tubes within the main annular chamber. This has the advantage of providing more rigid control of the primary and other airflows. It should be noted that although poor distribution of the fuel and air was a common defect of the original annular type combustion chamber arrangement, in later types this has been much improved.

Figure 3-2 shows an example of a cannular arrangement.

3.8   Fuel Injection and Vaporisation.

Two basic methods have evolved for the injection and vaporisation of the fuel, The first is based on the injection of a finely divided (atomised) fuel into a turbulent stream of air, the mixture then being vaporised and burnt.

The other method employs the principle of pre-vaporisation and mixing of the vaporised fuel with an airstream before entering the combustion zone.

3.9   Atomisation of the Fuel.

Various methods of fuel atomising are employed by different engine manufacturers. As an example of an atomising system the swirl type will be considered.

Essentially a swirl atomiser operates in a similar manner to a water sprinkler. Fuel is fed, under pressure, to a cylindrical or conical cavity into which a number of streams of fuel are arranged to enter almost tangentially. Due to their direction of entry into the cavity, a vortex is set up and the swirling fuel leaves via a single orifice on the axis of the cavity in atomised form. The underlying principle of vortex flow is that the tangential velocity of the fuel increases towards the centre with a resultant pressure drop; this results in the path that any particle tends to follow when it leaves the orifice being peculiar to its position and different from every one of its neighbours. The fuel tries to leave the orifice in the form of a hollow cone and, were it not for the restraining effects of viscosity and surface tension, would resolve itself into a cloud of particles of little more than molecular size. Viscosity and surface tension hold the liquid together, particularly at low pressures when the swirl energy available for disintegration is small.

Figure 3-7 shows what happens at the orifice of an example swirl atomiser as the pressure is increased.

At the lowest pressures the fuel leaves at a mere trickle, slightly modified by its original tangential entry. At a slightly higher pressure the effect of the tangential velocity causes the fuel to form a hollow cone on leaving the orifice, but the viscosity draws the fuel together as a continuous film which later comes together again forming the so called 'bubble'.

At a still higher pressure, the film no longer reforms as a bubble, but starts to break up at the edges, forming what is called the 'tulip'. As the pressure is increased further the tulip shortens, atomisation occurring nearer and nearer to the orifice, and over the optimum working pressure range the fuel emerges in the form of a large number of tiny droplets almost as soon as it leaves the orifice.

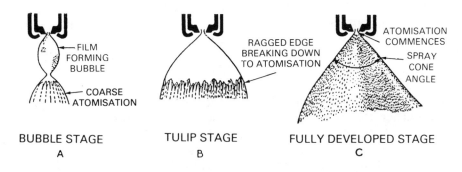

Figure 3–7 Development of Atomisation.

3.10 Burners.

The function of the burner is to inject fuel in a readily ignitable form into the flame tubes of the combustion chambers. Four basic types of burner will be discussed here:

(a)   Lubbock.

(b)   Simplex.

(c)   Duplex.

(d)   Spill.

Lubbock Type Burners.
Figure 3-8 shows an example of a Lubbock burner. In this type the area of the tangential slots through which the fuel enters the swirl chamber is controlled. As the pressure in the fuel line increases, the effective area of the slots, and therefore the amount of fuel discharged, are both increased. This action pressurises the fuel lines at low flows without raising the maximum pressure requirements to any great extent; and it gives good results. Some trouble has been experienced with this type, however, due to sticking of the piston that operates the variable area slots, and in most cases the adoption of a simple swirl atomiser has been the general solution. But because of these problems and improved alternative designs the Lubbock burner is virtually a thing of the past.

Simplex Type Burner.
The Simplex burner was widely used on many early gas turbine engines. Figure 3-9 shows an example of the type. It consists of a chamber, which generates a swirl into the fuel, and a fixed area atomising orifice. This design gave good atomisation at the higher fuel flow rates, that is, at the higher burner pressures, generally however, its performance at the low pressure ranges, such as at low engine speeds, was very poor. In particular its performance at high altitude was extremely poor in that 'flame outs', often caused by the shortfall of the burner's performance, occurred quite often. The reason for the poor low pressure performance was primarily due to the basic principle of its design being that of a 'square law' burner, that is, the flow through the burner was proportional to the square of the pressure drop across it. This meant that if the minimum pressure for effective atomisation was 25psi the pressure needed to give maximum flow would be 2500psi. Generally the fuel pumps available at the time were unable to deliver such pressures.

Duplex or Duple Burners.
The Duplex burner employs two fuel manifolds: the Primary and the Main manifold. The actual burner also utilises two orifices, the primary (fed by the primary manifold) designed to deal with the low flows, and the second or main orifice which copes with the higher flows as the burner pressure increases.

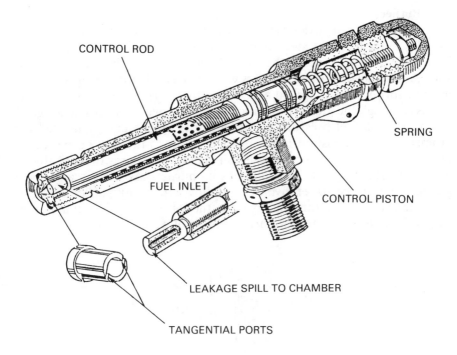

CONTROL ROD

SPRING

FUEL INLET

CONTROL PISTON

LEAKAGE SPILL TO CHAMBER

TANGENTIAL PORTS

Figure 3–8 A Lubbock Burner Assembly.

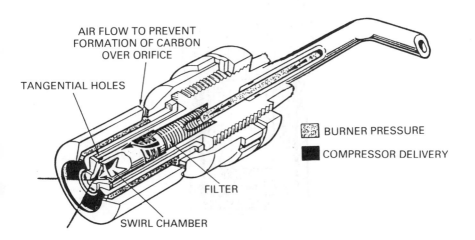

AIR FLOW TO PREVENT FORMATION OF CARBON OVER ORIFICE

TANGENTIAL HOLES

BURNER PRESSURE

COMPRESSOR DELIVERY

FILTER

SWIRL CHAMBER

Figure 3–9 Simplex Burner.

181

Spill Burner.
The spill burner can be described as being a Simplex burner with an additional passage from the swirl chamber for spilling fuel away. This makes it possible to supply fuel to the swirl chamber at a continuous high pressure. As the fuel flow rate decreases with increase of altitude, or reduction in rpm, surplus fuel is spilled away from the swirl chamber, leaving less to pass through the atomising orifice. Since the swirl chamber is designed to convert the fuel pressure energy into the kinetic energy needed for atomisation, the constant high pressure supply to the spill burner (even at very low flows into the combustion chamber) ensures there is atomisation of the fuel at all times. When spill burners are used in an engine means are required to remove the spill flow under any particular set of operating conditions; this usually takes the form of an additional pump. Figure 3-10 shows the interior arrangement of a spill burner.

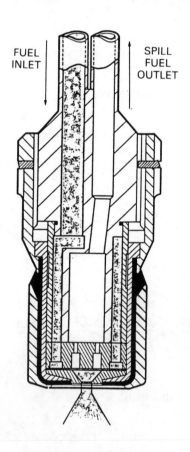

FUEL
INLET

SPILL
FUEL
OUTLET

Figure 3–10 Spill Burner.

Section 3 Test Yourself

Combustion Systems

1. The swirl assembly, or vanes, of a combustion chamber are fitted:

   (a) to generate a rotary motion to the mixture before it enters the combustion chamber.

   (b) to generate a rotary motion to the air in the secondary air flow.

   (c) to generate a rotary motion to the air in the inlet to the primary combustion zone.

   Ref. 3.5.

2. The action of the swirl vanes in a combustion system is to create:

   (a) a smooth flow.

   (b) a back flow.

   (c) a straightened flow.

   Ref. 3.5.

3. Pressure in the individual combustion chambers is balanced:

   (a) by the nozzle guide vane action at the outlet of the chambers.

   (b) by pressure balance tubes between each combustion chamber.

   (c) through the inlet manifold.

   Ref. 3.5.

4. The fuel is atomised:

   (a) in the combustion zone.

   (b) immediately after the compressor.

   (c) just prior to the combustion zone.

   Ref. 3.9.

5. In a multiple combustion chamber system:

   (a) each chamber is fitted with an igniter.

   (b) each alternate chamber is fitted with an igniter.

   (c) two or sometimes three igniters are fitted.

   Ref. 3.5.

4

Turbines

4.1 Introduction.

The turbine element of the modern gas turbine engine has either or both of the following primary functions; firstly to provide the power to drive the compressor and accessories and secondly, in the case of engines which do not make use solely of a jet for propulsion, of providing power to drive a shaft which in turn may drive a propeller or the rotors of a helicopter. In the example of a pure jet engine, the turbine extracts energy from the hot gases released by the combustion chambers and expanding them to a lower pressure and temperature. Very high stresses are encountered in this process as tip speeds in excess of 1350 feet per second may be experienced for efficient operation. The continuous flow of gas to which the turbine is exposed may have an entry temperature of between 700 and 1200 degrees centigrade, and may reach a velocity of 2000 feet per second in parts of the turbine.

To produce the required driving torque, the turbine may consist of several stages, each stage consisting of one row of stationary nozzle guide vanes and one row of moving blades or turbine rotors. Figure 4-1 shows an example of a turbine assembly as fitted to a conventional gas turbine engine.

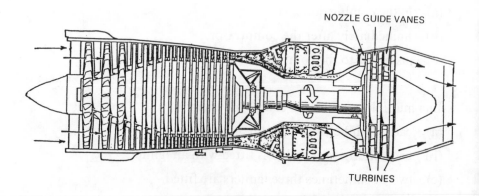

Figure 4–1 Location of Nozzle Guide Vanes and Turbines.

The number of stages is dependent upon whether the engine has one shaft or two, and on the amount of power required from the gas flow, the rotational speed at which it must be produced and the diameter of the turbine permitted. In recent years the tendency has been to increase the number of stages to reduce the stage loading.

The operational requirement of the engine dictates the number of shafts and hence the number of turbine stages; modern high pressure ratio engines usually have two shafts, one driving the low pressure compressor, or spool, the other driving the high pressure compressor. The rear turbine drives the low pressure compressor at the front of the engine and is normally termed the low pressure turbine, the front turbine drives the high pressure compressor and is termed the high pressure turbine. The turbines which drive the compressor, or compressors, are termed the power turbines, e.g. the low pressure power turbine etc.

Figure 4-2 shows an example of a twin spool compressor and its related turbines.

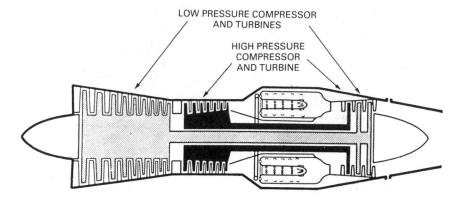

Figure 4–2 Turbine Arrangement in a Twin Spool Turbojet.

4.2 Turbine Principle of Operation

The mean blade speed of a turbine has a considerable effect on the efficiency of the output for a given turbine stage. This is primarily due to the gas velocity through the nozzle guide vanes (situated just prior to the first turbine rotor assembly) and the turbine blades being reduced as the blade speed increases, and the loss of pressure is proportional to the square of the gas speed. Stress in the turbine disc, also increases as the square of the speed unless the section thickness, hence the weight, is increased disproportionately. For this reason the design of the turbine has to be a compromise between efficiency and weight.

The design of the nozzle guide vanes and turbine blade passages is primarily based on aerodynamic considerations and as such the majority of such components are of aerofoil shape. The shapes employed are such that the turbine functions partly under impulse and partly under reaction conditions, that is to say, the turbine blades experience an impulse force due to the initial impact of the gas on the blades and a reaction force as a result of the expansion and acceleration of the gas through the blade passages. Although blade design will vary the proportion of each principle incorporated in the turbine, in general it is approximately 50 per cent impulse and 50 per cent reaction.

Figure 4-3 shows a comparison between an impulse/reaction turbine and a pure impulse turbine.

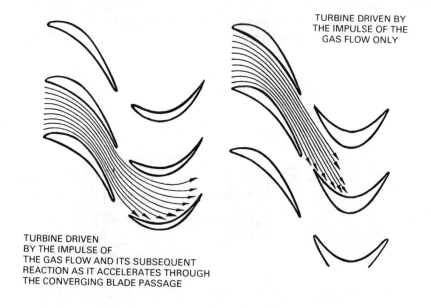

TURBINE DRIVEN BY THE IMPULSE OF THE GAS FLOW ONLY

TURBINE DRIVEN BY THE IMPULSE OF THE GAS FLOW AND ITS SUBSEQUENT REACTION AS IT ACCELERATES THROUGH THE CONVERGING BLADE PASSAGE

Figure 4–3 Impulse and Reaction Blades.

A gas turbine functions by the transfer of energy between the combustion gases and the turbine blades. This transfer is never 100 per cent because of thermodynamic and mechanical losses, but current designs achieve approximately 90 per cent.

When the gas is expanded by the process of combustion it is forced from the combustion chambers through the nozzles prior to the rotor where, due to their convergent shape, it is accelerated to just below the speed of sound. On passing through the nozzle guide vanes the gas is given a 'spin' or 'swirl' in the direction of rotation of the turbine rotor blades. On impact with the blades and during the subsequent reaction through the

186

blades, energy is absorbed from the gas causing the turbine to rotate at high speed and so provide the torque to the turbine shaft for driving the compressor.

As the gas passes through the turbine stages the temperature will drop as the gas gives up some of its energy, the pressure will fall and the velocity will initially fall and then increase in the jet pipe.

Figure 4-4 shows the gas flow pattern through the nozzle and turbine blades.

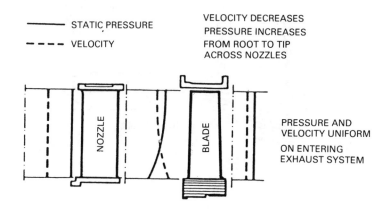

Figure 4–4 Gas Flow through Nozzle Guide Vanes
and Turbine Blades.

The torque or turning power applied to the turbine is governed by the rate of gas flow and the energy change of the gas between the inlet and outlet of the turbine blades. Therefore if the energy is absorbed efficiently the whirl will be removed from the gas stream so that the flow from the turbine exit will be virtually straightened out to given an axial flow in the exhaust system. Excessive residual whirl reduces the efficiency of the exhaust system and also produces vibration in the exhaust jet pipe.

It can be seen that the nozzle and blades of the turbine are manufactured with a state of twist, producing a greater stagger angle at the tip than that at the root. (See Fig. 4-5.)

The reason for the twist is to make the gas flow from the combustion chambers do equal work at all positions along the length of the blade and to ensure the gas flow enters the exhaust system with a uniform axial velocity. Reference to Fig. 4-4 shows this.

The degree of reaction from the turbine blades varies from the root to the tip of the blade, the reaction being greatest at the tip and least at the root with the mean section having a value of approximately 50 per cent.

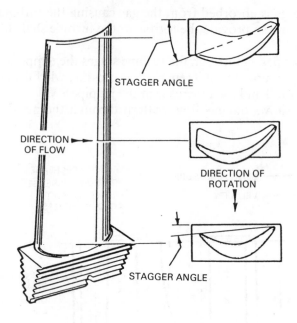

Figure 4–5 Blade Twist and Stagger Angle.

4.3 Turbine Losses.

The overall efficiency of the turbine is normally approximately 90 to 95 per cent. The losses which prevent the turbine being 100 per cent efficient are due to a number of causes: a typical three stage turbine would suffer a 3.5 to 4 per cent loss due to aerodynamic losses in the turbine blades; a further 4.5 per cent would be due to aerodynamic losses in the nozzle guide vanes, and the remainder to gas losses over the rotor blades and through the exhaust system.

4.4 Construction.

The primary components of the turbine assembly are the nozzle guide vanes, the turbine disc, and the turbine blades.

The rotating assembly, comprising the blades mounted on their discs and the disc being mounted on the main shaft or shafts, is normally carried in ball and/or roller bearings. The main turbine shaft may be directly connected to the compressor at the front end of the engine, or it may be coupled to the compressor via a self-aligning coupling.

(a) Nozzle Guide Vanes.

The aerofoil shape of the nozzle guide vanes and the blade passage between the adjacent vanes forms a convergent duct. They are located in the turbine casing by one of several methods all of which allow for expansion.

The nozzle guide vanes are subjected to very high thermal stresses and gas loads and they are usually hollow to allow the passage of cooling air delivered from the engine compressor.

Figure 4-6 displays the attachment arrangement of the blades to the disc and the cooling air flow.

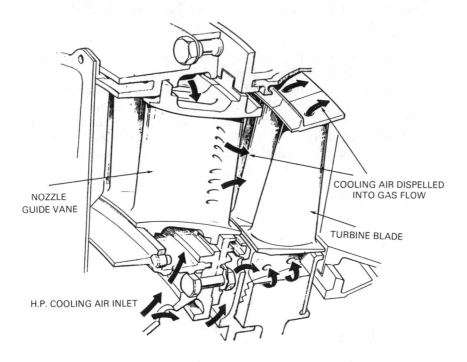

NOZZLE
GUIDE VANE

COOLING AIR DISPELLED
INTO GAS FLOW

TURBINE BLADE

H.P. COOLING AIR INLET

Figure 4–6 Blade Attachment and Blade Cooling.

(b) Turbine Disc.

The turbine disc is forged and then machined either with an integral shaft or with a flange on to which the shaft may be bolted. It also has provision for the attachment of the turbine blades. To limit the heat conduction from the turbine blades to the disc, a flow of cooling air is passed across both sides of each disc.

(c) Turbine Blades.

Turbine blades are made (forged) from nickel-based alloys that provide great strength at very high temperatures, but it is their physical performance at high temperature that limits the performance of the engine.

The turbine blades are basically of an aerofoil shape. Unlike the compressor blades, the profiles do not follow a particular class of aerofoil shape. The shape of the turbine blade is designed to provide passages between the adjacent blades which give a steady acceleration of the gas flow up to the 'throat' where the area is least and the velocity reaches that required at exit to produce the required degree of reaction.

The cross-sectional area of each blade is determined by the permitted stress in the material used and by the size of cooling holes or ducts. High efficiency demands thin edges trailing but the huge temperature variations during engine starting and stopping would induce cracking in very thin edges, so a compromise has to be struck. The method employed for attaching the blades to the disc is of the utmost importance. Various methods have been explored to moderate the stress and high temperatures experienced by the blades and this also results in a limiting factor on the rim speed.

Figure 4-7 shows three methods that have been used to attach the blades to the disc.

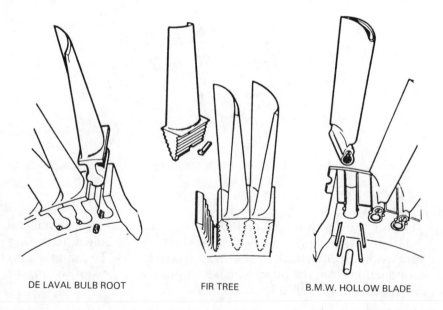

DE LAVAL BULB ROOT   FIR TREE   B.M.W. HOLLOW BLADE

Figure 4–7 Blade Attachment Methods.

190

The type of attachment most commonly used on modern gas turbines is the 'Fir Tree' method. This type of attachment involves very accurate machining to ensure that the loading is equally shared by all the serrations. The blade is free in the serrations when the engine is stationary and is stiffened in the root by centrifugal force when the turbine is rotating.

4.5 Reduction in Loss of Efficiency.

Loss of efficiency occurs across the blade tips of the turbine and to combat this problem shrouds are fitted to the tips of the blades. The shrouds are formed by forging a small segment at the tip of each individual blade and when assembled on the disc form a continuous peripheral ring around the blade tips. Figure 4-8 shows examples of turbine blade shrouding.

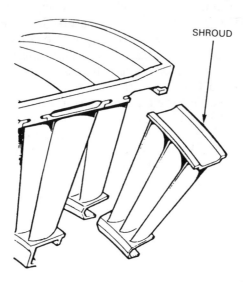

SHROUD

Figure 4–8 Blade Shrouding.

The shrouding of some turbine blades is achieved by the manufacture and installation of the turbine blades in groups of three or four blades, complete with their respective shrouds.

More recent turbine assembly designs employ Active Clearance Control where air is bled from the compressor to cool, and control the outer casing expansion rate in the vicinity of the turbine thereby controlling the clearance between the blade tips and the inner face of the engine casing. Blades used in Active Clearance Control systems do not have shrouds, an abrasive liner is fitted to the inner face of the engine casing at the turbine to maintain minimum clearance. Engine turbine efficiency with this system is considerably improved.

4.6   Compressor and Turbine Matching.

It is very important that the flow characteristics of the turbine be matched with the compressor in order that the maximum efficiency may be obtained and engine performance maximised. If the compressor and turbine are not matched this could result in too high a flow which would cause the compressor to choke and a loss of efficiency would occur very rapidly. Similarly, if the nozzle guide vanes were allowed too low a maximum flow then a back pressure could build up causing the compressor to surge.

4.7   Turbine Blade Creep.

One of the major limiting factors to higher turbine entry temperatures is the effects of the gas temperature on the nozzle guide vanes and the turbine blades, and the tensile stress imposed on the turbine disc and blades by the high rotational speeds. The high stresses on the component parts of the turbine assembly make it necessary to restrict the turbine entry temperature so that the various components may do their very arduous job, and to do it for a reasonable working life.

The combination of high rotational speeds, setting up considerable centrifugal force, coupled with very high temperatures result in the blades beginning to 'creep'. In other words, 'creep' is the action of the blades stretching due to the high temperatures and centrifugal force.

If such blade creep were allowed to continue unchecked, the tips of the blades would foul the outer casing, and/or stretch to the point when the blades fracture.

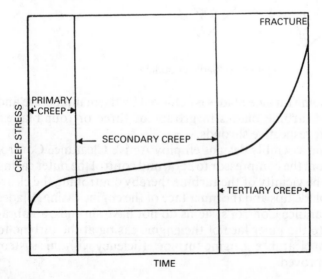

Figure 4–9 Stages of Blade Creep.

192

During normal operation the blades will glow red hot and must be strong enough to withstand the centrifugal force on them at the high rotational speeds, eg a blade weighing only two ounces may exert a load of over two tons at maximum speed. It must at the same time withstand the high bending loads applied by the gas to produce the many thousands of turbine horse-power to drive the compressor. Blades must also be resistant to fatigue and thermal shock, so they will not fail under the influence of high frequency fluctuations in the gas flow conditions, and finally they must be resistant to corrosion and oxidation.

Figure 4-9 shows a graph of the three basic stages of 'creep' and ultimately, if the blades are not changed, their subsequent fracture. On many modern gas turbine engines, air is used to cool the turbine blades in a similar manner to that of the nozzle guide vanes, which along with modern materials, minimises 'creep'.

4.8   Free Turbines.

In free turbine engines the turbine is mounted on a separate set of ball or roller bearings and is not connected to the compressor in any way. Its principle of operation is basically the same as the main or power turbines. The energy imparted into the free turbine may be used to drive a propeller, when it is more commonly known as a turboshaft or turboprop engine, or as a free turbine which may be used to drive a helicopter rotor via the appropriate gearboxes.

Figure 4-10 shows an example helicopter gas turbine of the free turbine type.

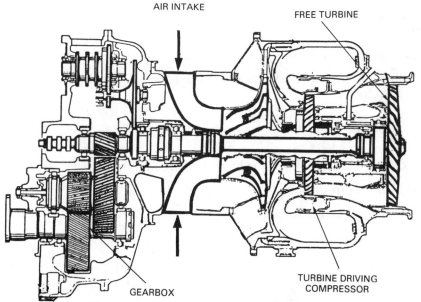

Figure 4–10 Free Turbine Engine.

Section 4 Test Yourself

Turbines

1. Nozzle guide vanes:

   (a)   tend to straighten the gas flow.

   (b)   are fitted immediately after the turbine assembly.

   (c)   give the gas a swirl.

   Ref. 4.2.

2. The nozzle guide vanes are normally:

   (a)   divergent.

   (b)   convergent.

   (c)   concave.

   Ref. 4.2.

3. The gas temperature:

   (a)   increases as it passes through the turbine.

   (b)   remains constant as it passes through the turbine.

   (c)   reduces as it passes through the turbine.

   Ref. 4.2.

4. The nozzles and blades of the turbine are manufactured with a state of twist to:

   (a)   generate a state of swirl as it passes through the assembly.

   (b)   ensure the gas flow enters the exhaust system at uniform axial velocity.

   (c)   increase blade reaction.

   Ref. 4.2.

5. Loss of efficiency of turbine blade tips are minimised by:

   (a)   blade tip shrouds.

   (b)   fir tree attachments.

   (c)   air bleed.

   Ref. 4.5.

6. Turbine blade 'creep' may be reduced by:

    (a)   blade tip shrouds.

    (b)   material and air cooling.

    (c)   creep restrainers.

Ref. 4.7 & 4.4.

7. The main turbine/compressor engine shaft is normally mounted on:

    (a)   needle roller bearings.

    (b)   ball bearings only.

    (c)   ball or roller bearings.

Ref. 4.4.

8. Modern gas turbine engine turbine blades are normally attached by:

    (a)   the fir tree method.

    (b)   the De Laval Bulb Root.

    (c)   the BMW, Hollow Blade.

Ref. 4.4.

9. A free turbine is:

    (a)   connected to the high pressure compressor of a two-spool engine.

    (b)   not connected to the compressor.

    (c)   connected to the low pressure compressor.

Ref. 4.8.

10. As the gas flow passes through the turbine assembly the velocity of the gas flow will:

    (a)   initially fall and then rise in the jet pipe.

    (b)   remain relatively constant.

    (c)   initially rise and then fall in the jet pipe.

Ref. 4.2.

4a

Exhaust System

4a.1　Introduction.

The exhaust system of the gas turbine engine passes the discharge gases to atmosphere. The gas leaves the turbine and, on most subsonic aircraft, the gases from a turbojet engine, are directed at high velocity and pressure to produce thrust. In a turboprop engine the exhaust gas velocities and pressures are relatively low as most of the energy has been absorbed in the turbines to drive the compressor and also the propeller.

The design of the exhaust system exerts a considerable influence on the performance of the engine. The areas of the jet pipe and propelling, or outlet, nozzle affect the turbine entry temperature, the mass airflow and the velocity and pressure of the exhaust jet.

The temperature of the exhaust gases entering the exhaust system is normally between 550deg C and 850deg C according to the type of engine. Turboprop and Bypass engines have a much cooler exhaust gas temperature. With the use of afterburning, or reheat, the temperatures in the jet pipe could be as high as 1500deg C or higher, however, by virtue of the pattern of the flame and the system of cooling the impact of the higher temperature is not felt by the walls of the jet pipe. A higher temperature than normal will nevertheless dictate the use of materials and a form of construction which will resist cracking and distortion and also minimise the conduction of heat to the surrounding aircraft structure. The afterburner jet pipe also requires a variable exhaust, or propelling, nozzle. This may take the form of a simple two position nozzle or a truly variable position nozzle which can be positioned at any point between fully closed and fully open. The purpose of such nozzles is to give the engine the capability of matching the different volumes of gas flow which occur when afterburning is on or off.

4a.2　The Basic Exhaust System.

Fig. 4a-1 shows a basic exhaust system.

As the gas leaves the turbine it has a velocity in the order 750 to 1200 feet per second; however, as velocities of this order produce high frictional losses the speed of flow is decreased by diffusion. The slow down is

196

achieved by the use of a divergent duct formed between the exhaust pipe and the exhaust cone, or exhaust unit. This has the effect of maintaining a fairly constant gas stream pressure from turbine to exhaust outlet. Temperature will fall very slightly in the exhaust pipe and velocity will decrease as the gas passes through the turbine and will then slightly increase as it passes from the turbine to the exhaust outlet where, depending on the outlet nozzle design, it will accelerate.

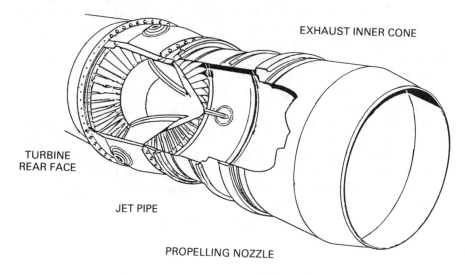

Figure 4a–1 A Basic Exhaust System.

The exhaust cone, just aft of the turbine outlet, prevents the exhaust gases from flowing across the rear face of the turbine disc. The velocity at the exhaust unit outlet is held to about Mach 0.5, that is approximately 950 feet per second. Losses also occur due to residual whirl velocity in the gas stream from the turbine, and to reduce these effects, the support struts of the exhaust cone are designed to straighten out the gas flow as it leaves the turbine.

The exhaust gases pass to atmosphere through the propelling nozzle which, in a basic exhaust system, normally forms a convergent duct, this will in turn cause the gas velocity to increase. In a turbojet engine the exit velocity of the exhaust gas is subsonic only at low thrust conditions. During most operating conditions the exit velocity reaches the speed of sound (in relation to the exhaust gas temperature) and the propelling nozzle is then said to be choked: that is no further increase in velocity can be obtained unless the temperature is increased. As the upstream total pressure is increased above the value at which the propelling nozzle chokes, the static pressure of the gases at exit increase above atmospheric

197

pressure. This pressure difference across the propelling nozzle gives what is known as pressure thrust and is effective over the nozzle exit area. This is additional thrust to that obtained due to the momentum change of the gas stream. It is important that the propelling nozzle is of the correct size in order to obtain the correct balance of pressure, temperature and thrust. With a small nozzle these values increase, but, there is then a possibility of the engine surging, whilst with a large nozzle the values obtained are too low. On some engines variable nozzles are used to increase or decrease nozzle area to suit the conditions required. When this type of nozzle is used, an increase in flow area through the nozzle enables easier starting and reduces the risk of surge, this being primarily due to a reduction in the turbine back pressure. With a reduced nozzle area the maximum thrust is increased. The variation in the nozzle area also enables low specific fuel consumption to be attained.

The bypass engine has two gas streams which are ejected through the jet pipe to atmosphere, the cool bypass airflow and the hot turbine discharge gases. Although the bypass airflow may be exhausted separately, on some engines it is the usual practice to mix the two flows before they leave the engine. This is done by a mixer unit which allows the bypass air to flow into the exhaust gas flow in a manner which ensures a thorough mixing of the two flows.

Figure 4a-2 shows an example of a bypass air mixer unit.

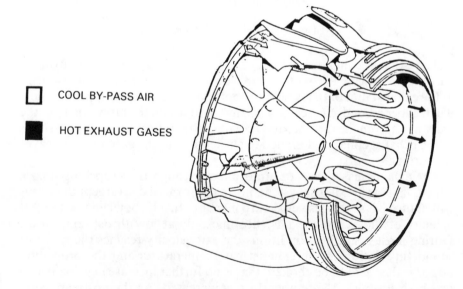

COOL BY-PASS AIR

HOT EXHAUST GASES

Figure 4a–2 By-pass Air Mixer Unit.

4b

Reheat/Afterburning

4b.1   Introduction.

Reheat, or afterburning, is a method employed on some engines to augment the basic thrust to provide additional power for take-off, and in some cases accelerate to cruise speed. Few civil aircraft use reheat or afterburning.

The alternative to reheat would be to employ a larger and more powerful engine at the expense of increased weight, larger frontal area and fuel consumption. As such penalties are not always acceptable, reheat is the usual alternative.

Reheat is a system primarily designed to augment thrust for short periods of time and consists of the introduction and burning of fuel between the turbine and the jet pipe propelling nozzle utilising the unspent oxygen remaining in the exhaust gases to support combustion. The resultant increase in the temperature of the exhaust gas gives an increased velocity to the jet leaving the propelling nozzle and thus increases the engine thrust.

As the temperature of the reheat flame may be in excess of 1700deg C, the burners are normally located so that the flame is concentrated around the axis of the jet pipe, thereby allowing a proportion of the turbine discharge gas to flow along the wall of the jet pipe and therefore maintain the wall of the jet pipe at a safe temperature value.

Figure 4b-1 shows the location of an afterburner in a jet pipe assembly.

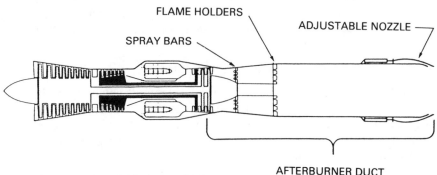

Figure 4b–1 Location of Afterburner Unit.

199

Normally a reheat jet pipe assembly is larger than a conventional jet pipe would be for the same engine, in order to achieve a reduced velocity gas stream. To provide for operations under all conditions, a reheat jet pipe is fitted either with a two position propelling nozzle or a variable propelling nozzle. The nozzle is closed during non-reheat operation. However, when reheat is selected the nozzle opens to provide a suitable exit area for the increased gas stream. This prevents an excessive build-up of back pressure which would affect the normal operation of the engine.

The thrust of an afterburning engine is slightly less, without afterburning, than that of a similar engine without provision for afterburning, because of the restrictions caused to the gas flow by the afterburner equipment in the jet pipe. The overall weight of the engine is also increased due to the additional equipment and the larger and stronger jet pipe.

4b.2   Afterburner Operation.

The flow velocity of the gas stream leaving the turbine is in the order of 750 to 1200 feet per second, but because this velocity is far too high for a stable flame to be maintained, the flow is diffused before it enters the afterburner combustion zone. The flow velocity is thereby reduced and the pressure increases. It must be noted however, that the speed of burning of kerosene at normal mixture ratios is only a few feet per second and any fuel lit, even in the diffused gas stream would quickly be extinguished. A flame stabiliser is therefore fitted downstream of the fuel burners to provide a region in which turbulent eddies are formed to assist combustion, and where the local gas velocity is further reduced to a figure at which flame stabilisation occurs whilst combustion is in operation.

An atomised fuel spray is fed into the jet pipe through a number of burners. The burners are arranged to provide an even distribution of fuel over the whole flame area. Combustion is initiated by an igniter plug adjacent to the burner, or by a hot sheet of flame which originates in the engine combustion chamber, this latter method is known as hot shot ignition. Due to the increased temperature the gases expand and finally accelerate through the propelling nozzle to provide additional thrust.

4b.3   Thrust Increase with Afterburning.

The amount of thrust increase from reheat depends solely upon the ratio of the absolute jet pipe temperatures before and after the extra fuel has been burnt. Some minor losses may be incurred, due mainly to restrictions created by the afterburning equipment in the jet pipe, and also by gas flow momentum changes.

4b.4   Afterburning Control.

The afterburner/reheat system requires two basic functions to be controlled: the fuel flow and the propelling nozzle; it is important that these functions work perfectly in co-ordination with each other. When afterburning is selected on, the propelling nozzle area automatically increases. The amount the propelling nozzle opens will be dependent upon the degree of afterburning selected which, in turn, dictates the fuel flow to the afterburners. When the nozzle area is increased the fuel flow increases, and when the nozzle area is reduced the fuel flow decreases. The fuel flow sensing device ensures that the pressure ratio across the turbine remains unchanged and that the engine is unaffected by the operation of the afterburning, regardless of the nozzle area and fuel flow.

Due to the large fuel flows required to supply the afterburner when it is in operation, an additional fuel pump is needed. This pump is normally of a centrifugal type and is energised automatically when reheat is selected.

4c

Thrust Reversal

4c.1   Introduction.

The progressive development of the modern airliner has seen a considerable increase in both aircraft weight and landing speed; as a result constant research has sought means of reducing the length of the landing run. A major contribution has been the fitting of thrust reversal to the gas turbine engine. Thrust reversal is normally fitted only to turbojet engines, and provides a simple method of rapidly slowing the aircraft by reversing the direction of the exhaust gases, thus using engine power as a deceleration force. Use of this method avoids overheating of wheel brakes, and makes landing on wet, or ice and snow covered runways much safer. Some aircraft have been designed to use thrust reversal in flight to reduce aircraft speed; this is not, however, the normal modern practice.

Figure 4c-1 shows examples of the effects of use of thrust reversal against wheel brakes only.

4c.2   Turboprop Aircraft.

On turboprop powered aircraft, thrust reversal is achieved by reversing the pitch of the propellers, this method is widely used and is discussed in depth in Part 3 of this volume.

4c.3.   Principle of Operation.

There are several methods employed to achieve the controlled reversal of thrust, but the principle is generally the same, and it is only the mechanism used that tends to differ. Two methods are described in this chapter.

(a) Clamshell Door System.

Normally this type of arrangement is operated pneumatically, that is, compressed air is used to control the position of the doors. Normal engine operation is not affected by the system because the reversing ducts remain closed by the doors until reverse thrust is selected by the pilot.

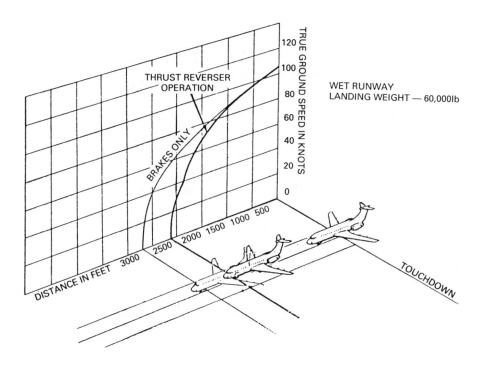

Figure 4c–1 Effects of Thrust Reversal Against
Wheel Brakes Only.

On selection of reverse thrust the doors rotate to uncover the ducts and close the normal gas stream exit. Deflector vanes then direct the gas stream in a forward direction so that the jet thrust opposes the forward motion of the aircraft. Ideally the gas should be directed in a completely forward direction but this is generally impracticable and a discharge angle of approximately 45 degrees is normally chosen. Reverse thrust power is normally about half the amount available for forward propulsion.

There are a number of safety features incorporated in the system. The pilot is prevented from selecting thrust reversal unless the engine is running at a low power setting. On selection, the engine throttle cannot be opened to a high power setting if the doors fail to move into a full thrust reverse position. Should the operating pressure fall during thrust reversal, a mechanical lock holds the doors in the fully forward, or full thrust reversal, position. This lock cannot be released until the air pressure is restored.

Figure 4c-2 shows an example thrust reversal unit and Fig. 4c-3 shows a more detailed example of the clamshell type.

203

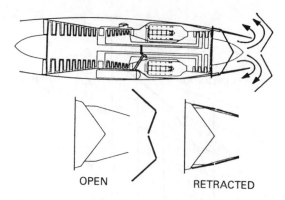

Figure 4c–2 Example Thrust Reversal Unit.

(b) Retractable Ejector System.
The retractable ejector system is normally both hydraulically and pneumatically operated and uses a bucket type door to reverse the jet stream.

On selection of reverse thrust, hydraulic pressure moves the ejector rearwards over the propelling nozzle, the buckets are then rotated by a pneumatic actuator to deflect the gas stream in a forward direction. A number of safety features are fitted to provide the same basic safety functions as those fitted to the clamshell door type.

4c-4   Thrust Reverser Position Indication.

The position of the thrust reversers is indicated by a system of lights which varies from aircraft type to type.

4c-5   Cold Stream Reverser System.

This system is employed primarily on High By-Pass engines and utilises the by-pass air as the thrust reversal medium which is therefore Cold Air. The system, in normal forward use, allows by-pass air to pass through the duct to the rear of the engine. When reverse thrust is selected the cold air is diverted by blocker doors to produce the reverse thrust as shown in Fig 4c-4. The normal Hot Gas Thrust, when reverse thrust is selected, is spoilt.

THRUST REVERSAL

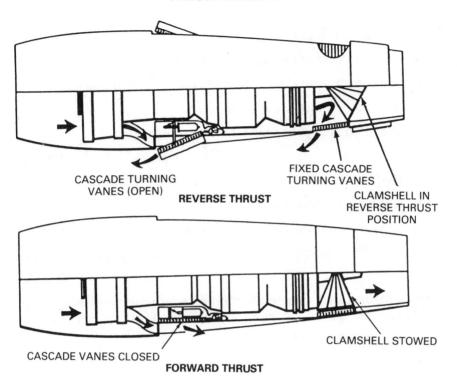

CASCADE TURNING VANES (OPEN)

REVERSE THRUST

FIXED CASCADE TURNING VANES

CLAMSHELL IN REVERSE THRUST POSITION

CASCADE VANES CLOSED

FORWARD THRUST

CLAMSHELL STOWED

Figure 4c–3 Clamshell Type Thrust Reverser.

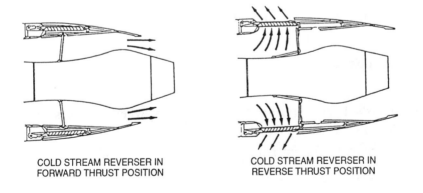

COLD STREAM REVERSER IN FORWARD THRUST POSITION

COLD STREAM REVERSER IN REVERSE THRUST POSITION

Figure 4c–4 Cold Air Thrust Reversal.

Test Yourself 4a, b & c

1. The support struts of the cone in an exhaust system:

(a) are sometimes used to straighten out the exhaust gases.

(b) give the exhaust gases a swirl effect.

(c) are fitted always to support the cone only.

Ref. 4a.2.

2. In a By-Pass engine, the by-pass exhaust is:

(a) always exhausted separately.

(b) always mixed with the normal exhaust gas in the jet pipe.

(c) sometimes mixed with the normal exhaust gases in the jet pipe.

Ref. 4a.2.

3. In an engine fitted with an afterburner, relative to an identical engine without an afterburner, under normal operation without reheat it:

(a) will produce the same power.

(b) will produce greater power.

(c) will produce less power.

Ref. 4b.1.

4. In a reheat system, with a variable position propelling nozzle, when reheat is selected:

(a) the nozzle will remain in the same position.

(b) the nozzle will open.

(c) the nozzle will close.

Ref. 4b.1.

5. In a clamshell door type thrust reversal system, when reverse is selected, the exhaust gases are:

(a) discharged at approximately 45 degrees.

(b) discharged at 90 degrees.

(c) fully reversed.

Ref. 4c.3.

5

Fuel Systems

5.1 Introduction.

The primary function of an aircraft gas turbine fuel system is to supply clean fuel, free from vapour, to the engine at the required pressure and flow rates and under a wide variety of operating conditions. Generally speaking, the fuel system is designed to satisfy the requirements of the particular aircraft in which it is installed.

5.2 Basic Fuel System.

The following is a basic fuel system to familiarise the reader with the essential components and their function within the fuel system.

(a) Fuel Tank.
The fuel tank is the primary component in which the fuel is stored within the airframe structure. The locations of the fuel tanks on larger aircraft are varied. Figure 5-1 shows some of the typical locations of a large fuel system.

(b) Fuel Tank Types.
There are three basic types of fuel tank used on commercial aircraft.

    (i)   Rigid.
This type of fuel tank is constructed from aluminium alloy, or similar light alloy, and takes the form of a rigid structure supported within a convenient space within the airframe. Figure 5-2 shows an example of a rigid fuel tank.

    (ii)   Flexible Fuel Tanks.
This type of fuel tank is normally manufactured from synthetic rubber and is carried within a lightweight housing specially shaped to contain it within the airframe structure. Flexible tanks, sometimes called bag tanks, may be manufactured in irregular shapes to make good use of every

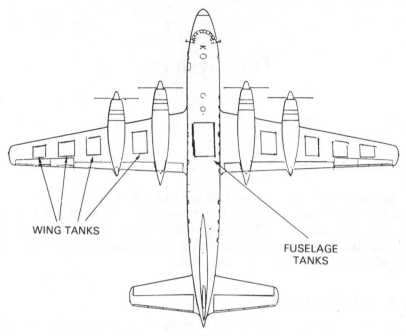

Figure 5–1 Fuel Tank Locations.

valuable space for fuel. Figure 5-2 shows an example flexible fuel tank.

(iii) Integral Tanks.
The volume which forms the fuel tank is an integral part of the airframe structure which is specially sealed to make it fuel tight. This type of tank is widely used on modern aircraft as it makes full use of the space available and saves considerable weight. (Fig. 5-2.)

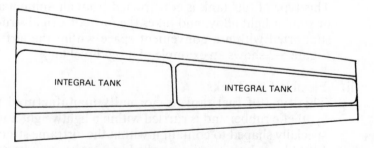

TANK AREA PART OF STRUCTURE BETWEEN MAIN AND REAR SPARS. PARTS OF LEADING AND TRAILING EDGES MAY ALSO FORM FUEL STORAGE TANKS

Figure 5–2 An Example Integral Tank.

208

(c) General.

The fuel tank incorporates:

(i)   A fuel contents sensor which, through a transmitter, indicates the fuel contents in the cockpit.

(ii)   A filter at the outlet from the tank and sometimes a filter is also fitted within the filler neck.

(iii)   On many types a means of pressurising the tank, usually by bleed air from the engine compressor, suitably cooled and pressure regulated. The object of pressurising the tank is to prevent the fuel bubbling at high altitude.

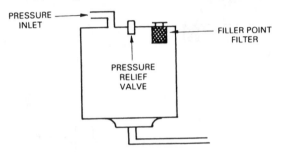

(d) Low Pressure Fuel Pump.

The low pressure fuel pump, usually called the 'Booster Pump', is normally electrically operated and is often connected to the underside of the fuel tank. It is controlled by an on/off switch in the cockpit. Its primary purpose is to maintain a low pressure (normally at least atmospheric pressure) in the fuel system between the pump itself and the main or engine driven pump (High Pressure Pump) in order to prevent or minimise vapour locks occurring in the components and pipelines. The Booster Pump is also provided with a by-pass so that in the event of its failure fuel can still be drawn through it by the engine driven pump to maintain a fuel supply to the engine. Adjacent

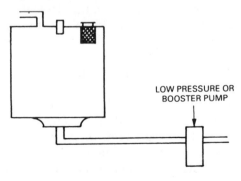

to the Booster Pump selector switch is an indicator light which, when the pump is switched on, illuminates until pressure has built up in the system to a specific value, whereupon the light extinguishes.

(e) Fuel ON/OFF Cock (Low Pressure Fuel Cock).
This is a simple Fuel ON, Fuel OFF cock or valve, which may be operated from the cockpit by an electric actuator, or mechanically through a linkage from a lever mounted in the cockpit which is operated manually.

Some larger aircraft have an emergency mechanical system to operate the Low Pressure cock in the event the electrical system fails.

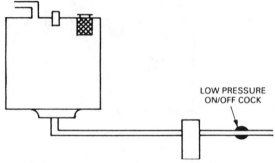

LOW PRESSURE
ON/OFF COCK

(f) Low Pressure Filter.
A filter is fitted in the low pressure fuel system to ensure a clean supply of fuel to the engine. The filter is normally fitted with a relief valve or by-pass valve so that if the filter element (which removes dirt from the fuel) becomes blocked, or clogged, a supply of unfiltered fuel will continue to be pumped to the engine. Problems can arise from ice particles forming in the fuel. Water can accumulate in suspension in the fuel and, as the aircraft climbs to high altitude and the temperature falls, the water in the fuel may form ice particles. Initially the filter element will prevent such ice particles passing further into the fuel system and fuel will continue to be supplied to the engine. Eventually, however, the ice will build up and block the element and also the relief or by-pass valve thereby leading to fuel starvation of the engine. It should be noted that as long as the water content of the fuel is in liquid form it presents no serious danger to the engine, therefore if the water is prevented from forming into ice particles fuel starvation will be avoided. To achieve this, the fuel is heated prior to the filter, thereby preventing the formation of ice in the fuel and therefore precluding the filter element becoming blocked by ice. The fuel may be heated by bleed air from the high pressure zone of the compressor, or alternatively may be heated by a heat exchanger utilising the oil from the engine lubrication system, in which event the oil will be cooled at

the same time. Temperature control is exercised in both systems to maintain a specific fuel temperature.

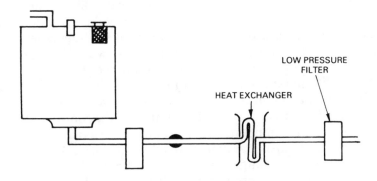

(g) High Pressure Fuel Pump (Engine-Driven Pump).
The majority of engine-driven pumps are of the swash plate type and are capable of maintaining a constant pressure and varying the volume of fuel they deliver according to the demands of the engine. An operational diagram of a Swash Plate pump is shown in Fig. 5-3.

Swash Plate Type Pump Principle of Operation, Variable Volume Type.

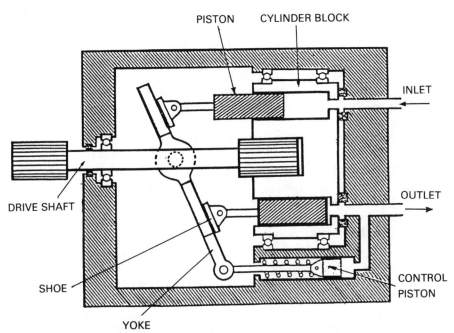

Figure 5–3 Sectional Diagram of Swash Plate Pump.

211

This type of pump is similar in construction to the fixed volume pump of the same basic type, but the cylinder block and drive shaft are co-axial. The pistons are attached to shoes which rotate against a stationary yoke, and the angle between the yoke and cylinder block is varied to increase or decrease pump stroke to suit system requirements. When pressure in the system is low, as would be the case when the throttle is opened, spring pressure on the control piston turns the yoke to its maximum angle, and the pistons are at full stroke, delivering maximum output to the system. When the actuator has completed its stroke, pressure builds up until the control piston moves the yoke to the minimum stroke piston; in this position a small flow through the pump is maintained, to lubricate the working parts, overcome internal leakage and dissipate heat. On some pumps a solenoid-operated depressurising valve is used to block delivery to the system, and to off-load the pump.

(h) Fuel Flow Control System.
In most modern gas turbine fuel systems the principle of a Flow Control System is used; earlier engines operated with a pressure controlled fuel system. In the flow control system the fuel pump delivery pressure is sensitive to engine speed, therefore at low engine rpm the fuel pump delivery pressure is quite low. The flow control system is very compact and with the exception of the engine speed governor, all other devices are contained within one combined fuel control unit.

The High Pressure Fuel Pump delivery pressure is controlled by the Fuel Control Unit and the rpm of the pump is controlled by the Engine Speed Governor. The servo pressure in the pump (which dictates the piston stroke and, therefore, the delivery of the pump) is supplied by the Altitude Sensing Unit, which is part of the Fuel Control Unit.

At any steady running condition below governed speed, the fuel pump delivery is controlled to a fixed value by the Altitude Sensing Unit. As the throttle is slowly opened the pressure in the pump servo piston supply increases, in turn the pump output increases. Any variation in engine air intake pressure, due to a change in aircraft forward speed or altitude, is sensed by a capsule in the Altitude Sensing Unit, causing the unit to reduce the pump delivery if the intake pressure should reduce; and the opposite will occur should the intake pressure increase.

During a rapid acceleration, the rapid movement of the throttle will cause an increased supply of fuel to the combustion chambers which will not be matched by an adequate supply of air from the compressor. The result of this unbalanced fuel/air ratio will be an increase in engine gas temperature and possibly compressor surge. It is essential therefore, to have an Acceleration Control Unit to give a corresponding lag in the rate of fuel flow increase.

The components in the fuel control system are very complex and this description is purely to give the reader a basic understanding of their purpose.

(i) High Pressure Fuel Cock (Fuel Shut-Off Cock).
The High Pressure cock is essentially a sophisticated on/off cock. They may be operated manually, as on many older aircraft types, or automatically in conjunction with the throttle as part of an automatic engine start system. Normally the fuel is pressurised before the high pressure cock is opened, and to ensure the fuel flows smoothly there is a pressurising valve incorporated within the assembly. On engine shut-down the high pressure cock is closed to starve the engine of fuel. On some modern fuel systems the high pressure cock control in the cockpit takes the form of a circuit breaker as opposed to a lever.

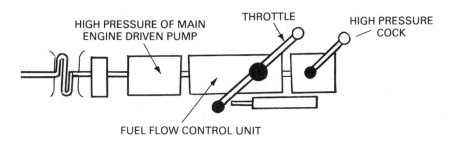

HIGH PRESSURE OF MAIN ENGINE DRIVEN PUMP — THROTTLE — HIGH PRESSURE COCK — FUEL FLOW CONTROL UNIT

5.3 Engine Fuel Manifold.

Fuel is supplied from the fuel supply system to the engine fuel manifold system. On most modern aircraft there are two manifolds: the main burner manifold and the primary burner manifold, both of which are explained in the section on combustion chambers.

5.4 Water Injection.

(a) Introduction.
As with a piston engine, the maximum power output of a gas turbine engine depends largely upon the density of the airflow passing through the engine. As altitude is increased the density of the atmosphere reduces and as a result power declines. Equally power will be lost, or a reduction in thrust will occur, when the ambient air temperature increases. Under such conditions power output may be

restored, or in some cases boosted for take off, by cooling the airflow with water or water/methanol. If methanol is added to the water it gives anti-freeze properties, and also provides an additional source of fuel.

(b) Injection.
There are two basic methods of introducing the coolant (water/methanol) into the engine airflow:

(i) The coolant on some engines is sprayed directly into the intake, or compressor inlet. When the injection system is switched on, water/methanol is pumped from a tank mounted in the airframe to a control unit. The control unit meters the flow of mixture to the compressor inlet through a metering valve which is operated by a servo piston. Engine oil is used as the medium to operate the servo system and a

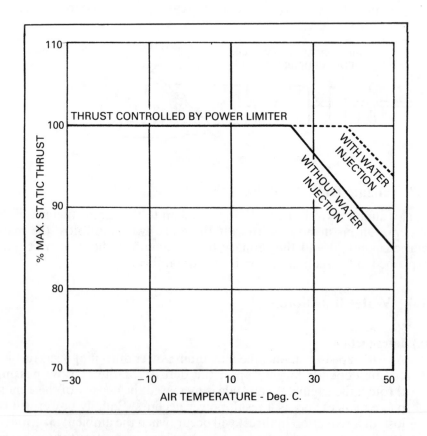

Figure 5–5 Turbojet with Water Injection.

servo valve controls the supply of engine oil. The degree of servo valve opening is set by a control system which is sensitive to oil pressure, (propeller shaft torque in the case of turboprops), to oil pressure, and to atmospheric pressure acting on a capsule within the control unit assembly. Inlet injection systems are normally used on centrifugal compressor engines.

(ii) The alternative method of water/methanol injection is the combustion chamber injection system, which is more suitable to axial flow compressor engines. On selecting water/methanol injection, the coolant flows from the tank, in the airframe, to an air driven turbine pump which delivers it to the water flow sensing unit. The water, or water/methanol, flows from the sensing unit down each burner feed arm and is sprayed from jets onto the flame tube swirl vanes, thus cooling the air passing into the chamber combustion zone. The coolant pressure between the sensing unit and the discharge jets is sensed by the fuel control system, which automatically resets the engine speed governor to give the higher maximum engine speed required for boosted power for certain take-off conditions, such as take-off in high temperature situations.

The water flow sensing unit opens only when the correct pressure difference is obtained between compressor air delivery pressure and water pressure. The system is brought into operation when the engine throttle lever is moved to take-off position, causing microswitches to operate and select the air for the turbine pump. The sensing unit also forms a non-return valve to prevent air pressure feeding back from the discharge jets. Provision is also made for an indicator light to illuminate when water, or water/methanol is flowing.

Figures 5-5 and 5-6 show the effects of coolant injection in a turbojet engine and a turboprop engine.

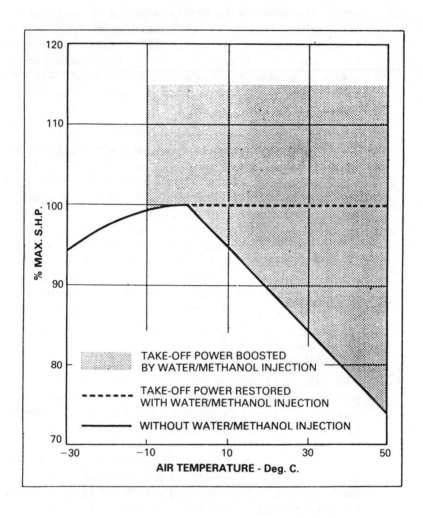

Figure 5–6 Effects of Water Injection in a Turboprop.

Section 5 Test Yourself

Fuel Systems

1. The low pressure fuel pump:

   (a)   is normally driven mechanically by the engine.

   (b)   is normally electrically driven.

   (c)   is driven hydraulically by the engine lubrication system.

Ref. 5.2.

2. The low pressure filter is prevented from being blocked by ice particles in the fuel by:

   (a)   a by-pass valve being fitted to the filter.

   (b)   pre-heating the fuel.

   (c)   an ice guard mounted prior to the filter.

Ref. 5.2.

3. The high pressure fuel pump is normally driven:

   (a)   mechanically by the engine.

   (b)   hydraulically.

   (c)   electrically by the engine.

Ref. 5.2.

4. The high pressure fuel cock:

   (a)   controls fuel flow from the tank to the fuel flow control unit.

   (b)   is used to control fuel flow to the engine.

   (c)   is used to pressurise the fuel tank.

Ref. 5.2.

5. Fuel is fed to the engine from the supply system via:

   (a)   the fuel manifold.

   (b)   the fuel injection jets.

   (c)   the injector control unit.

Ref. 5.2.

6

Engine Starting Systems

6.1   Introduction.

To start a gas turbine engine two systems are required: ignition and fuel feed, both discussed in depth in chapter three.

The fuel system provides atomised fuel to the burners located in the combustion chambers, and the ignition system supplies a spark to ignite the fuel air mixture on start up. Ignition is also provided at other times and these will be discussed later in this chapter.

In order to achieve the correct air/fuel ratio for ignition (in the order of 15:1 to 18:1) a flow of air must be supplied to the combustion chambers, and this is normally achieved by rotating the compressor at sufficient rpm to produce an adequate airflow.

During engine starting the two systems, fuel and ignition, must operate simultaneously and this is co-ordinated and controlled automatically after initiation of the start cycle, by an electrical circuit.

It is important to note at this stage the ideal theoretical air/fuel ratio is in the order of 15:1, however for practical purposes an air/fuel ratio in the order of 18:1 is more desirable in producing a combustion temperature of approximately 1600 to 1800deg C.

6.2   Start Sequence.

The start sequence is automatically co-ordinated and controlled in most modern systems, and is typically as follows:

(a) Start Selected.
The selection of engine start will initiate rotation of the compressor in order to create the necessary airflow to sustain engine operation. The most common methods used to initiate rotation are by an electrically operated starter motor or an air start system.

(b)   As the start button is depressed, with electrical power 'on' the starter motor or air system rotates the engine, and at the same time ignition is also switched 'on'.

(c)   After a pre-set time delay, which will normally correspond to a given build up of engine rpm, the HP cock will open to admit fuel to the combustion chambers.

Note: Some systems require the HP cock to be opened manually when the required engine rpm are reached.

(d) Normally light-up occurs between 5 to 10 seconds after start sequence is initiated, at which time the engine should have reached some 20 per cent of the maximum engine rpm.

(e) If combustion is successful the engine should reach self sustaining speed at 35 per cent of maximum engine rpm after a period of some 15 to 20 seconds after the commencement of the start sequence.

(f) The starter electrical circuit will normally cancel shortly after self sustaining speed.

(g) Idle rpm (some 55 to 60 per cent engine rpm), will be reached approximately 30 seconds after the start button has been depressed.

Note: The figures stated above are approximate.

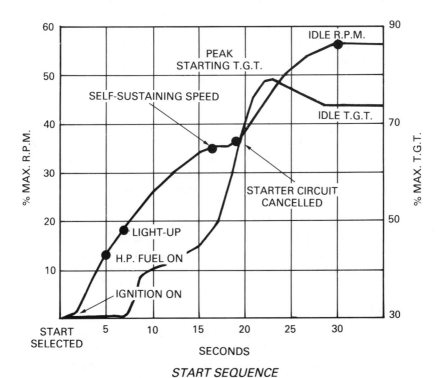

START SEQUENCE

6.3   Methods of Engine Starting.

(a) Electrical Start System.

This system employs an electric motor coupled to the engine via a reduction gear mechanism and a ratchet or clutch assembly. The electric motor is normally DC and, through the ratchet or clutch mechanism, automatically disengages after the engine has started.

Depending on the system adopted, the electrical supply may be of a low or high voltage and is passed through a circuit of relays and resistances which permits the full voltage to be progressively increased as the starter gains speed and provides the power for the ignition system. The electrical supply is automatically cancelled when the starter load is reduced, ie when the engine has successfully started or when the time cycle is completed.

Figure 6-1 shows a typical electrical start system.

(b) Air Starting System.

Air starting is used on many modern civil aircraft because it is simple, economical to use, and comparatively light in weight. The system employs an air turbine motor which is coupled to the engine via a clutch or ratchet assembly.

The starter turbine is supplied with air either from a ground source or from the aircraft's auxiliary power unit, the air being fed to the starter turbine causing it to rotate and, in turn, rotate the gas turbine engine. Like the electrical start system, the air start system is automatically controlled once the start sequence has been initiated. An electrically operated air control valve is opened when engine start is selected and is automatically closed at a predetermined starter speed. The clutch also automatically disengages as the engine accelerates up to idling rpm and rotation of the starter ceases.

Figure 6-2 shows an example air start system.

Note: In starting a twin-spooled compressor engine, the high pressure compressor is spun up by the starter motor and the airflow created rotates the low pressure compressor. The high pressure compressor is started first to reduce the tendency of surge.

6.4   Ignition.

As already stated in para 6.2, initiation of ignition is an automatic function once the start sequence has been selected, and it is also cancelled automatically. However, ignition is not only used during the start sequence: it may also be used during take-off, relighting the engine after

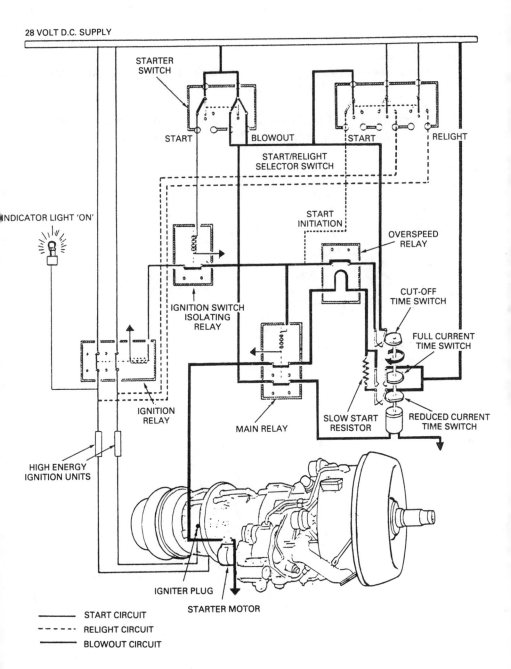

28 VOLT D.C. SUPPLY

STARTER
SWITCH

START   BLOWOUT   START   RELIGHT

START/RELIGHT
SELECTOR SWITCH

INDICATOR LIGHT 'ON'

START
INITIATION

OVERSPEED
RELAY

CUT-OFF
TIME SWITCH

IGNITION SWITCH
ISOLATING
RELAY

FULL CURRENT
TIME SWITCH

IGNITION
RELAY

SLOW START
RESISTOR

REDUCED CURRENT
TIME SWITCH

MAIN RELAY

HIGH ENERGY
IGNITION UNITS

IGNITER PLUG

STARTER MOTOR

——— START CIRCUIT
- - - - RELIGHT CIRCUIT
━━━ BLOWOUT CIRCUIT

Figure 6–1 Low Voltage Start Circuit.

221

a 'flame-out' has occurred, and continuous operation in adverse weather conditions.

(a) Relighting.
As can be seen in Fig. 6-1, provision is made for relighting the engine in the event of a flame-out.

(b) On many aircraft provision is also made to sustain the operation of the ignition units during take-off or during flight in adverse weather

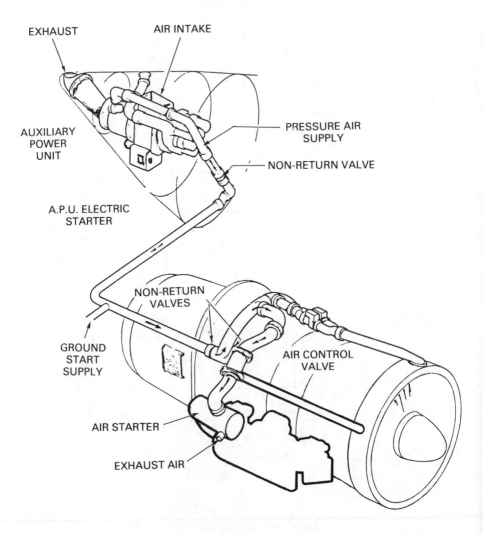

EXHAUST

AIR INTAKE

AUXILIARY
POWER
UNIT

PRESSURE AIR
SUPPLY

NON-RETURN VALVE

A.P.U. ELECTRIC
STARTER

NON-RETURN
VALVES

GROUND
START
SUPPLY

AIR CONTROL
VALVE

AIR STARTER

EXHAUST AIR

Figure 6–2 Air Starter System.

222

conditions. In particular, during take-off, should a flame-out occur due to compressor surge or stall, the igniters may immediately relight, or re-ignite the air/fuel mixture and so avoid a much more serious situation developing. Ignition is also switched on during flights through heavy tropical storms where, again, there is an increased risk of flame-out.

6.5 Relighting.

If a flame-out occurs in flight the airflow passing through the engine will maintain a degree of rotation of the compressor and turbine assembly. To relight the engine all that is required is the operation of the ignition, assuming an adequate fuel supply is available. Operation of the complete start sequence is not required, as the engine is still rotating (windmilling). A separate switch is provided in the ignition system to permit the start sequence to be by-passed and ignition only provided; this is termed the relight switch. The ability of the engine to successfully relight varies with forward speed and altitude of the aircraft. Details relating to relight procedures are given in Engine Performance and Handling.

Section 6 Test Yourself Engine Starting Systems

1. In an automatic electrical starting system the:

   (a) ignition commences ten seconds after the start button has been pushed.

   (b) ignition commences at the same time the starter motor engages.

   (c) ignition commences when fuel starts flowing into the combustion system.

   Ref. 6.2.

2. In an electrically operated gas turbine start system, the electric motor:

   (a) must be manually disconnected when the engine has reached the required rpm.

   (b) is automatically switched off when the required rpm are reached.

   (c) is automatically switched off after a specified period of time or the engine is at sustaining rpm.

   Ref. 6.3.

3. When relighting the engine due to a flame-out:

   (a) the full start sequence must be used.

   (b) the full start sequence may be by-passed and use of the relight button is made.

   (c) auto ignition must be selected.

   Ref. 6.5.

4. In an air start system:

   (a) air is blown through the compressor inlet to rotate the engine.

   (b) air is blown through the turbine to rotate the engine.

   (c) air is supplied to an air starter motor.

   Ref. 6.3.

5. On a twin-spooled compressor engine, on starting:

   (a) both compressor elements are rotated by the starter motor.

   (b) the low pressure compressor is started by the motor.

   (c) the high pressure compressor is started by the motor.

   Ref. 6.3.

7

Lubrication Systems

7.1 Introduction.

The primary function of the gas turbine engine lubrication system is to supply oil to the main bearings of the main drive shaft in order both to provide adequate lubrication and also to cool the bearings. Figure 7-1 shows the location of the main bearings in a typical gas turbine engine. The number of main bearings varies depending on engine type, but generally there are at least four or five and they are normally of a ball or roller type. As well as lubricating the main bearings oil is also fed to ancillary drive gearboxes which drive such components as generators, hydraulic pumps and many other such items. In turboprop engines, the lubrication system also provides oil to the reduction gearing of the propeller drive mechanism.

The majority of gas turbine engine lubrication systems are of a self contained recirculatory type, that is a system with its own storage tank from which a pump draws the lubricating oil and circulates it round the system, lubricating and cooling the bearings, gears, drives and other components, and then returns the oil to the tank.

7.2 Recirculatory Lubrication System.

(a) Tank.

The recirculatory type system first requires a storage tank which holds a reserve of oil to compensate for minor leakage, expansion of the oil due to temperature increase, and also allows a space above the oil in the tank for frothing.

The tank usually incorporates a filter in the filler neck to prevent any foreign objects entering the tank and contaminating the oil. Some tanks also have an additional filter at the outlet from the tank.

Figure 7-2 shows an example oil tank.

(b) Oil Pump.

The pump is normally a fixed, or constant volume, type, delivering the same flow rate at constant engine rpm. The pump is driven by the

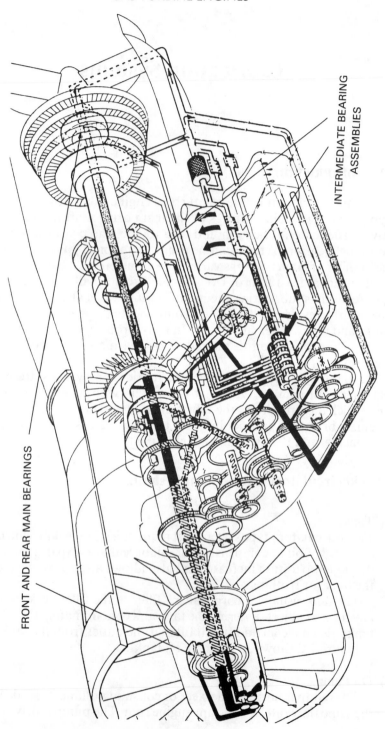

INTERMEDIATE BEARING ASSEMBLIES

FRONT AND REAR MAIN BEARINGS

Figure 7-1 Location of Main Bearings

engine and therefore its rpm, and of course its output, is directly related to engine rpm. The pressure in the system is not controlled by the pump, but by a Pressure Relief Valve situated after the pump.

The majority of modern gas turbine lubrication systems are fitted with more than one pump and they usually fall into two main types. There are normally two pressure pumps which supply the oil to the areas of the engine to be lubricated and a number of scavenge pumps which ensure the return oil is sucked from the bearings and other components and returned to the oil tank and main pressure pumps.

Figure 7-3 shows an example pump.

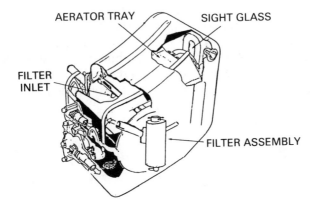

Figure 7–2 Oil Tank.

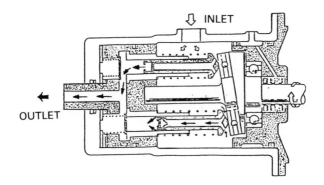

Figure 7–3 Fixed Volume Oil Pump. Pressure is controlled by a Pressure Relief Valve.

(c) Strainers.
In each return line a strainer is fitted to remove any particles of dirt, metal, or other form of contamination to prevent their continuing recirculation and the consequent damage they may inflict on the system and its components.

(d) Bearing Oil Seals.
The main bearings, usually of a ball or roller type, are subjected to very high temperatures, and to mitigate this the housings of the bearings and the bearings themselves are primarily cooled by the lubricating oil. The oil is pumped through the bearing housings under pressure and as such must be sealed to prevent the oil leaking out into the other areas of the engine. Even after the cooling effects of the oil the temperatures remain very high, far too high to allow the use of conventional rubber or nylon type seals. The type of sealing used, therefore, takes the form of a combined groove or thread shape backed up by air pressure to prevent the oil leaking out of its housing. Figure 7-4 shows some examples of air controlled seals.

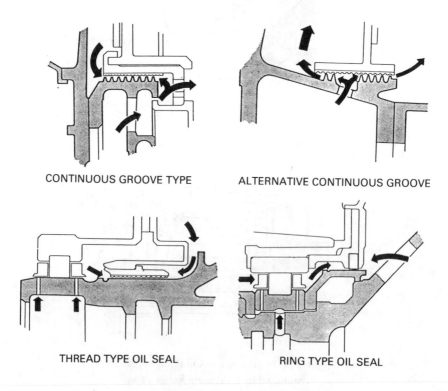

CONTINUOUS GROOVE TYPE   ALTERNATIVE CONTINUOUS GROOVE

THREAD TYPE OIL SEAL   RING TYPE OIL SEAL

Figure 7–4 Examples of Air Controlled Oil Seals.

(e) Magnetic Chip Detectors.

At strategic points in the system magnetic chip detectors are located. These are small plugs which are magnetic and attract ferrite-based metal particles which may be in the lubricating oil. By examination of the chip detector and careful examination of any particles on it, the system can be health monitored. For example, certain types of particle may indicate the pump bearings are beginning to wear excessively.

Figure 7-5 shows an example installation of chip detectors.

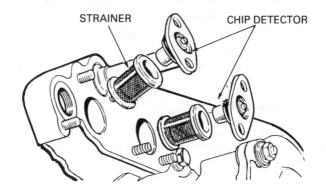

STRAINER   CHIP DETECTOR

Figure 7–5 Example Chip Detector.

7.3 Expendable Lubrication System.

The expendable, or total loss, lubricating system is included in this book for comparison purposes. Generally this type of system was used on earlier types of engine and is only seen on older operational machines. Also the use of this type of system tended to be confined to small engines. The system is light in weight, as it requires no oil cooler, scavenge pumps or filters, and therefore is very simple in design.

The expendable lubricating system consists primarily of:

(a) Oil Supply.

This may be achieved by one of two methods, either by an oil pump or by pressurising the oil tank. In the case of the pressurised oil tank method, this is automatically selected by the operation of the high pressure fuel cock during the engine start sequence.

(b) Oil Tank.

It must be remembered, once the oil has been used for lubricating the engine bearings it is then dumped overboard, and no attempt is made to recirculate the oil. As a result the oil tank must be large enough to hold sufficient oil for the duration of the flight. Generally the flight duration of such engines is comparatively short. A typical consumption rate of oil for such an engine type would be 1.2 litres per hour.

(c) Oil Metering Valve.

An oil metering valve is fitted to ensure a balanced supply of oil of the front bearing and centre bearing. The rear bearing is normally supplied with oil that has been used to lubricate the front and main, or centre, bearings. After lubricating the rear bearing the oil is then ejected into the engine gas flow from the exhaust.

Figure 7-6 shows an example of an expendable lubrication system.

7.4   Lubricating Oils.

Generally gas turbine engines use a low viscosity (thin) lubricating oil which is normally synthetic based, ie does not originate from mineral based crude oil.

Gas turbine lubricating oils must retain their lubricating properties while operating at high temperatures and also remain resistant to oxidation in such conditions. There are many types of synthetic oils used for gas turbine engines and they are necessarily manufactured to rigid specifications. Only those recommended for a particular engine must be used.

The gas turbine engine is able to use low viscosity oils due mainly to the absence of reciprocating components and heavy gear loadings. The power requirement is therefore considerably reduced and starting the engine is less of a problem, particularly at low temperatures. Normal engine starts can be achieved with gas turbines at temperatures as low as -40 degrees C.

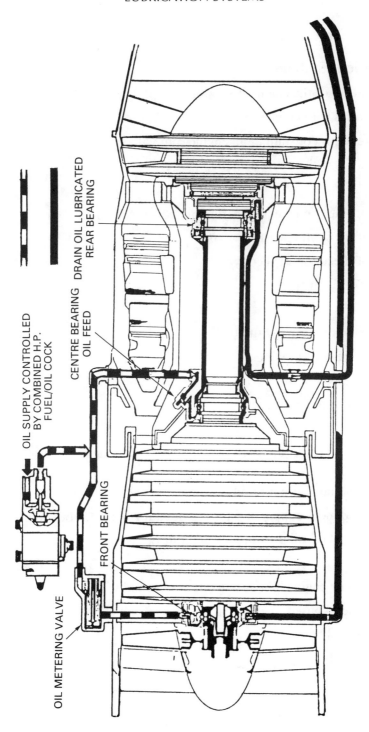

Figure 7–6 Expendable Lubrication System.

Section 7 Test Yourself

Lubrications Systems

1. The output of the engine-driven oil pump:

   (a) varies with engine rpm.

   (b) remains constant at all engine rpm values.

   (c) varies with engine demand.

Ref. 7.2.

2. Gas turbine engine main bearing oil seals are normally:

   (a) of the synthetic rubber type.

   (b) of the air controlled type.

   (c) of a nylon type.

Ref. 7.2.

3. Strainers are normally fitted:

   (a) in the pressure line.

   (b) in the oil tank.

   (c) in the return line.

Ref. 7.2.

4. Oil metering valves are normally fitted to the engine lubrication system to ensure:

   (a) an equal amount of oil is supplied to each bearing.

   (b) a balanced supply of oil is provided for the front bearing.

   (c) a constant oil pressure throughout the system.

Ref. 7.3.

5. Gas turbine engine lubricating oils are normally:

   (a) mineral based.

   (b) natural based.

   (c) synthetic based.

Ref. 7.4.

8

Fire Protection

8.1 Introduction.

Gas turbine installations and their associated equipment are designed and constructed to minimise the occurrence of an engine fire. It is essential, however, that if a failure does occur provision is made to detect and rapidly extinguish any fire, and where possible, through the construction of the aircraft airframe, coupled with the extinguishing systems, also ensure that the fire is prevented from spreading.

8.2   Fire Prevention.

The following features are some of the practices adopted by most engine and aircraft manufacturers to reduce the risk of fire and to prevent the spreading of a fire should it occur.

During the design and manufacture of the engine great effort is applied to ensure that all potential sources of flammable liquids and fluids are isolated from the 'hot end' of the engine.

External fuel and oil pipelines and components are usually located around the compressor casings and separated from the combustion and turbine areas of the engine by fireproof bulkheads or heat shields. The areas around the jet pipe, or exhaust, are constructed in a similar manner. Such zones are usually ventilated to prevent the accumulation of fuel vapours which could present a fire risk.

All pipelines which carry fuel, lubricating oils, and hydraulic fluids are made fire resistant, and all electrical wiring, components and connections are made 'flameproof', that is to say, they are incapable of igniting an inflammable vapour due to internal sparking. Sparking due to discharges of static electricity is prevented by 'Bonding', ie all electrical and other components are connected to each other to provide continuity and, therefore, prevent the build-up of static electricity in any one location which could ultimately result in a sudden discharge large enough to ignite fuel vapours or other combustible materials. The method most commonly used to bond components together is via bonding leads.

The engine bays and cowlings are manufactured with adequate drainage to remove overboard all flammable fuels or fluids both in flight and on the ground.

233

To further reduce the build-up of vapours in the engine bays or pods, air is sometimes bled from the boundary layer and ducted through the engine bay and then out to atmosphere. Usually such air bleed systems can be controlled by the pilot so that they can be shut off if a fire extinguisher is fired, or selected. Without such provision the extinguishant would be removed from the engine bay by the ventilating airflow thereby preventing it fulfilling its function of smothering the fire.

8.3   Fire Detection.

It is essential that, should a fire occur, it be rapidly detected in order that it can be extinguished before it becomes too large. It is also important that the detection system is reliable and will not give false fire warnings due to short circuiting from such causes as vibration, chafing or the presence of moisture.

The fire detection system may be of the continuous element type or it may consist of a number of individually located detector units. Both methods operate on the principle that the presence of a fire is signalled by a change in the electrical impedance or the output voltage of the detector circuit. (Remember, temperature increase in electrical terms results in a reduction in resistance.) The variation of resistance or voltage will depend on the type of system used. The change of temperature, caused by the fire will create a signal which through an amplifier operates the warning indicator. Fire indication is normally through a light and/or an audible warning such as a bell, and the warning is cancelled only when the temperature returns to normal.

Test buttons or switches are normally provided to test the detection warning light circuits prior to flight.

Figure 8-1 shows an example installation of a detector system.

8.4   Fire Containment.

In the event of a fire occurring in an aircraft engine, or in its respective bay or pod, it is vital to contain the fire in that area and prevent it from spreading to other parts of the aircraft. The cowlings which surround the engine are normally manufactured from light alloy which would be unable to contain the fire when the aircraft is static on the ground. In flight however, the airflow around the cowlings provides sufficient cooling to render them fireproof. Bulkheads which are designed to contain a fire, normally termed 'fireproof bulkheads' or 'firewalls' and do not have the benefit of airflow over them in flight, are usually manufactured from steel or titanium.

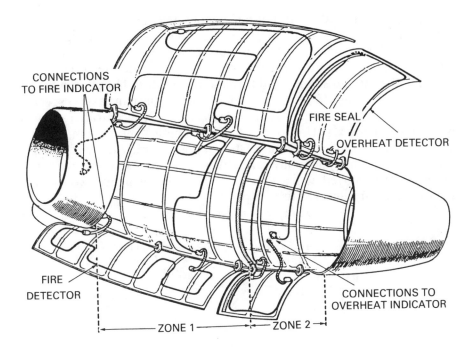

CONNECTIONS
TO FIRE INDICATOR

FIRE SEAL

OVERHEAT DETECTOR

FIRE
DETECTOR

CONNECTIONS TO
OVERHEAT INDICATOR

ZONE 1 — ZONE 2

Figure 8–1 Fire Dectector System.

8.5   Fire Extinguishing System.

Normally when a fire is detected, in particular on multi-engined aircraft, it is usual to shut down the engine immediately. If the cause of the fire is a fuel leak, allowing the engine to continue running simply means the fire will continue to be fed by the engine's fuel system. In shutting the engine down the high pressure fuel cock will be closed, starving the engine of further fuel. It is also essential to isolate the fuel system related to the affected engine by closing the low pressure fuel cock. Any fuel pumps or other components within the isolated area of fuel supply should be switched off.

The fire extinguishants used most commonly for gas turbine engines are methyl-bromide or one of the freon compounds. The fire extinguisher is normally cylindrical in shape and is pressurised. Such extinguishers are termed 'Fixed Fire Extinguishers', that is to say they are not portable as may be found clipped to the cockpit or cabin wall. Methyl-bromide extinguishers are normally coloured grey or blue.

The extinguisher is located outside the fire zone for which it is intended. Normally such extinguishers would be located in the wing or an area of the airframe fairly close to its fire zone.

235

The methyl-bromide extinguisher is operated electrically by a push button in the cockpit; as the button is depressed a small cartridge in the valve assembly attached to the extinguisher is fired, releasing the extinguishant and directing it through a pipe or tube to the fire zone. In the fire zone the extinguishant is fed through tubes which have a number of holes in them, designed to create a spray of extinguishant over a specific area of the engine or engine bay. The spray is highly concentrated and will normally last for a period of 0.5 to 2.0 seconds. The system may be designed with a single fire extinguisher and is generally termed a 'single shot' system. Some systems are called 'two-shot systems' where two extinguishers are employed with a selector switch which will give two shots at the suspected or indicated fire.

Figure 8-2 shows an example of a two-shot system.

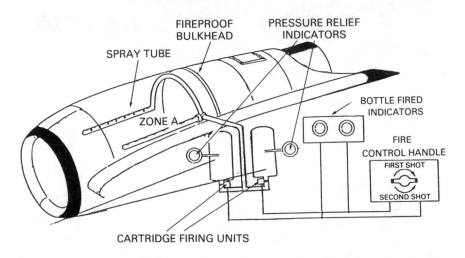

Figure 8–2 Two-Shot Fire Extinguisher System.

To guard against an extinguisher overpressurising due to excess temperature, a relief valve in the valve assembly opens to allow the extinguishant to escape to atmosphere. A small tube carries the extinguishant from the relief valve to a convenient port and then to atmosphere. In the end of the port is installed a small disc or diaphragm which may be coloured red or green. The extinguishant will burst the disc on escaping to atmosphere, thereby providing the pilot with a quick external check whether the extinguisher has overpressurised and discharged.

Figure 8-3 shows a methyl-bromide extinguisher and its related valve assembly.

236

8.6   Extinguisher.

Extinguishers vary in construction but normally comprise two main components (i) the steel or copper container and (ii) the discharge or operating head. A sectioned view of an extinguisher widely used in a two-shot system is shown in Fig. 8-3. The container is in the form of a steel cylinder and has an externally threaded neck to which the discharge head is screwed and soldered. The discharge head contains two annular machined diaphragms, each bearing an externally-threaded spigot on which a hollow plug is screwed to form an annulus between its inner end and its respective diaphragm. Each annulus is connected by a 'flash' hole to a port containing the appropriate cartridge unit. Below, and concentric with each diaphragm and charge plug, is an adjustable hollow junction box fitted with a union to which an extinguisher discharge pipe is connected. The lower end of the junction box is closed by a cap which embodies a discharge indicator pin.

A banjo coupling is fitted in the main body of the operating head and serves as a connection for a pressure discharge indicator.

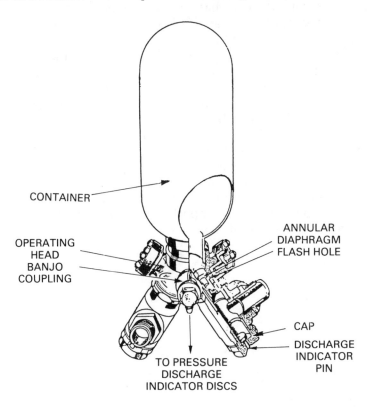

Figure 8–3 Methyl-Bromide Extinguisher.

When either of the cartridge units are fired, sufficient pressure is created in the adjacent annulus to rupture the associated diaphragm. The spigot and charge plug assembly is thereby detached and forced down the hollow junction box beyond the outlet union and discharge pipe through which the extinguishant then flows to the spray pipes, ring, and/or manifolds. (See Fig 8-3.)

8.7   Directional Flow Valves.

These valves are a special form of non-return valve designed for use in two-shot systems to allow the contents of one or several extinguishers to be directed into any one power plant. The methods of connection may vary between different aircraft systems, but the one shown in Figure 8-2 is typical and also serves to illustrate the two-shot operating sequence generally adopted. The extinguishers are controlled by individual firing switches each having three positions: No 1, OFF and No 2. When the port extinguisher switch is selected to the No 1 position, the relevant cartridge unit in the port extinguisher is fired and the extinguisher is discharged to the port power plant. If the fire has not been extinguished, selection of the No 2 position then causes the starboard extinguisher to be discharged also into the port power plant via the crossfeed line and port directional flow valve, the latter preventing extinguishant from entering the empty extinguisher of the port system. In order to extinguish a fire in the starboard engine, the starboard extinguisher switch is selected to its No 1 position, and the relevant cartridge unit is fired so that extinguishant is discharged to the starboard power plant. If selection of the No 2 position of the starboard extinguisher switch becomes necessary, then the port extinguisher will also be discharged into the starboard power plant via the appropriate crossfeed line and the starboard directional flow valve, which prevents charging the empty starboard extinguisher.

Note: In some types of aircraft, the cross connecting of selected extinguishers between engines is accomplished by means of transfer switches which are additional to the normal firing switches.

Section 8 Test Yourself

Fire Protection

1. The majority of fixed aircraft fire extinguisher systems use:

(a) Methyl-bromide extinguishant.

(b) CO_2 extinguishant.

(c) Carbon Tetra Fluoride extinguishant.

Ref. 8.5.

2. The extinguisher in a fixed fire extinguisher system is activated:

(a) manually by a mechanical valve.

(b) electrically.

(c) by CO_2 gas pressure.

Ref. 8.5.

3. A burst red disc at the atmospheric outlet of a fixed fire extinguisher system indicates:

(a) the system has been used to extinguish a fire.

(b) the system is unserviceable.

(c) the extinguisher has overpressurised.

Ref. 8.5.

4. In flight, engine cowlings are fireproofed by:

(a) the airflow.

(b) titanium.

(c) asbestos lagging.

Ref. 8.2.

5. Fire from electrical components due to static electricity build-up is minimised by:

(a) ventilation.

(b) bonding.

(c) boundary air cooling.

Ref. 8.2.

9

Ice Protection Systems

9.1 Introduction.

Icing of gas turbine engines can occur during flight when flying through clouds containing supercooled water droplets, and also during ground operations in conditions of poor visibility with an air temperature near freezing.

The gas turbine engine requires protection against the formation and build-up of ice in front of the engine in the intake region, and on the leading edges of air intake ducts.

Figure 9-1 shows the areas of the engine and intake which are equipped with ice protection devices.

9.2 Types of Ice Protection Employed on Gas Turbine Engines.

There are essentially two main types of ice protection system currently in use:

(a)   Hot Air Systems.

(b)   Electrical Systems.

9.3 Hot Air System.

The hot air system is widely used on turbojet engines and works on the principle of ducting hot air, normally bled from the high pressure region of the engine's compressor, to heat the skin surfaces at the engine intake and the leading edge of the engine inlet.

Figure 9-2 shows a hot air system and its components.

9.4 Hot Air System Operation.

Hot air is bled from the high pressure stages of the compressor, often the last stage, and is then ducted via a pressure regulating valve which controls the pressure within the system. The airflow passes through light alloy ducting to the surfaces requiring protection, and is capable of maintaining the surface skin temperature above 0deg C. After the air has

240

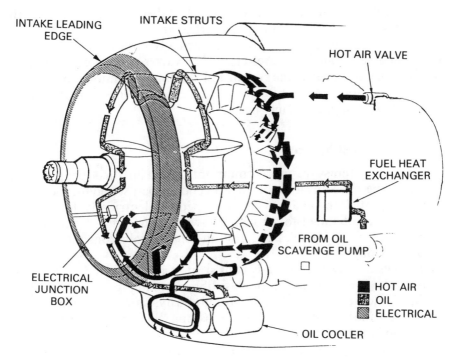

Figure 9–1 Ice Protection Devices.

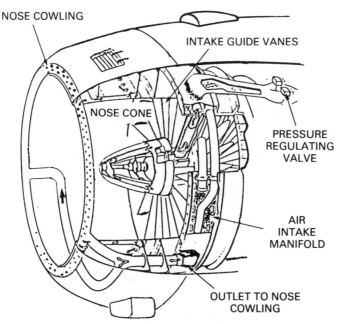

Figure 9–2 Hot Air De-icing.

241

circulated through the system it is either discharged back into the compressor inlet or is just dumped overboard.

The pressure regulator valves are normally electrically actuated by either manual or automatic selection. The valves prevent excessive pressures being developed in the system and also limit the amount of air taken from the compressor, thereby preventing excessive loss of performance, particularly at higher engine speeds.

9.5   Electrical System.

Electrical systems are more commonly used on turboprop engines primarily because this form of ice protection is best suited for the protection of propellers against ice formation. Electrically heated pad assemblies are bonded to air intake cowlings, the propeller blades and spinner (where applicable) and also on some installations the oil cooler intake cowling.

The electrically heated pads consist of strip conductors sandwiched between layers of Neoprene, or glass fibre cloth impregnated with epoxy resin. Some heaters are heated continuously, as an anti-icing system preventing the formation of ice on the leading edges, whilst other elements are heated intermittently.

The latter type of element is divided into sections by breaker strips which are heated continuously.

Figure 9-3 shows an electrically heated element assembly including the breaker strip type of installation.

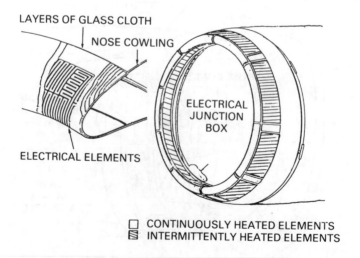

□ CONTINUOUSLY HEATED ELEMENTS
▨ INTERMITTENTLY HEATED ELEMENTS

Figure 9–3 Electrically Heated Element Assembly.

242

9.6   Electrical Ice Protection Operation.

Electrical power is supplied by an AC generator and to reduce the weight and size of the system, and in particular of the generator, the de-icing electrical loads are cycled between the engine, propeller and, sometimes, the airframe. Referring again to Fig. 9-3 it can be seen that part of the cowling is heated continuously and part intermittently. This type of operation will assist in keeping the weight and size of the generator to a minimum.

In normal operation, the continuously heated elements prevent any ice forming and thus serve an anti-icing function. By contrast, the intermittently heated elements allow ice to form, during their heat-off cycle. During the heat-on cycle ice that has adhered to the area will be removed, or allowed to break off, through the heating action of the elements coupled with the action of the airflow over the area.

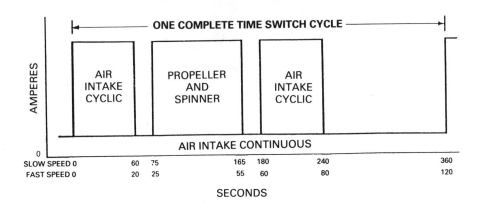

Figure 9–4 Cycle Sequence.

The continuously heated breaker strips limit the size of the area on which ice can form on the intermittently heated areas.

The cycling time of the intermittently heated elements is arranged to ensure that the engine will not be seriously affected by the amount of ice that may build-up during the heat-off period, and the heat-on time is long enough to ensure that any ice which has formed will be freed from the area.

A two-speed system is often used to accommodate the propeller and spinner requirements, a fast cycle at higher atmospheric temperatures when the water concentration is usually greater, and a slow cycle when lower atmospheric temperatures prevail.

Figure 9-4 shows an example cycling sequence chart.

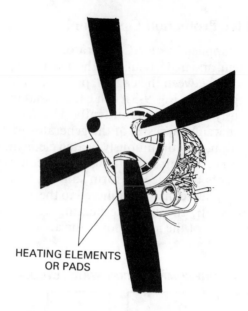

HEATING ELEMENTS
OR PADS

Figure 9–5 Electrically Heated Propeller
Ice Protection.

Note: Most electrical ice protection systems are supplied by frequency wild generators in order to minimise weight and size.

9.7 Electrically Heated Propeller Ice Protection.

The propeller ice protection system is part of the main engine ice protection system. The heated elements that are attached to the leading edge of the propeller blades do not cover the full length of the blade for two reasons: firstly, the forces experienced towards the blade tip are such that to achieve satisfactory bonding of the heating elements to the blade is almost impossible, and secondly, towards the tip of the propeller blade an element of dynamic heating tends to prevent the formation of ice.

Figure 9-5 shows the location of the heating elements or pads on a typical turboprop propeller.

Section 9 Test Yourself

Ice Protection Systems

1. Hot air for the purpose of ice protection systems is normally obtained from:

   (a) heater elements.

   (b) the low pressure stages of the compressor.

   (c) the high pressure stages of the compressor.

   Ref. 9.4.

2. The air pressure in the heated air system of ice protection is:

   (a) the same as the engine compressor pressure.

   (b) controlled by a pressure relief valve.

   (c) controlled by a pressure regulator valve.

   Ref. 9.4.

3. The electrically heated ice protection system:

   (a) heats air which is then ducted to specific areas.

   (b) heats pads which are bonded to certain points.

   (c) heats oil which is ducted to certain points.

   Ref. 9.5.

4. Ice is most likely to form:

   (a) at low atmospheric temperatures.

   (b) at high atmospheric temperatures.

   (c) at any atmospheric temperature.

   Ref. 9.6.

5. Propeller ice protection pads are:

   (a) heated by hot air.

   (b) located towards the blade tip.

   (c) located towards the blade root.

   Ref. 9.7.

10

Engine Performance and Handling

10.1 Introduction.

The handling requirements of gas turbine engines vary according to type, and this chapter is a guide to some of the more general features and problems. For specific data the particular engines manuals must be consulted.

10.2 Pre-Starting Precautions.

When possible the aircraft should be headed into wind during engine starting or for ground running. The area around the aircraft should be clear of all obstructions, loose equipment or any objects which could be drawn into the intake or damaged by the jet exhaust. It is very important that personnel in the vicinity of the aircraft are made aware of the engine's starting and/or running and are advised to keep clear.

10.3 Starting.

On most gas turbine aircraft the engine starting sequence is automatic once engine start has been selected. Prior to initiating the start sequence, the low pressure and high pressure fuel cocks must be turned ON, and the low pressure fuel pumps must be turned ON to allow a fuel flow to the engine-driven high pressure fuel pumps. Normally the throttle should be kept closed during the engine start sequence. On some installations protection devices prevent the start sequence being initiated unless the throttle is in the closed position. Failure to ensure that the throttle is closed during the start sequence can on some engines result in over-fuelling of the engine.

With an electrical starting system the start button should be pushed in and held for two to three seconds and then released. The starter sequence relay will first supply a low voltage current to drive the starter motor, then current to the booster coils for the ignition system igniters, and finally a high voltage current to the starter motor which then accelerates the engine at a great rate.

During the initial stages of engine acceleration the fuel pressure rises; the high pressure or engine-driven fuel pumps will have moved to the 'on load' or 'on stroke' position when the engine was previously shut down and will now be delivering fuel under pressure to the engine. The fuel is sprayed into the combustion chambers from the burners and ignited either, on some older type engines, by the torch igniters, or high energy ignition units. On some installations the fuel pressure may rise too rapidly and fuel may be discharged into the combustion chambers before the engine rpm are high enough for a satisfactory light-up because the air/fuel mixture will be incorrect. This situation may result in a 'Hung' start.

A 'Hung Start' will be indicated by the engine accelerating to a figure below 'Idle' rpm and failing to accelerate any higher. In other words, the mixture is too rich. If this situation should occur with a fully automatic sequence start system, the engine must be shut down and a fresh attempt made to restart.

Note: A 'Hung Start' is also known as a 'Hot Start'.

On some engine installations, if a 'Hung Start'; situation is liable to occur, it is recommended that the high pressure cock should be closed, or partially closed, at the commencement of the start sequence. This will minimise the risk of an incorrect fuel/air ratio at the low initial rpm, which could lead to overfuelling of the engine.

It should also be noted that at low engine rpm, an overfuelling situation can also lead to surging and an excessive engine gas temperature or jet pipe temperature.

After 'light up', the engine speed increases under the combined influence of the turbine and starter motor. After approximately 30 seconds, the current to the starter motor (electric start system) and igniter units or plugs is automatically cut off and the engine becomes self sustaining.

The starting sequence should never be interrupted, that is to say, disconnected or switched off. Should this be done then the start sequence, when re-connected, continues from the point at which it was stopped. This could result in flooding the engine with fuel and result in failure to start and, possibly, damage to the start system and/or engine.

10.4   Failure of the Engine to Start.

If the engine fails to start, as soon as this becomes apparent the high pressure fuel cock should be closed. The action of closing the high pressure fuel cock will reduce the fuel flooding of the engine. The most likely cause of start failure is insufficient electrical power to rotate the engine at sufficient rpm. After closing the high pressure cock the engine should be allowed to run down and stop and sufficient time thereafter allowed for all surplus fuel to drain through the fuel drain valves. Time must also be allowed for the starter motor to cool before any attempt is made to restart the engine.

Note: Insufficient power on engine starting will also reduce the effectiveness of the igniters.

10.5   Wet Start.

Should an engine fail to start, as in the previous paragraph, the interior of the combustion chambers will be wet with fuel, fuel will have drained and collected in the bottom of the engine, some fuel may also have passed through the turbine and collected in the exhaust or jet pipe. In some instances the fuel drain valves will not allow all fuel to drain out of the engine. It is also possible that ignition during the first attempt to start did not take place effectively, resulting in very little fuel actually being burned. If a normal start is now attempted and the accumulated fuel ignites, an internal engine fire could result generating excessive temperatures and possibly damage to the engine.

This type of internal engine fire is sometimes termed 'torching'. Should an engine fail to start and excessive amounts of accumulated fuel are suspected, before a further attempt is made to start the engine, a 'dry run' should be carried out. First ensure the engine and starter motor have been given adequate time to cool, and as much fuel as possible has drained from the engine. The engine should then be turned over by the starter motor with the high pressure cock, master starter switch, ignition, and all priming or booster pumps switched off. This will result in blowing air through the engine and thereby drying some of the accumulated fuel from the components before a further attempt is made to start the engine.

When a dry run is carried out, the starter motor must be given adequate time to cool before any further start sequence is initiated.

Note: It may be necessary to re-site the aircraft after an aborted 'wet start' because fuel that has drained from the aircraft will now constitute a serious fire hazard.

Although a dry run has been carried out to remove accumulations of fuel from the engine, a degree of 'torching' will sometimes take place at the second attempt to start the engine. Flames will be seen coming from the jet pipe; this will also be accompanied by a rise in engine gas temperature. Usually, however, this will not be a serious problem provided the engine gas temperature remains within limits and no attempt is made to shut the engine down at this specific time.

10.6   Engine Resonance.

During starting of the engine, resonance may occur on light-up and can be recognised by a rumbling sound from the engine. This situation usually occurs due to a degree of overfuelling, and may be overcome by partial closing of the high pressure fuel cock. As soon as the resonance subsides the high pressure fuel cock should be moved to the fully open position.

10.7   Immediately After Starting.

After the starting cycle is completed the engine should be allowed to idle for a brief period and the following should be checked:

(a)   Oil Pressure.

(b)   Burner or Fuel System Pressure.

(c)   Engine Gas Temperature or Jet Pipe Temperature.

(d)   All ancillary services.

(e)   That All Relevant Instrumentation is operating satisfactorily.

10.8   Warming Up the Engine.

The engine must be allowed to warm up to its normal operating temperature, which is carried out at ground idle rpm. Until the recommended operating temperature has been reached the throttle should not be moved. If any throttle adjustment is required then the throttle should be moved smoothly and slowly. Any rapid movements during this period may cause the engine to stall or surge.

10.9   Taxying.

Rapid and unnecessarily frequent opening and closing of the throttle should be avoided while taxying, because it can lead to overfuelling which, in turn, can cause surging and resonance, and this in turn will lead to increased engine gas temperature.

The initial response of the engine to throttle movement is generally slow, and considerable power may be required to start moving some larger types of aircraft. Once the aircraft starts to move, however, the power required during taxying is relatively small.

Axial flow engines are, as stated in previous chapters, susceptible to compressor stall and surge, particularly at low engine rpm, which can be considerably aggravated in crosswind conditions. The combination of low engine rpm and crosswinds is likely to occur during taxying and it may be necessary to use a slightly higher rpm to reduce stall tendencies. In extreme conditions the turning of the aircraft into wind to recover from engine stall may be the only answer. It is therefore essential to avoid rapid throttle movements in such situations. Should the engine stall, then the throttle must be closed slowly and then re-opened slowly to re-establish satisfactory airflow conditions through the engine and in particular the compressor. On very rare occasions it may be necessary to shut the engine down and then re-start.

10.10   Take-Off.

As in the case of aircraft taxying in crosswind conditions and the consequent danger of engine surge, the situation is even more critical during take-off in crosswind conditions. Should engine stall or surge occur during take-off, not only will engine power be lost at a critical time, the surge or stall could also lead to a 'flame-out'. Modern gas turbine engines are equipped with various aids to minimise the onset of engine stall and its related conditions; even so, every precaution must be taken to ensure any such situation does not arise. The throttle must be moved smoothly and slowly as engine rpm are increased for take-off, and the engine must be monitored closely to ensure there is not the slightest indication of the onset of surge or stall. Engine gas temperature must be correct, neither too high nor indeed, too low. Monitor that such devices, discussed in previous chapters are functioning correctly. For take-off Inlet Guide Vanes must be fully open, Intermediate Bleed Valves operating correctly, Variable Stators operating correctly, and rear or main Bleed Valves operating correctly.

Additionally, most modern aircraft require as further protection that the Auxiliary Power Unit be running during take-off as an insurance against main generator supply failure, and the igniter system operating to give instant re-light in the event of a flame-out occurring.

10.11   Climbing.

If the correct climbing speeds are not used, and particularly if the speed is too low, the rate of climb is therefore reduced. At high altitudes, unless the correct speed is used the aircraft will not climb at all. During climb at the recommended rpm and airspeed, a careful watch must be kept on the engine gas temperature (which should not exceed the permitted maximum), the throttle being closed slightly if necessary.

Under certain conditions some engines are prone to surge while climbing at higher altitudes. With centrifugal compressor engines the symptom of a surge is a muffled detonation in the engine and to reduce or rectify the situation, the throttle should be closed slightly and/or the airspeed increased.

With an axial flow engine there may be indication of surge by a loud 'cough' or 'bang' from the engine or there may be no audible warning before the surge, the first symptom being a loss of power or a 'flame-out'. If a sudden loss of power occurs the throttle must be closed immediately;

if a flame-out has also occurred then the high pressure fuel cock must be closed as well as the throttle. This type of surge normally only occurs if the climbing speed is lower than normal. If the climbing speed falls below the correct figure at high altitude, power should be reduced below the climb rpm while speed is restored by diving the aircraft until the correct speed is obtained.

In spite of the Barometric Pressure Control, the rpm for a given throttle setting may tend to increase with increase of altitude. With increase of altitude the atmosphere becomes less dense so reducing the back pressure on the engine and thereby causing the engine rpm to increase while the thrust will reduce.

Therefore to maintain constant rpm the throttle should be progressively closed. The more modern types of gas turbine with improved engine control systems have a reduced tendency for rpm to vary with altitude for a given power setting.

10.12   General Handling.

The principles of handling the gas turbine engine are determined by the fact that it best operates at a fixed throttle setting. The engine consists of a matched set of primary components which are designed to give an optimum performance at a given throttle setting, therefore any deviation from such matched settings, such as low fuel/air ratio, excessively high mass flow at intake, will be a deviation from normal engine operation. By the same token, movement of the throttle, from the optimum setting will also constitute a deviation from normal operation. It must also be noted that constant changes of the throttle setting will increase wear and therefore reduce the life of the engine.

Various devices such as variable inlet guide vanes (Swirl Vanes), Barometric Pressure Control, Automatic Control Unit, Bleed Valves and others, are there to assist the pilot in maintaining a balanced control of the engine when changing the thrust condition. Even with such devices, however, great care must be taken when operating the throttle. Should any device suffer a malfunction, successful control of the engine can still be maintained but even greater attention must be paid to throttle handling and the preservation of a good flow in the compressor.

At high altitudes gas turbine engines become extremely sensitive to throttle movement and the range of movement between idling and full power may be very small due to:

(a)   The lower limit which is dictated by the higher idling rpm required to provide adequate fuel pressure for combustion and/or cabin pressurising requirements.

(b)   The upper limit dictated by the throttle position above which the rpm and/or engine gas temperature limits are exceeded.

If the throttle is opened too rapidly this may result in a momentary increase in engine gas temperature followed by a flame-out. In this event, or if the engine is intentionally stopped in flight, the high pressure fuel cock should be closed immediately. Note that when relighting an engine at altitude the engine starter motor system should not normally be used as this may damage the engine; the airflow through the engine will normally give adequate rpm for relighting.

10.13   Centrifugal Compressor Engines.

With this type of engine there is little risk of flame extinction provided the throttle is moved smoothly and not too rapidly. The higher the altitude the higher the engine idling rpm, and the more sensitive the engine to throttle movement.

10.14   Axial Flow Type Engines.

If, when the throttle is opened, the rpm remain constant and the engine gas temperature rises to the maximum permitted level, the throttle should be fully closed immediately: these symptoms indicate that surging or a stalled compressor condition exists. After the throttle has been fully closed it may be opened again provided that the throttle movement is kept slow. At the same time special attention must be paid to the engine gas temperature to ensure that it remains within limits and a repeat surge or stall does not occur.

Low engine rpm should be avoided as much as possible; if, however, the rpm has been allowed to drop below the flight minimum value, when the throttle setting is thereafter increased the movement must be carried out slowly, again due to the possibility of surge or stall in the compressor. Particular attention must be paid to this when on the approach with the airspeed low and the aircraft sinking in a nose-up attitude which may cause the airflow to stall at the lips of the engine intakes. If the rpm are kept at or above the recommended value on the landing approach, until the decision actually to land has been made, such surge or stall conditions can be avoided.

Above 3000ft the effect of the Acceleration Control Unit is reduced on some engines, and any rapid acceleration of the engine causes overfuelling which can then lead to stalling or surging of the compressor. Engine acceleration deteriorates with increased altitude and care must therefore be taken when increasing power at high altitudes. For the same reason care must also be taken to avoid excessive engine gas temperature when accelerating.

10.15   High Altitude Surge.

Above 30,000–40,000 feet, when flying at a low indicated Airspeed and high rpm in very low temperatures, high altitude surge may occur. The risk of this type of surge can be avoided by keeping the rpm at the recommended value and minus 100 rpm for each 5 degrees below minus 55deg C.

10.16   Variable Position Inlet Guide Vanes (Variable Position Swirl Vanes).

The action of the variable position inlet guide vanes has no noticeable effect on engine running. Compressor efficiency, however, is reduced unless the guide vanes move to the fully open position at the recommended engine rpm. On modern gas turbines this action is fully automatic. The lowest specific fuel consumption can be obtained only by operating with the variable inlet guide vanes fully open. Remember when engine starting, the guide vanes should be in the fully closed position.

10.17   Mechanical Failure in Flight.

In the event of mechanical failure of the engine in flight the immediate action to be taken should be:

(a)   Close the throttle and HP cock.

(b)   Switch off the LP pumps, and if the failure is accompanied by a strong risk of fire, close the LP Fuel cocks also.

(c)   In twin-engined aircraft, shed all non-essential load and land the aircraft as soon as possible.

10.18   Engine Icing.

Centrifugal compressor engines do not encounter serious icing problems, mainly because of the combination of centrifugal force, temperature rise and rugged construction found in this type of gas turbine. The only condition which may present a problem to this type is the occurrence of severe ambient icing.

Axial flow compressors are seriously affected by the same atmospheric conditions that cause airframe icing. Ice may form on the inlet guide vanes causing a restricted and turbulent airflow with a consequent loss in thrust and rise in engine gas temperature. Heavy icing can cause an excessive engine gas temperature leading to turbine and engine failure.

10.19   Effect of RPM on Rate of Icing.

For a given icing intensity the closer the spacing of the inlet guide vanes, the more serious the effect of icing. For a given engine the rate of ice accumulation is roughly proportional to the icing intensity and the mass airflow through the engine, ie to engine rpm. The rate of engine icing can therefore be reduced by decreasing the engine rpm.

10.20   Effect of True Air Speed on the Rate of Icing.

The rate of icing for a given icing index is almost constant up to 250 knots True Air Speed (TAS), but beyond this the rate of icing increases rapidly with increasing TAS. This is because whilst the rate of engine icing is directly proportional to the liquid water content of the air gathered into the air intakes, the water content of the air in the intakes is not necessarily the same as that in the free airstream.

At low speeds, air is drawn into the intakes and at high speeds the air is rammed in, the transition speed, at which the pressure and temperature in the intake are atmospheric, is approximately 250 knots TAS. During the suction period the concentration of water content is virtually unchanged from that of the free airstream. At speeds above 250 knots, most of the suspended water droplets ahead of the projected area of the intake, tend to pass into the intake while some of the air in this same projected area is deflected round the intakes. The inertia of the droplets prevents them from being deflected and so the water content of the air in the intake is increased. A reduction of TAS to 250 knots will therefore reduce the rate of icing.

The reduced pressure caused by the compressor sucking air in the intake is at its lowest at zero speed. The pressure drop also increases with raise in rpm. The pressure drop is, of course, accompanied by a temperature drop. On the ground, or at very low speeds and high rpm, air at ambient temperature will be reduced to sub freezing temperatures as it enters the intake, and any water content would therefore freeze onto the inlet guide vanes. The suction temperature drop which occurs is of the order of 5 to 10deg C. This temperature drop occurs at high rpm at the lowest altitudes and decreases with decreasing rpm or increasing TAS. Under these conditions visible moisture is needed to form icing, therefore take-off in fog, at temperatures slightly above freezing, may result in ice forming.

Anti-icing systems and De-icing systems are discussed in previous chapters.

10.21 Approach and Landing, Turbojet Engines.

With turbojet engines, approach should be made under power to ensure that a quick response for additional thrust is available should it become necessary to adjust the glide path by use of the throttle. Minimum engine rpm are recommended for approach configurations for specific aircraft. The rpm should be kept at or above this figure until the decision to land has been made and the runway can be seen. In the event of the landing being aborted and the decision made to go round again, any movement of the throttle to maximum power should be made smoothly to avoid surge.

If the decision has been made to go round again after touch-down and the engine rpm has fallen below the recommended approach rpm, the throttle must be opened very carefully until the minimum approach rpm is reached or the engine will surge. When the throttle is opened up under these conditions the engine takes longer to accelerate to full power.

10.22 Stopping the Engine.

The engine must not be shut down, or stopped, until the engine temperature has fallen to the recommended figure. Normally after touch-down, and the aircraft having taxied in, the engine is cool enough to be stopped. Although slight variations in procedure exist with different engine and aircraft types, generally the throttle must be fully closed and the high pressure fuel cock turned off. If, however, the temperatures are above the recommended values, the engine should be run at approximately twice the idling rpm for a short period to allow it to cool. The throttle should then be closed and the engine allowed to idle for approximately 30 seconds, after which the high pressure cock can be turned off. The engine thereafter continues to run for several minutes until combustion has ceased and the engine has run down. The low pressure fuel cock should not be turned off until the engine has stopped turning. If the low pressure cock is turned off before the engine stops the high pressure fuel pump will be run dry and air will be drawn into the system, which will then need to be re-primed with fuel and bled. It should also be noted that if the low pressure cock is turned off before the high pressure cock, the run down time of the engine will be increased as well as the system being allowed to run dry.

10.23   Relighting Turbojet Engines.

In the event of a flame-out occurring in flight a relighting of the engine, providing there is no mechanical or system failure, is normally possible on modern gas turbine engines. With some engines relighting is possible up to 35,000 feet, but in most cases much lower altitudes are recommended and, generally, the lower the altitude the greater the degree of success.

If flame-out occurs the following actions should be taken.:

(a)   Close the high pressure fuel cock immediately to prevent the accumulation of fuel in the engine which would make relighting much more difficult.

(b)   Fly at the recommended relighting indicated air speed and altitude.

(c)   Ensure that at least one low pressure fuel cock and booster pump are on, that the fuel pressure warning light is out, and that there is enough fuel in the selected fuel tanks.

(d)   Switch on the relight and emergency booster pump if fitted.

(e)   Set the throttle to the recommended position. This will vary with aircraft types, as experience has shown that, while some engines relight more readily with the throttle in the fully closed position others relight more effectively with the throttle partially open.

(f)   Ensure that the master starting switch and ignition switch, if fitted, are in the ON position.

(g)   Press the relight button and open the high pressure fuel cock to the fully open position.

(h)   Immediately a rise in rpm or engine gas temperature is indicated, release the relight button and close the throttle. The engine should then accelerate to idling rpm for the altitude and may then be opened up slowly to the desired figure.

10.24   Gas Turbine Engine Ratings.

Introduction.

Generally engines of the turbojet type are rated in pounds of thrust developed, and this in turn is divided into specific thrust ratings for specific functions. Broadly they are as follows:

(a) Take-off Rated Thrust.

(b) Maximum Continuous.

(c) Maximum Climb.

(d) Maximum Cruise.

(e) Idle.

For practical purposes the engine rating is normally interpreted in terms of engine pressure ratio (EPR) or on some engines, mostly military, by a specific throttle setting.

(a) Take-off Rated Thrust.
Will normally be obtained at a throttle setting below the full forward position and may be sub-divided into two categories:

Take-off (Wet)
This is the maximum take-off thrust certified for engines that use water injection. The rating is selected by operating the water injection system and setting the throttle to obtain the computed 'Wet' Take-off Thrust in terms of engine pressure ratio. This rating is restricted normally to take-off, is time limited, and has altitude and ambient air or water limitations.

Take-off (Dry)
This is the maximum thrust certified without water injection. The rating is selected by setting the throttle to obtain the computed Take-off (Dry) thrust in terms of engine pressure ratio for the prevailing conditions of ambient temperature and barometric pressure. The rating is time limited, and is used only for take-off, and as required, for Reverse Thrust when landing.

(b) Maximum Continuous.
This thrust rating is the maximum thrust certified for continuous use and is normally used only at the discretion of the pilot or to ensure safe flight.

(c) Maximum Climb.
This is the maximum thrust approved for normal climb. The rating is obtained by adjusting the throttle to obtain a predetermined engine pressure ratio. On some engines Maximum Continuous and Maximum Climb thrusts are the same.

(d) Maximum Cruise.
This is the maximum thrust approved for cruise flight conditions and is obtained in the same manner as Maximum Continuous and Maximum Climb thrust.

(e) Ground Idle.
Ground Idle is the minimum thrust at which the engine must be operated at specific ground or flight conditions when the throttle lever is placed in the ground idle position.

Commercial engines are part throttle engines, that is, rated thrust is obtained at less than full throttle position. Taking their name from the shape of the take-off thrust curve, the so called part throttle engines are also known as 'Flat Rated' engines.

Note: Details of the handling of turboprop engines are dealt with in Part Three of this volume, "Propellers".

Section 10 Test Yourself

Engine Performance and Handling

1. A gas turbine engine, on starting, accelerates to a figure below idle rpm and fails to accelerate above that value, this indicates:

   (a)   a wet start.

   (b)   a hung start.

   (c)   a surge condition.

Ref. 10.3.

2. When the gas turbine engine is shut down, the high pressure fuel pump:

   (a)   will move to the off load position.

   (b)   will remain at the setting it is in at time of shut down.

   (c)   will move to the on load position.

Ref. 10.3.

3. Prior to engine starting, the throttle:

   (a)   must be set at ground idle.

   (b)   must be set at a value above ground idle.

   (c) must be closed.

Ref. 10.3.

4. If an engine fails to start, the:

   (a)   high pressure cock should be closed when the engine has stopped.

   (b)   high pressure cock should be closed as soon as ignition is switched off.

   (c)   high pressure cock should be closed as soon as failure to start becomes apparent.

Ref. 10.4.

5. On some engine types, resonance may be reduced, during starting by:

   (a)   increasing the throttle setting.

   (b)   fully closing the high pressure cock.

   (c)   partially closing the high pressure cock.

Ref. 10.6.

6. Torching is a term sometimes used to describe:

(a) the point of ignition on engine starting.

(b) the re-light after a flame-out.

(c) an internal engine fire.

Ref. 10.5.

7. Variable inlet guide vanes:

(a) must be fully open on engine starting.

(b) may be in any mid position on engine starting.

(c) must be fully closed on engine starting.

Ref. 10.16.

8. If, when stopping the gas turbine, the low pressure fuel cock is closed first:

(a) the engine run down time will increase.

(b) the engine run down time will be unaffected.

(c) the engine run down time will be reduced.

Ref. 10.22.

9. In the event a surge is suspected in the compressor of a gas turbine engine, the:

(a) throttle must be opened slowly.

(b) engine must be shut down.

(c) throttle must be closed slowly.

Ref. 10.14.

10. On most aircraft fitted with gas turbine engines, prior to engine shut down, if the engine temperatures are too high:

(a) the engine must be run at idle rpm until it cools down.

(b) the engine must be run at approximately twice idle rpm until it cools.

(c) the fuel/air mixture must be moved to rich.

Ref. 10.22.

11

Gas Turbine Controls and Instrumentation

11.1 Introduction

This chapter is intended to give the reader a basic knowledge of the general cockpit controls and instruments relating to the gas turbine engine in the average aircraft. Controls and instrumentation vary from one aircraft type to another, but most of the primary controls and instruments to be found are listed below.

11.2 Engine and Engine System Controls.

(a) **Throttle Lever.**
Selects the engine fuel flow and hence controls the engine speed. Normally mounted between the pilots' seats on the main control quadrant.

(b) **High Pressure Fuel Cock (HP Cock).**
Sometimes termed the High Pressure Shut Off cock, provides a means of stopping the engine in that it starves the engine of fuel when closed.

(c) **Low Pressure Fuel Cock (LP Cock).**
Normally controlled by an electric actuator which in turn is operated by a switch in the cockpit. This is essentially an on/off control for the fuel system from the fuel tank, or tanks, to the High Pressure Pump. Switches are also provided for transfer pumps to enable fuel to be controlled between tanks.

(d) **Thrust Reversal.**
This normally takes the form of a separate lever which gives instinctive control of engine power during reverse thrust operation.

(e) **Reheat.**
Reheat, or afterburning, is controlled by a lever in the cockpit. On most modern aircraft the variable exhaust or propelling nozzle is controlled automatically.

11.3   Gas Turbine Instrumentation.

Although engine installations may differ, depending upon the type of aircraft and engine, gas turbine engine control will usually depend upon use of the following instrumentation. Engine thrust indication will be dealt with separately.

(a)  **Tachometer** – Engine rotor rpm may be sensed by a mechanically-driven tachometer generator, mechanically-driven permanent magnet, or a pulse pick-up which senses passing compressor or fan blades, or passing gear teeth. The output signal from any of the above sensors is directed to an appropriate indicator in the cockpit, calibrated to read directly in per cent rpm. Dual axial flow compressor engines are usually provided with two tachometers, one indicating low pressure compressor speed (N_1), the other high pressure compressor speed (N_2).

For most axial flow compressor engines, the main purpose of the tachometer is to monitor rpm during an engine start and to indicate an overspeed condition, should one occur. Although Pratt & Whitney does not recommend the use of the tachometer for setting thrust on axial flow compressor engines, the low pressure compressor (N_1) tachometer on EPR-controlled engines may be used as an approximate reference for setting engine thrust in transient and certain other flight conditions. Whenever the N_1 tachometer is used to set engine thrust, the thrust setting should be more accurately adjusted on engine pressure ratio as soon as possible. On single compressor axial flow engines, it is strongly recommended that engine speed is not used as a primary means of setting or checking engine thrust. Refer to the discussion under Engine Thrust Indication which follows.

(b)  **Exhaust Gas Temperature Indicator** – Turbine engines may be instrumented for exhaust gas temperature indication at locations before, between, or behind the turbine stages. Exhaust gas temperature is an engine operating limit, and is used to monitor the mechanical integrity of the turbines, as well as to check engine operating conditions. Actually, the temperature at the turbine inlet is the important consideration, this being the most critical of all of the engine variables. However, as has been pointed out, it is impractical to measure turbine inlet temperature in most engines. Consequently, thermocouples are inserted at the turbine discharge instead, this temperature providing a relative indication of that at the inlet. Although the temperature at this point is much lower than that at the inlet, it enables the pilot to maintain surveillance over engine internal operating conditions.

Several thermocouples are normally used, spaced at intervals around the perimeter of the engine exhaust duct near the turbine exit. The exhaust gas temperature indicator in the aircraft shows the average of the temperatures measured by the individual thermocouples. The readings of the several thermocouples can usually also be obtained individually during ground engine maintenance by the use of a selective switch. The spread between the lowest and the highest thermocouple reading is useful in maintenance because it serves to indicate the presence of hot or cold spots in the engine exhaust pattern which may mean that something is wrong inside the engine.

(c) 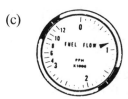 **Fuel Flow Indicator** – The fuel flow indicator shows the fuel flow to the fuel nozzles in pounds (or kilograms) per hour. Fuel flow is of fundamental interest for monitoring inflight fuel consumption, for checking engine performance, and for inflight cruise control. The relationship of abnormal fuel flow to the readings of the other instruments will provide one of the best indications of the probable cause of an engine malfunction.

(d)  **Oil Pressure Indicator** – To guard against engine failures resulting from inadequate lubrication and cooling of the various engine parts, the oil supply to critical areas must be monitored. The oil pressure indicator shows the pressure relayed by the oil pressure transmitter. On most installations, the oil pressure transmitter takes breather pressure into consideration, relaying the true pressure drop across the oil jets in the oil system.

(e) 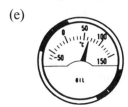 **Oil Inlet Temperature Indicator** – The ability of the engine oil to perform its job of lubricating and cooling is a function of the temperature of the oil, as well as the amount of oil supplied to the critical areas. An oil inlet temperature indicator is frequently provided to show the temperature of the oil as it enters the engine bearing compartments. Oil inlet temperature also serves as an indication of proper operation of the engine oil cooler.

(f)  **Fuel Inlet Pressure Indicator** – Fuel system characteristics frequently make it advisable to monitor the fuel pump inlet pressure. In case of fuel flow stoppage in flight, it is desirable to determine whether trouble has developed in the engine or in the aircraft fuel system, so that prompt corrective action may be taken. In addition, the fuel pump inlet pressure will indicate possible cavitation at the fuel pump inlet in flight, and will show during engine ground checks whether or not the fuel system is operating properly.

(g) **Air Temperature Indicator** – The air temperature indications currently used in aircraft are free air temperature (FAT), outside (OAT), ram (RAT), total (TAT) and static air temperature (SAT). Regardless of which temperature is instrumented in a specific aircraft model, the Flight Manual will show how to use it, in conjunction with applicable charts or tables, to set the EPR values which provide rated thrust levels. The EPR setting varies with the thrust level desired and with the true total air temperature existing at the front of the engine. (T_{t2}). Some aircraft have instrumentation which indicates T_{t2} values that may be used without correction to determine EPR settings.

Except for an indicator to measure engine thrust, the above represents the minimum instrumentation considered adequate for control of the engine. Some installations may have additional instruments.

(h) Engine Thrust Indication
The subject of the means by which a pilot sets and monitors the thrust produced by the engines installed in his aircraft has been mentioned a number of times in the foregoing text. The following repeats what has been said earlier as well as discussing thrust indication in detail.

  On some engines, engine rpm and exhaust gas temperature (EGT), are used together for indicating and setting thrust on an engine installed in an aircraft. In such cases, the full rated thrust of the engine for take-off is obtained by the pilot at 100 per cent rpm and a specified EGT. The specified EGT is established on a thrust-measuring ground test stand by varying the exhaust nozzle area of the engine as necessary to achieve the desired temperature.

 On some centrifugal compressor engines, thrust is indicated by rpm alone, and full rated thrust for take-off is obtained when the tachometer reads 100 per cent.

Virtually all axial flow turbojets and turbofans, military and commercial, use engine pressure ratio (EPR) as a measure of engine thrust. EPR indicators compare the total turbine discharge pressure to the total pressure of the air entering the compressor, then indicate the ratio of these pressures. Engines instrumented for EPR have a fixed exhaust nozzle area. Two fixed areas are used on afterburning engines, one for non-afterburning operation and the other for afterburning operation.

For engines with a fixed nozzle area, the actual exhaust gas temperatures obtained during operation are usually below the prescribed limits, as shown by Fig. 11-1. Although it is permissible for an engine to operate at the temperature limit for any given thrust rating, an engine that does so may have something wrong which causes the engine to run abnormally hot.

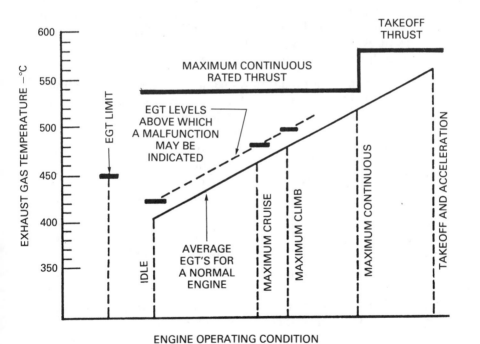

Figure 11–1 Exhaust Gas Temperature Limits for Typical Commercial Engine.

With the exception noted in para (a), engine rpm is considered a very poor parameter for setting and checking engine thrust on axial flow turbojet and turbofan engines having fixed exhaust nozzle areas. Many complications arise when rpm is utilised as the controlling variable on such engines. The most important of these are:

(i) Since the high pressure compressor rpm on dual axial flow engines, or the rpm of the whole compressor on single compressor engines, is governed by the fuel control, rpm does not provide an accurate means of determining whether or not the complete engine is functioning properly. As an example, rpm will not enable an engine operator to detect a damaged or dirty compressor unless rpm is carefully used in conjunction with other engine variables such as fuel flow, exhaust gas temperature, and engine pressure ratio.

(ii) Because the engines are 'trimmed' by a fuel control adjustment to produce full rated thrust at a fixed throttle position on a standard day, rpm for any given thrust condition will vary slightly among individual engines, depending upon the engine trim speed. The variation in rpm must be taken into consideration whenever rpm is used to measure the thrust being developed by the engine. This introduces a complication which cannot be tolerated whenever precise thrust settings are necessary during flight.

(iii) On dual compressor axial flow engines, one per cent variation in rpm results in approximately four per cent variation in thrust at the higher thrust settings for the low pressure compressor (N_1), and five per cent variation for the high pressure compressor (N_2), whereas one per cent variation in turbine discharge pressure or engine pressure ratio results in only one and one half per cent variation in thrust. The five per cent variation in thrust for one per cent variation in rpm also holds true for single compressor axial flow engines.

(iv) Rpm does not vary in direct proportion to the thrust being produced by the engine over the entire thrust range.

For these reasons some manufacturers recommend that turbine discharge pressure, or engine pressure ratio, be used as the engine variable for indicating thrust on axial flow engines with fixed area exhaust nozzles. The use of either of these is not only much simpler under most conditions than the use of rpm for engines of this type, but is considerably more accurate as well.

11.4 Instrumentation for Measuring Thrust (and Power for Turboprops).

For engines other than those using fully variable exhaust nozzles, turbine discharge pressure or engine pressure ratio can be used to indicate or set engine thrust because they vary proportionally to the thrust the engine is developing. Most turbojet- and turbofan-powered aircraft today are instrumented for engine pressure ratio, and this is the parameter generally used to set or measure engine thrust during take-off, climb and cruise. For very accurate thrust measurement, such as during ground trimming of an engine, turbine discharge pressure is often employed to measure thrust. In such cases, it is common practice temporarily to connect a turbine discharge pressure indicator to the engine for the duration of the engine trim run.

This is how the two methods of engine pressure measurement function:

Turbine Discharge Pressure Indicator – This instrument indicates the internal engine pressure upstream of the jet nozzle, immediately aft of the last stage of the turbine (P_{t5} or P_{t7}), and serves as an indication of the pressure available across the nozzle to generate thrust. Turbine discharge pressure must be used in conjunction with T_{t2} and P_{t2}, as will be explained later.

11.5 Engine Pressure Ratio Indicator.

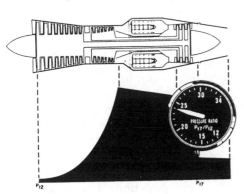

This instrument indicates the engine pressure ratio as a measure of the thrust being developed by the engine. This is the ratio of the turbine discharge total pressure to the equivalent of the compressor inlet total pressure (P_{t5}/P_{t2} or P_{t7}/P_{t2}). Values for P_{t2} must be corrected for inlet duct loss on the engine pressure ratio curves or charts by the aircraft manufacturer. Therefore, both for static (ie take-off) and flight use, the actual value for P_{t2} will vary among different aircraft types and models because of installation effects. However, the relation of P_{t2} at the engine face to both P_{am} for static conditions and for P_{am} plus P, (the pressure due to ram) in flight is determined during early flight testing for each aircraft model, and is used thereafter as the reference pressure for P_{t5}/P_{t2} or P_{t7}/P_{t2}. The true (field) barometric pressure on the take-off runway is P_{am} and P_{am} plus P, is equivalent to total pressure at, or near, the compressor inlet when airborne. Because it is inadvisable to instrument the compressor inlet directly for P_{t2}, the P_{t2} sensor for the pressure ratio indicator may be placed at some other location on the aircraft, preferably as near the engine air inlet as possible. When the appropriate corrections have been made to the inflight charts in the aircraft Flight or Operation Manual, any rated thrust, or percentage of rated thrust, in terms of engine pressure ratio may be set with the aircraft throttle as a function of the total air temperature of T_{t2}.

Because the thrust developed by the engine is indicated by the pressure ratio between the pressure at the engine air inlet and the discharge pressure at the jet nozzle, turbine discharge pressure, by itself, should not be used directly as an accurate indication of the engine output. Compressor inlet pressure (P_{t2}) must be taken into account on curves or charts whenever turbine discharge pressure alone is instrumented on the aircraft. For static engine operation this will usually be accomplished by showing barometric pressure, corrected for inlet duct loss, rather than P_{t2} values on the curves or charts. Inflight curves or tables will usually show airspeed and altitude and this will eliminate the need for virtually delineating P_{t2} values in the operating data. Engine pressure ratio indicators have the P_{t2} value introduced into the system, automatically taking this factor into account on the observed instrument reading.

Torquemeter (Turboprop Engines) – Because only a small part of the propulsive force produced by a turboprop is due to jet thrust, neither turbine discharge pressure nor engine pressure ratio is used to indicate the power being produced by the engine. Instead, a torquemeter is employed to measure the level of shaft power that the engine is developing both on the ground and in flight. As the method of measuring torque varies, the engine Maintenance Manual should be consulted for a description of the manner in which a particular torquemeter system functions. In most systems, however, torquemeter oil pressure is used to actuate a torque indicating instrument in the aircraft. The torquemeter instrument portrays torquemeter oil pressure (which is proportional to engine power) in pounds per square inch (psi). Some torquemeter instruments are calibrated to read in terms of pound-feet (lb-ft) of torque, and some may read in shaft horsepower (SHP), directly.

11.6   Related Terms.

c_p, c_v — Specific heats at constant pressure and volume

C — Coefficient or constant

ESHP — Equivalent shaft horsepower (turboprop)

ESFC — Equivalent specific fuel consumption (turboprop)

F_g — Gross thrust (lb)

F_{11} — Net thrust (lb)

g — Acceleration due to gravity, and mass conversion factor, 32.174

k, γ — Gamma – ratio of specific heats (c_p, c_v)

M — Mach number (velocity of airspeed divided by the speed of sound at the appropriate air temperature)

N — Compressor speed (rpm or per cent) for a single compressor engine

N_1 — Speed (rpm or per cent) of the low pressure compressor of a dual compressor engine, or the compressor speed (rpm or per cent) of a single compressor engine equipped with a free turbine.

N_2 — Speed (rpm or per cent) of the high pressure compressor of a dual compressor engine, or the free turbine speed (rpm or per cent) of a single compressor engine equipped with a free turbine.

N_3 — Free turbine speed (rpm or per cent) of a dual compressor engine equipped with a free turbine.

NOTE: The symbols, N_g and N_f, are sometimes used to represent rpm for a free-turbine-type, turboprop or turboshaft engine. N_g is the symbol for the speed of the basic engine, or gas generator. N_f is the speed of the free turbine, or power turbine, as it is often called.

P — Absolute pressure (gauge pressure plus atmospheric pressure – psia)

p — Gauge pressure (psig)

T — Absolute temperature (°R or °K)

t — Temperature (°F or °C)

V — Velocity (usually in ft/sec)

v — Volume (in appropriate units)

W — Weight (usually in lb)

w — Rate of flow (gas, such as air, or liquid, such as fuel, usually in lb/sec or lb/hr)

Δ (Delta) — Difference or change (ie ΔP represents a pressure difference, such as one between the two sides of a fuel filter) δ (Delta)   —   Standard correction factor for pressure (relative absolute pressure)

η (Eta)   —   Efficiency

θ (Theta)   —   Standard correction factor for temperature (relative absolute temperature)

ρ (Rho)   —   Density

The subscripts used with a number of the above letters and symbols more accurately define the quantity in each case. The Engine Station subscripts listed below simply show at what point in the engine each quantity is being taken. For example, P_{t2} means total (t) absolute pressure (P) taken at Station 7 in the engine.

Key Points – Gas Turbines

Theory

1   Charles' Law states that a volume of a given mass of gas at constant pressure is proportional to its absolute temperature.

2   If the volume of a mass of air is 546 cubic feet at 1°C, it will be 2 cubic feet smaller at 0°C.

3   Adiabatic gas compression means there is no external loss or gain of heat.

4   A nozzle is choked when the gas flow through it is sonic and can give additional thrust.

5   A turbojet engine is smooth-running, because it has no reciprocating parts.

6   Gas turbine efficiency increases with increasing altitude.

7   The performance of the turbojet engine is measured by the thrust produced at the propelling nozzle.

8   The power developed by a gas turbine engine depends on the mass airflow through the engine.

9   The propulsive thrust of a gas turbine is produced by the reaction to the acceleration of a stream of gas (Newton's Third Law).

10   As aircraft speed increases, propulsive efficiency increases, due to ram effect. (Total head pressure).

11   As altitude increases, fuel flow is less because of decreased air density.

12   On a cold day, the engine performance will produce higher thrust and lower TGT than on a hot day.

13   With the aircraft stationary and full power selected, thrust is 100% and propulsive efficiency is ZERO.

14   Combustion takes place at a constant pressure.

15   During the working cycle, combustion takes place continuously.

16   A by-pass engine is an engine in which a proportion of the compressor air is not used for combustion purposes.

17   Air enters the engine through a divergent duct (air intake) where the velocity decreases and the pressure increases.

18   A by-pass ratio of 0.7 to 1 means 0.7 by-pass air to 1 part passing through the HP compressor.

19   The sequence of events in a gas turbine is induction, compression, combustion, expansion and exhaust.

20   The power required to drive the compressor and components is approximately 60% of the energy available after combustion.

21   At a constant temperature, if the volume of a gas is halved, the pressure is doubled.

22   A by-pass engine will give improved propulsive efficiency and specific fuel consumption.

23   High by-pass ratio engines have a lower SFC, because there is a lower jet pipe velocity which increases propulsive efficiency.

Construction

Compressors/Intakes

1   Compression ratio is the ratio between compressor inlet pressure and compressor outlet pressure.

2   Stator blades on an axial flow compressor convert kinetic energy to pressure energy.

3   Inlet guide vanes (IGVs) reduce the possibility of compressor stall, by guiding the intake air on to the first stage of rotor blades at the correct angle.

4   Bleed valves are open at low rpm to bleed off some compressor air, to reduce the possibility of a surge.

5   In a twin-spool engine, the LP and HP compressors are driven by their respective turbines, the LP running at a lower speed than the HP.

6   Cascade vanes are used to change the direction of the airflow off the centrifugal compressor/diffuser ring into the combustion chamber.

7   Air conditioning/pressurisation air and anti-icing air are taken from the compressor.

8   In the duct between the compressor and combustion chamber, the velocity decreases and pressure increases (Highest pressure in engine).

9   Compressor blades are twisted to give the correct angle of incidence along the blade in relation to its speed.

10   Compressor blades become shorter towards the rear of the compressor, to maintain axial velocity as the pressure increases.

11   The purpose of the rotating guide vanes on a centrifugal compressor is to direct the air smoothly into the impeller.

12   The most efficient engine air intake on subsonic or low supersonic aircraft is the pitot type.

13   Intakes are designed to decelerate the free airstream flow.

14   A complete 'stage' of an axial flow compressor consists of one rotor and one stator.

15   Stator vanes are often shrouded, to minimise vibration.

16   Vibration monitors filter out low frequency vibration and measure vibration in Relative Amplitude.

17   The vibration transducer feeds directly into the gauge in the cockpit.

Turbines/Exhaust Assembly

1   Nozzle guide vanes (NGVs) are fitted to accelerate the gas flow and direct it onto the turbine at the correct angle of attack.

2   Across the turbines, velocity, pressure and temperature decrease.

3   Turbine blade creep is a product of heat and centrifugal force.

4   A tight fit between the turbine disc and blades is ensured by centrifugal force and blade compression loads.

5   Turbine gas temperature (TGT) is measured as an indication of turbine serviceability.

6   The top temperature control protects the turbine blades from over-heating, by reducing the fuel supply to the burners.

7   A free turbine is one which is not connected to a compressor, only an output drive.

8   The gas enters the jet pipe from the turbine at a velocity of 650 to 1,200 ft/sec (Mach 0.5).

9   The effect of increasing the area of the jet (propelling) nozzle would be a decrease in thrust.

10   In a turboprop engine, most of the energy extracted at the turbine is used to drive the propeller, leaving only a small amount of residual thrust.

11   The jet pipe is insulated from the airframe by a combination of cooling air and insulation material.

12   In a modular constructed engine, certain components can be changed between overhauls, increasing time between overhauls, thereby reducing maintenance and overhaul costs.

13   Turbine blade tips often have shrouds fitted, to reduce gas leakage across the blade tips.

14   If a thermocouple in the exhaust assembly goes U/S, then the EGT gauge will read lower.

15   Thermocouples do NOT need an electrical supply.

Combustion Chambers

1   In the combustion chamber, the pressure remains constant and combustion is self-supporting.

2   The chemically correct mixture ratio of air to fuel is 15:1, but the overall air/fuel ratio can vary between 45:1 and 130:1 during normal running conditions.

3   The highest temperature, of approximately 2,000°C, is experienced in the combustion zone.

4   A swirl vane is fitted in the nose of the flame tube around the burner head and its function is to anchor and stabilise the flame.

5   A toroidal vortex is a region in the combustion chamber of low velocity recirculation which anchors and stabilises the flame.

6   Air is directed to the shroud around the burner head, to minimise carbon formation.

7   Approximately 20% of the compressor air is taken by the snout of the flame tube.

Systems

Fuel Systems

1   The LP cock isolates the airframe fuel system from the engine fuel system, to enable maintenance to be carried out.

2   The LP cock should not be used to shut down the engine, because the fuel pump and other fuel components would run dry.

3   The LP cock would be turned off in the event of a crash, to minimise the possibility of an engine fire.

4   The danger of ice formation in the fuel system filters is reduced by using a heating system or a fuel cooled oil cooler.

5   When the engine is stopped, the fuel pump servo-piston spring will put the pump to maximum stroke.

6   If the swashplate (yoke) of the fuel pump is perpendicular to the axis of the pump drive shaft, the flow will be minimum.

7   The maximum rpm of the engine is affected by the specific gravity of the fuel, ie, higher SG – lower max rpm.

8   The hydro-mechanical governor which controls maximum engine rpm is unaffected by the SG of the fuel.

9   The barometric pressure control (BPC) varies the fuel flow to the burners by means of spill valves which are adjusted by changes in aircraft speed, altitude and throttle position.

10   Attenuators are fitted in the flow control unit (FCU), to damp out pressure surges.

11   The accelerator control unit (ACU) is fitted to limit the rate of fuel flow increase during acceleration, to correspond with mass airflow through the engine.

12   The ACU will prevent stalling and surging during fast accelerations.

13   The pressure control system and the proportional flow control system are both hydro-mechanical.

14 The combined acceleration and speed control system and the pressure ratio control system are both mechanical systems.

15 The pressure ratio control system uses a gear type fuel pump.

16 The gas turbine is stopped by closing the HP cock.

17 The top temperature control protects the turbine blades by reducing the fuel flow to the burners when critical TGTs are reached.

18 The maximum engine rpm of a pressure ratio control system is controlled by an auxiliary throttle valve which partially closes, opening the pressure drop spill valve, which reduces the fuel flow to the spray nozzles.

19 Governor creep is indicated during a climb by increasing rpm.

20 Idling rpm would be lower on a cold day, because of increased mass airflow, unless compensated by the fuel control unit (FCU).

21 Flight idle rpm will be lower at low altitude and higher at high altitude, unless controlled by the FCU.

Lubrication, Cooling and Sealing, Reverse Thrust

1 The type of oil used in a gas turbine is synthetic, anti-freeze, low viscosity and has a high flash point.

2 The scavenge pump has a greater capacity than the pressure pumps, but the pressure pump provides a higher pressure.

3 The return oil is filtered by a scavenge filter.

4 To give early warning of bearing failure, magnetic chip detectors are fitted in scavenge lines.

5 Reverse thrust is used to reduce aircraft speed after landing, by changing the direction of the exhaust gas flow.

6 Cascade vanes are fitted in reverse thrust systems, to reduce airflow turbulence and guide the exhaust gases forward.

7 Reverse thrust should not be engaged at low aircraft speed, because of the danger of ingestion of hot exhaust gases into the intake.

8 Reverse thrust cannot be engaged unless the engine is at idle.

9 An interstage seal is used to form controlled restriction to the passage of air or gas.

10 Oil is prevented from leaking by seals and air pressure.

Starting and Ignition

1   The starting sequence of an electric engine starter is normally terminated by a time switch.

2   During the starting sequence, light-up should take place at 17.5% rpm.

3   When light-up takes place, interconnectors spread the flame to adjacent flame tubes.

4   Self-sustaining rpm is the lowest speed at which the engine will run independently of external help.

5   Iso-propyl-nitrate (AVPIN) is a mono-fuel.

6   Combustion is initiated by igniter plugs.

7   The reason for igniter plug gaps being larger than those of conventional spark plugs is due to lower operating pressures in the flame tube.

8   High energy ignition is used to make relighting at altitude more reliable.

9   To test a high energy igniter plug, listen for a 'crack' when the relight switch is pressed.

10 The expression 'relighting' means restarting an engine in flight after a flame-out.

11 A choke is fitted to an ignition unit to extend the duration of the electrical discharge across the plug.

12 The discharge resistor is fitted to dissipate any residual stored energy in the unit within one minute of the system being switched off.

13 The high energy ignition system provides ignition by using capacitors in the unit.

14 During flight in heavy rain, igniters are set to ON and give a low capacity discharge all the time.

15 High energy igniter systems receive a low voltage which builds up to give high energy discharge.

Ice Protection, Thrust Augmentation and Fire Protection

1   In an electrical system of ice protection, the heating elements operate part-continuously and part-intermittently (turboprop).

2　　The use of engine anti-icing is recommended when there is visible moisture and the OAT is below +10°C.

3　　Anti-icing air is normally taken from the compressor and, when functioning, will increase TGT.

4　　Water injection is used to restore thrust in high ambient temperatures and/or at high altitude airfields.

5　　Water/methanol or water sprayed into a gas turbine will restore thrust by evaporating and cooling the air, thus increasing mass airflow.

6　　Methanol in the water/methanol injection system also acts as an anti-freeze.

7　　In case of fire, the cool zone of a gas turbine is maintained at a higher pressure than the hot zone.

8　　To indicate the relieving of a fire extinguisher due to excessive thermal expansion, plastic indicators in the fuselage skin would be blown out.

9　　A 'two-shot' fire extinguishing system is one where two fire extinguishers can be discharged into an engine bay.

10　　The correct procedure for dealing with an engine fire is: silence the warning bell, shut-down the engine and operate the fire extinguisher.

11　　For fire detection, the continuous wire type detector uses the principle that, with an increase in temperature, the resistance will DECREASE until the circuit is made and the warning light comes on.

12　　If capacitance is used instead of resistance in continuous wire type detectors, the capacitance will INCREASE with increase in temperature.

13　　A manual test of the engine fire warning system will give a steady red light.

14　　If the fire warning light were to come on in flight, it would give a continuous red light.

15　　Fire extinguisher discharge lasts from .5 to 2 seconds.

16　　Turbojet uses hot air for anti-icing. Turboprop uses electrical de-icing.

Ground Handling

1   Jet aircraft are positioned into wind for ground runs, to prevent the re-entry of hot gases into the air intake.

2   If jet pipe resonance is experienced on start-up, the HP cock should be partially closed and then opened fully immediately the resonance stops.

3   A 'hung' start occurs when the engine lights up, but fails to accelerate.

4   When ground running at high rpm, the throttle should be closed slowly and the engine allowed to idle before shutting down, to allow the engine to cool down and relieve thermal stresses.

5   'Run-down' time is the time taken for an engine to stop after the HP cock is closed.

6   Gas turbine pressure ratio (EPR) is the ratio of the jet pipe pressure to the compressor inlet pressure.

7   Reduction in engine efficiency could by caused by ice formation in the intake.

8   Compressor run-down time is dependent upon the freedom of the compressor, turbines and engine-driven accessories.

9   Heavy tropical rain at high ambient temperatures may require the use of ignitors during take-off.

10   A 'hung' start is accompanied by a low fuel flow and a high EGT.

12

The Modern Gas Turbine Engine

12.1 Introduction.

The progressive demand for greater efficiency, economy and quieter engines has produced a number of variations of the basic gas turbine engine.

Few commercial aircraft are powered by a conventional turbojet as discussed in previous chapters. The majority now use by-pass engines or turboprops. The following listed engines are the main types in use at the present time:

12.2 Turbojet.

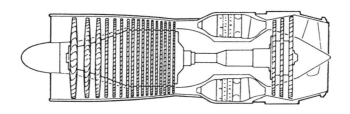

Figure 12–1 Single-Spool Axial Flow Turbojet.

The example shown is a single-spool engine having one compressor driven by a turbine via a single common drive shaft. The compressor is therefore rotating at exactly the same rpm as the turbine.

At low rpm this engine is very prone to stall and surge and generally requires devices such as compressor bleeds (interstage bleeds) and dump valves to avoid or reduce the compressor stall tendencies.

12.3   Twin-Spool By-pass Turbojet (Low By-pass).

The compressor of this engine is in two parts, a low pressure compressor consisting of four stages at the front of the unit. These are driven by the rearmost set of turbines via a common drive shaft. Aft of the Low Pressure compressor is the High Pressure compressor which is separately driven by the high pressure turbine (located in front of the low pressure turbine) via its own concentric drive shaft. Each spool is able to rotate independently of the other and thereby allows compressor pressure to be increased at a much steadier rate so that stall tendencies are much reduced.

The low pressure compressor of this engine supplies air to the core, or hot engine, as well as to the by-pass duct. This permits a much lighter construction and produces a greater power-to-weight ratio. The by-pass ratio is 1 to 1, ie the output of the low pressure compressor is divided equally between the by-pass duct and the core engine.

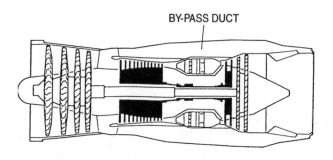

BY-PASS DUCT

Figure 12–2 Twin-Spool By-Pass Turbojet (low by-pass ratio).

12.4   Triple-Spool By-pass Turbojet (High By-pass)

This engine type has three spools, that is, the compressor is in three stages each driven by its own dedicated turbine assembly.

From front to rear of the engines the compressors are: low pressure compressor, intermediate compressor and high pressure compressor.

Low Pressure Compressor.
This consists of the Large Front Fan which, in general terms, delivers 5 parts of air through the by-pass duct for every part delivered to the intermediate compressor and core, or hot, engine. The by-pass ratio of this engine is thus 5:1.

Most of the thrust produced by this engine is developed by the Low Pressure compressor or Large Front Fan. It should be noted, however,

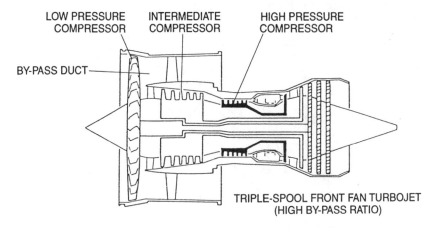

LOW PRESSURE COMPRESSOR INTERMEDIATE COMPRESSOR HIGH PRESSURE COMPRESSOR

BY-PASS DUCT

TRIPLE-SPOOL FRONT FAN TURBOJET
(HIGH BY-PASS RATIO)

Figure 12–3.

that for a given mass flow through the engine a pure turbojet (single spool) will produce more thrust than a High by-pass engine. Remember Thrust = Mass × acceleration.

Intermediate and High Pressure Compressors.
These compressor assemblies further raise the total core engine pressure prior to the combustion process.

Primary Advantages of the High By-pass Turbojet.

(a) Because the compression ratios are lower, the compressor assemblies can be made much lighter in weight. Engine for engine a High by-pass engine may be as much as 10% lighter and therefore has a better power-to-weight ratio.

(b) Whilst the air mass velocity is lower it is, however, produced across a much wider area.

(c) Fuel consumption is much improved, so the engine is more economic.

(d) As mass velocity is less, the engine is much quieter.

The accompanying graph plots the comparisons.

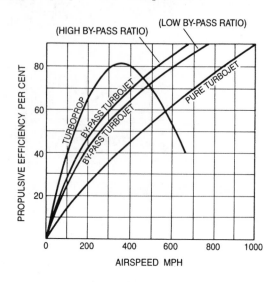

At aircraft speeds below approximately 450 miles per hour, the pure jet engine is less efficient than a propeller-type engine, since its propulsive efficiency depends largely on its forward speed; the pure turbojet engine is, therefore, most suitable for high forward speeds. Propeller efficiency, however, decreases rapidly above 350 miles per hour due to the disturbance of the airflow caused by the high tip speeds of the propeller. These characteristics have led to some departure from the use of pure turbojet propulsion in favour of the turboprop combinations of propeller and gas turbine where aircraft operate at medium speeds.

The advantages of the propeller/turbine combination have to some extent been offset by the introduction of the by-pass, ducted fan and propfan engines. These engines deal with larger comparative airflows and lower jet velocities than the pure jet engine, thus having a propulsive efficiency which is comparable to that of the turboprop and at the same time permitting higher flight speeds.

In a high by-pass gas turbine engine when the Engine Indication and Crew Alerting System is used, the following abbreviations are employed:

LARGE FRONT FAN (LOW PRESSURE COMPRESSOR)	N1
INTERMEDIATE COMPRESSOR	N2
HIGH PRESSURE COMPRESSOR	N3

Note: Cold air thrust reversal is used by this type of engine as described earlier.

12.5 Twin-spool turboshaft (With Free Power Turbine)

This type of engine may be used as a small turboprop or, more commonly, to power helicopters. There are a number of interesting points to note about this engine:

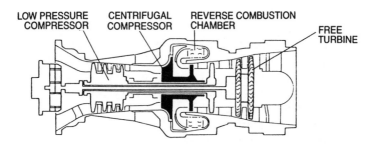

Figure 12–4 Twin-Spool Turbo-Shaft
(with free-power turbine).

Firstly, the second, or high pressure, compressor is of centrifugal type therefore enabling the air from the low pressure compressor to be turned through 90° whilst increasing the pressure. Secondly, the air is then directed into the combustion chamber where it again reverses its flow direction before once more turning through 180° to pass through the high and low pressure turbines. This reverse flow through the combustion stage enables the engine to be much shorter.

The number of spools employed in an engine will vary to suit design requirements. Layout of components will also vary. The engines chosen in this chapter are intended only as examples and are based mostly on Rolls-Royce designs.

12.6 Engine Indication and Crew Alerting System (EICAS).

This modern electronic form of indicating engine and other automatic system information is covered in the ELECTRICS volume of this series (Volume 3), together with the ECAM system. Both of these systems provide engine performance information.

In general Boeing aircraft are equipped with EICAS and Airbus aircraft with ECAM. The following is a basic EICAS system as used in Boeing 757 and 767 aircraft.

12.7 EICAS – Primary and Secondary Engine Displays.

1 General
EICAS has been designed to categorize alerts and displays according to function and use. This has resulted in three modes of display: Operational, Status and Maintenance.

2 Operational Mode
The Operational Mode displays those engine parameters and crew alerts required in flight, and provides continuous monitoring of aircraft and engine systems.

The upper display is dedicated to primary engine parameters, and crew alerts for monitoring by the crew. The lower display is showing secondary engine parameters.

At power-up all engine parameters appear automatically.

3 Status Mode
The status mode displays data needed by the crew to determine the readiness of the airplane for dispatch, and is closely associated with the minimum equipment list (MEL). The status mode displays control surface position, selected sub-system parameters, and systems/equipment status messages. The status mode is manually selected and shown on the lower display.

4 Maintenance Modes
The maintenance modes display maintenance information to aid the ground crew in troubleshooting and verification testing of the major subsystems. The maintenance modes are manually selected and shown on the lower display.

5 Cathode Ray Tube Display Features
Cathode ray tube displays seven colours defined as follows:

White — General colour used for all scales, normal operating range of pointers digital readouts, digital readout boxes.

Red — Used for warning messages, redline limit on scales, exceedance condition for pointers, digital readouts, and digital readout boxes.

Green — Use for thrust mode readout and EPR/N1 target cursor.

Blue — Not used for any EICAS displays, (displayed during EICAS test only.)

Yellow — Used for caution and advisory messages, yellow band on scales, yellow band condition for pointer, digital readouts, and digital readout boxes.

Magenta
(Pink) — Used for in flight start envelope, windmilling cursor, and cross bleed messages.

Cyan
(Blue) — Used for all parameter names, status cue, and total air temperature name.

Background colour is black.

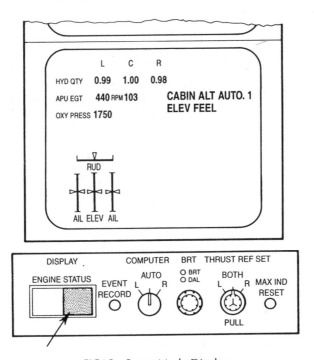

EICAS—Status Mode Display.

12.8 EICAS – Status Mode Display

1 General

Status mode displays provides data needed by the crew to determine the readiness of the aircraft for dispatch and are closely associated with the Minimum Equipment List (MEL).

12.9 Display

The status mode can be displayed on the lower CRT and is manually selected by the crew using the display select panel status switch. The display shows control surface position, selected subsystems parameters, and system/equipment status messages. This is done manually on the ground, as part of pre-flight check of dispatch items. Use of the status mode in flight can be useful in anticipating possible ground maintenance actions. For this purpose, a STATUS cue is provided on the upper left corner of the lower CRT whenever a change is status messages occurs and the STATUS page is not displayed.

The systems status message(s) are displayed on the right section of the page.

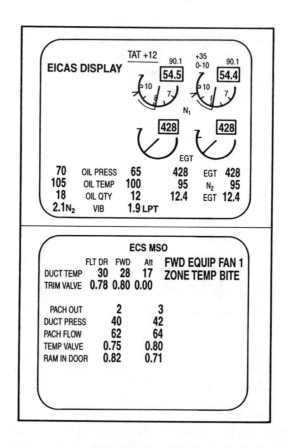

EICAS Display – Maintenance Mode – ECS/MSG
Format in Real Time.

12.10 EICAS – Maintenance Mode Display – ECS/MSG Format in Real Time

1 General

The maintenance mode displays are designed to provide a flight deck display of maintenance information for the convenience of flight crew when making post-flight logbook entries, and to aid the ground crew in troubleshooting and verification testing of the major subsystems. They are also used to record system parameters at the time of an in-flight fault, for later readout on the ground. These formats are not available to the crew in flight unless a by-pass switch option is selected by the airlines, to allow monitoring of the maintenance mode display on non-revenue flights.

2 Environmental Control Systems/Messages – Display

The ECS/MSG page format is one of five maintenance mode displays that can be selected on the maintenance control panel and displayed

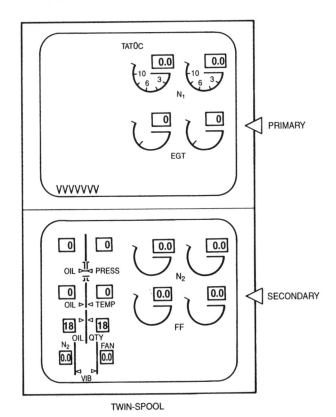

TWIN-SPOOL

EICAS—Primary and Secondary Engine Display.

on the lower CRT, in place of the secondary engine parameters or status display. This format provides parameters of the aircycle cooling pack and the zone temperature control system. It also provides maintenance messages for all aircraft systems on the upper right corner of the display.

Any time a maintenance page is displayed, the upper CRT operates in compact full format.

3 Maintenance Messages

All the maintenance messages (M) can appear on the ECS/MSG format page only when this format is selected. These messages, white in colour, are for most cases a repeat of the status messages displayed on the status format.

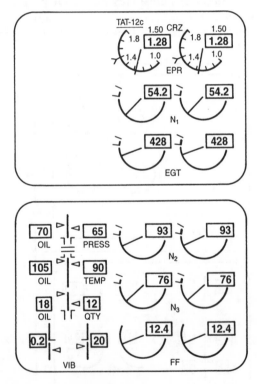

TRIPLE-SPOOL

At power-up, all engine parameters appear automatically.

EICAS—Standby Engine Indicator (SEI).

2.11 Standby Engine Indicator (SEI)

General
The Standby Engine Indicator displays in digital readout all critical engine parameters.
    The values on the left and right of the display are safe limit decals.

EICAS – Display Select Panel – Controls
Primary unit for both pilots to control EICAS functions and displays.
All the controls on this panel can be used in flight and on the ground.

1   Engine Display Switch
    A momentary push switch used to remove or display secondary engine parameters on the lower display unit.

2   Status Display Switch
    A momentary push switch used to display (on the lower display unit) control surface positions, hydraulic fluid quantity; crew oxygen pressure, APU engine gas temperature, and status messages related items requiring crew awareness prior to dispatch or in flight.

3   **Event Record Switch**
A momentary push switch when used with the aircraft in the air or on the ground records all environmental control system, electrical, hydraulic, and performance/auxiliary power unit parameter data for storage in the manual event non-volatile memory.

4   **Computer Select Switch**
A three-position rotary switch for selecting display signal source. In AUTO position, left computer is primary signal source. Automatic switching to right computer occurs when left computer becomes invalid. In the L (left) position, the left computer is supplying the display signals, and in the R (right) position, the right computer is supplying display signals.

5   **Display Units Brightness Control**
Dual concentric controls with the inner control increasing brightness of both display units when rotated in the clockwise direction. The outer control increases the brightness of the upper display unit and decreases the brightness of the lower display unit when rotated in a clockwise direction. Rotating the outer control counterclockwise has the opposite effect.

6   **Thrust Reference Index Set Controls**
A dual concentric rotary switch combined with a two way push-pull switch. The inner control is continuously rotating with twelve detents per revolution. When initially set (pulled out), the readout, corresponding to the engine selector switch position, defaults to 1.55 EPR (104% N1). Clockwise rotation of the control increases the corresponding readout with a rotation sensitivity of 0.01 EPR (0.1% N1) per detent. Once a readout has been modified manually, its last input data will be retained regardless of the engine selector switch position, until the inner control is reset (pushed in). The outer control is a three-position rotary switch used to select the L (left), Both, or R (right) engine(s) indicator.

7   **Maximum Indicator Reset Switch**
A momentary push switch used to clear maximum exceedance readouts from the display unit. Only that data for which the exceedance no longer exists is cleared.

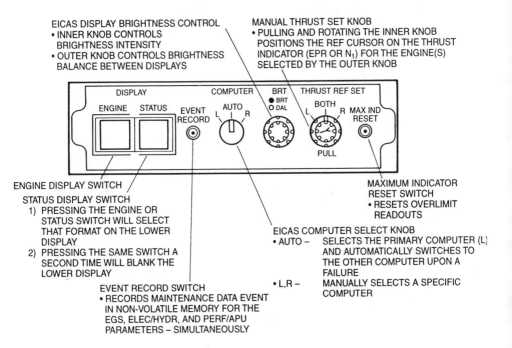

EICAS DISPLAY BRIGHTNESS CONTROL
• INNER KNOB CONTROLS
  BRIGHTNESS INTENSITY
• OUTER KNOB CONTROLS BRIGHTNESS
  BALANCE BETWEEN DISPLAYS

MANUAL THRUST SET KNOB
• PULLING AND ROTATING THE INNER KNOB
  POSITIONS THE REF CURSOR ON THE THRUST
  INDICATOR (EPR OR N₁) FOR THE ENGINE(S)
  SELECTED BY THE OUTER KNOB

ENGINE DISPLAY SWITCH
STATUS DISPLAY SWITCH
1) PRESSING THE ENGINE OR
   STATUS SWITCH WILL SELECT
   THAT FORMAT ON THE LOWER
   DISPLAY
2) PRESSING THE SAME SWITCH A
   SECOND TIME WILL BLANK THE
   LOWER DISPLAY

MAXIMUM INDICATOR
RESET SWITCH
• RESETS OVERLIMIT
  READOUTS

EICAS COMPUTER SELECT KNOB
• AUTO – SELECTS THE PRIMARY COMPUTER (L)
          AND AUTOMATICALLY SWITCHES TO
          THE OTHER COMPUTER UPON A
          FAILURE
• L,R –   MANUALLY SELECTS A SPECIFIC
          COMPUTER

EVENT RECORD SWITCH
• RECORDS MAINTENANCE DATA EVENT
  IN NON-VOLATILE MEMORY FOR THE
  EGS, ELEC/HYDR, AND PERF/APU
  PARAMETERS – SIMULTANEOUSLY

12.12 EICAS – Operational Format

1 Power Up

At power-up, all engine parameters appear automatically.

2 Status Switch

Pressing the Status switch, the lower CRT changes to the Status mode.

3 Engine Switch

Pressing the Engine switch returns the secondary engine parameters to the lower CRT.
To return to the Status mode, press Status switch again.

4 Lower CRT-Blank

The lower CRT can be turned to normal blank mode either by pressing the Status switch if the Status page is displayed, or by pressing the Engine switch if the secondary engine parameters are displayed.

5   Lower CRT from Blank to Engine or Status Display

When the lower display is BLANK, pressing the Engine switch displays Secondary engine parameters; pressing the Status switch displays Status mode.

12.13 EICAS – Alert Messages – Interface

1   General

The EICAS System monitors over 400 inputs from engine and system sensors for the generation of alert, status, and maintenance messages, depending on the urgency of the detected abnormality. Alert messages are displayed in red and yellow, and Status and Maintenance messages in white.

2   Alert Messages

There are three levels of Alert Message: warnings, cautions and advisories that are displayed on the left side of the upper CRT depending upon the urgency of the malfunction, and are displayed in parallel with individual lights in the flight compartment.

Up to 11 messages can appear on the upper CRT. If an overflow condition exists, page 1 notation replaces the eleventh line.

The following graphics explain the various Alert messages and the cancel/recall capability.

3   Status and Maintenance Messages

These messages, in white, are displayed on the lower CRT on status, or maintenance ECS/MSG page format respectively. These messages will be covered under status and LCS/MSG formats.

EICAS – Alert Message Levels - Definitions

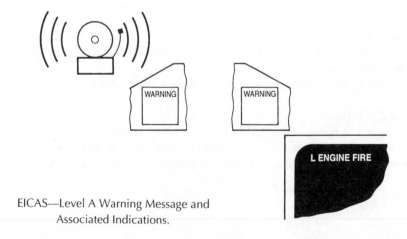

EICAS—Level A Warning Message and
Associated Indications.

A. Level A Warnings

These warnings require immediate crew corrective action. They are displayed in red on a CRT, and in red on master warning lights and panel lights. Their associated aurals sounds are: fire bell, and European sounding siren.

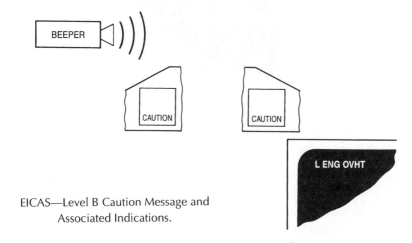

EICAS—Level B Caution Message and
Associated Indications.

B. Level B Cautions

These cautions require immediate crew awareness and future crew action. They are displayed in yellow on a CRT, and in amber on master caution lights, and panel lights. Their associated aural sound is a caution aural repeated twice.

C. Level C Advisories

These advisories require crew awareness. They are displayed in yellow on CRT and amber on panel lights.
No master caution lights and no aural tones are associated with this level.

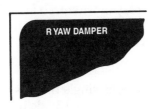

• NO AURAL TONES

• NO MASTER LIGHTS

EICAS—Level C Advisory Message.

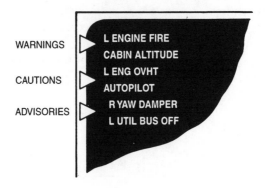

WARNINGS

▷ L ENGINE FIRE
CABIN ALTITUDE

CAUTIONS

▷ L ENG OVHT
AUTOPILOT

ADVISORIES

▷ R YAW DAMPER
L UTIL BUS OFF

EICAS–Alert Messages Overview.

12.14 EICAS – Master Caution Lights/Cancel and Recall Switches

1 Master Caution Lights
Single action light switch displays an amber message CAUTION when illuminated by EICAS computer in conjunction with a caution message displayed on the upper CRT.
Pressing either light switch turns both lights off.
Lamp replaced by removing lens cover.

2 Cancel and Recall Switches
These switches are associated with the alert messages (caution and advisory only) that can be displayed on the upper CRT.

A. Cancel Switch
Momentary push, single pole, single throw switch.
When activated provides less than +3v dc to EICAS computer and removes caution and advisory messages currently displayed, or paging capability to display those stored in memory that are in excess of the eleven message combinations currently displayed.
Warnings are not cancellable.

B. Recall Switch
Momentary push, single pole, single throw switch.
When activated provides less than +3v dc to EICAS computer.
Re-displays the caution and advisory messages removed by cancel switch.

Practice Paper 1

1. On leaving the compressor, the air:

    (a)   passes into the primary zone of the combustion chamber.

    (b)   passes through the diffuser.

    (c)   passes into the primary and secondary zone of the combustion chamber.

    (d)   passes into the swirl assembly of the combustion chamber.

Ref. 1.3

2. Fuel, on entering the combustion chamber, is primarily atomised by:

    (a)   the swirl vanes.

    (b)   the diffuser.

    (c)   the dilution holes.

    (d)   the burner feed.

Ref. 1.3

3. The diffuser after the compressor:

    (a)   converts the velocity energy into pressure energy.

    (b)   converts the pressure energy into velocity energy.

    (c)   straightens the airflow.

    (d)   creates a swirl effect in the airflow.

Ref. 1.3

4. In a basic turbojet engine, of the total energy produced, approximately:

    (a)   60% leaves the engine as thrust.

    (b)   40% leaves the engine as thrust.

    (c)   90% leaves the engine as thrust.

    (d)   25% leaves the engine as thrust.

Ref. 1.3

5. At subsonic speeds, a turbojet engine requires:

   (a)   a convergent intake.

   (b)   a variable intake.

   (c)   a convergent/divergent intake.

   (d)   a divergent intake.

Ref. 1.8

6. The compressor is:

   (a)   rotated by free stream air.

   (b)   driven by the inlet guide vanes.

   (c)   driven by an electric motor.

   (d)   driven by the turbine.

Ref. 1.3

7. A basic centrifugal compressor, generally produces a pressure ratio of:

   (a)   4 to 4.5 to one.

   (b)   30 to one

   (c)   130 to one.

   (d)   15 to one.

Ref. 2.4

8. Modern centrifugal compressors produce a balance of air compression between that done by the impeller, and that done by the diffuser as approximately:

   (a)   20% to 80%.

   (b)   40% to 60%.

   (c)   50% to 50%.

   (d)   10% to 90%.

Ref. 2.5

9. Double sided, Double entry centrifugal compressors:

    (a)   have additional efficiency loss due to heat transfers through the disc or shroud.

    (b)   are more difficult to balance.

    (c)   are less efficient due to limited rpm.

    (d)   have additional efficiency loss due to reduced operating.

Ref. 2.5

10. The compressor blades of an axial flow compressor are curved throughout their length and:

    (a)   their angle of incidence increases from root to tip.

    (b)   their angle of incidence reduces from root to tip.

    (c)   their angle of attack reduces from root to tip.

    (d)   their angle of attack increases from root to tip.

Ref. 2.9

11. The compression ratio of the compressor:

    (a)   is the measure of air pressure between each stage.

    (b)   is the measure of air pressure between the diffuser and combustion chambers.

    (c)   is the measure of air pressure between compressor inlet and compressor outlet.

    (d)   is the measure of air pressure between free stream pressure and compressor outlet.

Ref. 2.10

12. Compressor surge may be minimised by use of:

    (a)   fixed inlet guide vanes.

    (b)   compressor bleed.

    (c)   turbo-fans.

    (d)   swirl vanes.

Ref. 2.14

13. Air release valves, in the compressor of a gas turbine, are opened:

   (a)   automatically.

   (b)   manually by the pilot.

   (c)   only to supply cabin conditioning when required.

   (d)   only after the engine is above ground idle rpm.

Ref. 2.17

14. When starting a twin-spool compressor engine:

   (a)   both spools are rotated to avoid surge.

   (b)   the low pressure spool is rotated first to avoid surge.

   (c)   the high pressure spool is rotated first to avoid surge.

   (d)   the free turbine only is rotated to avoid surge.

Ref. 2.18

15. Turbine blade tip turbulence:

   (a)   may be reduced by blade creep.

   (b)   may be reduced by disc shrouding.

   (c)   may be reduced by blade tip shrouding.

   (d)   may be reduced by fir tree shrouding.

Ref. 4.5

16. Blade creep is:

   (a)   reduced by tip shrouding.

   (b)   a permanent lengthening of the blade.

   (c)   a temporary lengthening of the blade.

   (d)   reduced by disc shrouding.

Ref. 4.7

17. The main bearings of the compressor/turbine drive shaft are mounted via:

   (a)   needle roller bearings.

   (b)   nylon bearings.

   (c)   ball bearings.

   (d)   ball or roller bearings.

Ref. 4.4

18. Reverse thrust power available is:
   (a) 90%.
   (b) 100%.
   (c) 50%.
   (d) 25%.

Ref. 4c.3

19. Reverse thrust is directed:
   (a) completely in the opposite direction to normal flow.
   (b) at 90 degrees to the relative airflow.
   (c) at 45 degrees to the relative airflow.
   (d) at 15 degrees to the relative airflow.

Ref. 4c.3

20. Ice is prevented from:
   (a) blocking the HP filter by pre heating the fuel.
   (b) blocking the LP filter by pre heating the fuel.
   (c) forming in the fuel by pre heating the fuel tank.
   (d) blocking the LP filter by pre heating the filter element.

Ref. 5.2

Part 3

Propellers

1

Basic Principles of Propellers

1.1 Introduction

The propeller is a means of converting the power developed by the aircraft's engine into a propulsive force. A rotating propeller imparts a rearward motion to a mass of air, and the reaction to this is a forward force on the propeller blades.

The basic cross-sectional shape of the propeller blade is that of an aerofoil similar to the wing or other such lift generating surface. The propeller is driven by the aircraft's engine, either directly from the crankshaft, or via a gearbox which will usually reduce the rpm of the propeller in relation to the engine rpm.

With the aircraft's engine running, when the propeller blade moves through the air, forces are generated, which are known as thrust and torque, and which may be regarded as near equivalents to the forces of lift and drag produced by a wing.

Thrust is the propulsive force, and torque the resistance to rotation, or propeller load. The magnitude of the thrust and torque produced will be dependent upon the size, shape and number of blades, the blade angle, speed of rotation of the propeller, the air density, and the forward speed.

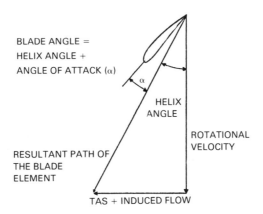

Figure 1–1 Resultant motion and angle of attack.

303

1.2   Blade Terminology

As each blade is basically of aerofoil cross-section, thrust will be produced most efficiently at a particular angle of attack, the angle of attack being the angle between the chord line of the propeller blade at a particular blade station, or position along the blade, and the relative airflow. Figure 1-1 illustrates this.

The angle of attack will vary both with operating conditions and with the camber of the blade section; however, for a given blade and given in-flight conditions, it will be relatively constant along the blade length. The rotational speed of a particular cross-section of the blade will increase the farther it is from the axis of rotation, that is, the centre of the propeller shaft, and as the forward speed of all parts of the blade is the same the relative airflow will vary along the length of the blade. It is therefore necessary to decrease the blade angle from blade root to tip to generate balanced thrust conditions. Figure 1-2 shows the basic angles and twisting moments of the propeller blade.

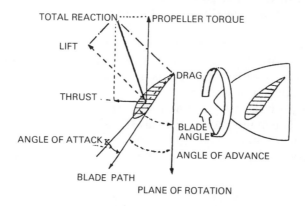

Figure 1–2   Resolution of forces.

1.3   Geometric Pitch

The geometric pitch of a propeller is the distance which it should move forward in one revolution without slip, much like how far a screw thread will move into its hole in one revolution. The air, however, is not solid and the propeller does not achieve its geometric pitch because a certain amount of slip will occur. Geometric pitch without slip is theoretically equal to $2\pi r \tan \theta$, where r is the radius, or station, of a particular cross-section, and θ is the blade angle at that point. Fixed pitch propellers are usually classified by their diameter and pitch, being related to the blade angle at three-quarter radius, or other nominated station. See Figure 1-3.

304

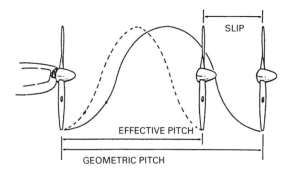

Figure 1–3 Propeller slip.

1.4 Forces on a Propeller

The construction of a propeller has to be strong enough to resist the various forces which act upon it during the course of its normal operation. It must also resist the effects of the elements to which it is constantly exposed, in particular moisture and constant changes of temperature. Erosion due to dust particles in the atmosphere is also a problem, and must be considered.

The forces acting on the propeller are centrifugal, bending and twisting.

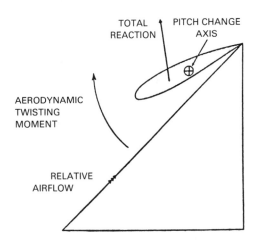

Figure 1–4 Aerodynamic twisting moment.

305

(a) Centrifugal Forces

Centrifugal forces will cause radial stress in the blades and the propeller hub, and when acting on the material which is not on the axis of the blade will cause a twisting moment. This can be seen in Figure 1-4.

Centrifugal force on a propeller can be divided into two components within the plane or rotation. The first is the radial force parallel to the blade axis, and the other is a force at 90 degrees to the blade axis.

The radial component, or force parallel to the blade axis, produces radial stress, whilst the force at 90 degrees to the blade axis will tend to turn the blade to a finer pitch by creating a twisting action.

This turning effect is the centrifugal twisting moment and is shown in Figure 1-5.

It should be noted that the wider the blade, the greater the twisting moment.

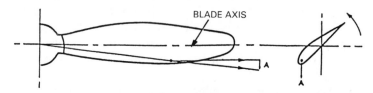

Figure 1-5 Centrifugal twisting moment.

(b) Thrust Forces

Thrust forces will tend to bend the blades of the propeller forwards in the direction of flight. This is illustrated in Figure 1-6.

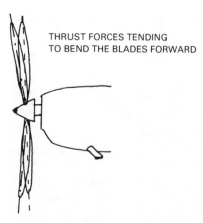

Figure 1-6 Thrust forces.

(c) Torque Forces

Torque forces will set up a bending tendency of the blades in the direction of rotation. This is shown in Figure 1-7.

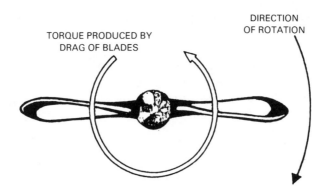

Figure 1-7 Torque forces.

(d) Air Loads

The air loads will tend to oppose the centrifugal twisting moment and coarsen blade pitch. Both through design and naturally the air loads and centrifugal twisting moment tend to cancel each other out.

1.5   Propeller Design

The propeller for a particular aircraft is designed to meet the specific requirements for that installation and the designer has to consider the following aspects of its operation.

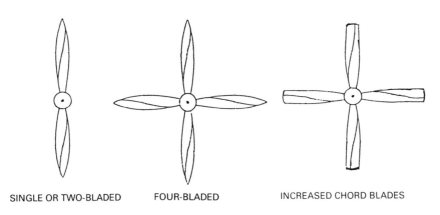

SINGLE OR TWO-BLADED   FOUR-BLADED   INCREASED CHORD BLADES

Figure 1-8.

(a) Propeller Diameter and Number of Blades
These factors will depend on the power the propeller is required to absorb, the take-off thrust it is required to produce, and the noise limits which have to be met.

Large diameter propellers normally result in better performance than small diameter propellers, and the blade area is selected to ensure that the lift coefficients are kept in the range where the blade sections are most efficient. Wide chord blades, and/or large diameter blades, lead to heavy propellers; an increase in the number of blades may increase cost, but reduces noise. Figure 1-8 illustrates some variations in propeller blade configuration.

(b) Propeller Tip Speeds
High propeller tip speeds will absorb greater power than low tip speeds. However, if the tip speed is allowed to approach the speed of sound, efficiency will diminish and this consideration limits the practical diameter and rotational speed combinations. High propeller tip speeds are also the primary source of propeller noise, and although large diameter propellers will produce a much better performance they are constrained to the lower rpm to avoid such high tip speeds.

1.6 Propeller Design Conclusions

Generally, the propeller is a compromise to satisfy the various conflicting requirements. Small two-bladed propellers, of suitable profile, are satisfactory for low powered piston engine aircraft, but for high powered piston engines or turboprops, three- or four-, and sometimes more, bladed propellers are the norm. In some cases, contra-rotating propellers are used which are normally driven through reduction gearing to enable high power engines to operate the propeller at efficient speeds.

1.7 Propeller Mounting

Firstly, the method by which the propeller assembly is mounted on the engine can be divided into two distinct methods:

(a) Tractor Propeller
This type of mounting positions the propeller on the front of the engine.

(b) Pusher Propeller
This type is mounted to the rear of the engine.

Figure 1-9 shows the two main types of mounting and a combination of the tractor and pusher types mounted in-line on a small aircraft.

A further division of propeller types can be made in the form of left-handed and right-handed propellers.

(c) Left-Handed Propeller

A left-handed propeller is one which when viewed from the cockpit rotates in an anti-clockwise direction.

From outside of the aircraft, and viewed from the front, the left-handed propeller will rotate in a clockwise direction.

(d) It also follows that a right-handed propeller will be seen to rotate clockwise from the cockpit, and anti-clockwise when viewed from the front of the aircraft.

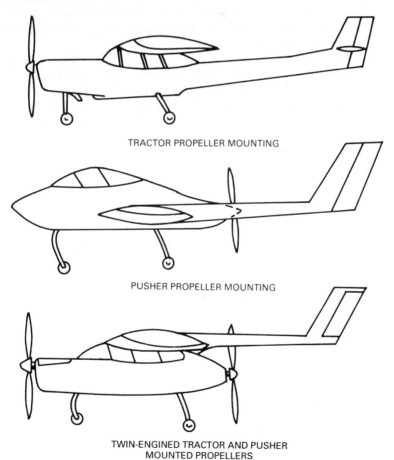

TRACTOR PROPELLER MOUNTING

PUSHER PROPELLER MOUNTING

TWIN-ENGINED TRACTOR AND PUSHER
MOUNTED PROPELLERS

Figure 1–9 Propeller mountings.

1.8 Consolidation

(a) General

In order to convert engine power to thrust, a piston engine requires a propeller, the thrust being obtained by accelerating an air mass, the reaction to this acceleration aft being to move the aircraft forward, ie:

$$FORCE = MASS \times ACCELERATION.$$

In terms of energy:

$$KINETIC\ ENERGY = \tfrac{1}{2}\ MASS \times VELOCITY$$

A propeller system gives a large air mass a small acceleration, whereas a turbojet gives a small air mass a large acceleration. The propeller system, therefore, uses less kinetic energy than a jet engine to achieve a given thrust.

However, due to limitations in propeller rpm because of its effect on tip speed, the propeller-driven aircraft is more efficient at speeds up to 300 knots. Beyond this speed, propeller efficiency falls off rapidly due to shock waves and vibration, whereas the jet propelled aircraft becomes more efficient. Figure 1-10 shows a comparison of propulsive efficiency.

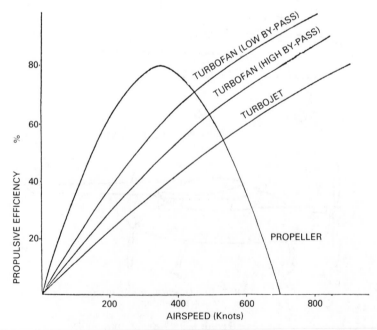

Figure 1–10 Comparison of propulsive efficiency.

(b) Propeller Terminology

The propeller rotates in a plane perpendicular to the thrust axis and, at a given point on the blade, its velocity can be represented by a vector. In relation to the blade, the relative airflow will be resultant of the rotational and aircraft velocities. Figure 1-11 shows the vectors as stated with other propeller terms.

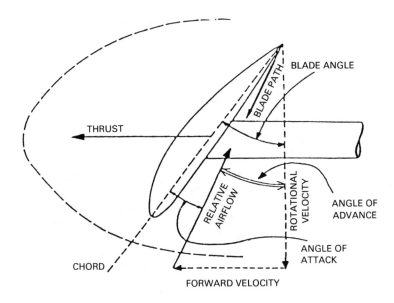

Figure 1–11.

Angle of Advance (Helix Angle), the angle between the relative airflow and the rotational velocity.

Blade Angle, the angle between the plane of rotation and the blade face, or the chord, at a given point.

Angle of Attack, the angle between the relative airflow and the chord.

These three angles may be linked together:
BLADE ANGLE = ANGLE OF ATTACK + ANGLE OF ADVANCE (HELIX ANGLE)

Tractor Propeller, a propeller mounted in front of the engine and therefore pulling the aircraft.

Pusher Propeller, a propeller mounted to the rear of the engine and therefore pushing the aircraft. Air is still accelerated aft of the aircraft.

311

Ground Clearance, the clearance between the propeller tip and the ground, with the aircraft in normal flying altitude.

Fuselage Clearance, the clearance between the propeller tip and the side of the fuselage; usually relevant only on multi-engined aircraft.

(c) Forces Acting on a Blade
The aerodynamic force produced by setting the blade at a small positive angle of attack may be resolved with respect to the direction of motion of the aircraft.

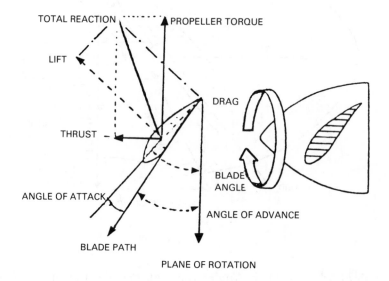

Figure 1–12 Resolution of forces.

As can be seen in Figure 1-12, the reaction thus resolved is in the form of lift and drag vectors. Whilst the drag component is important when considering retardation effect on the blade, the breakdown of the resultant into thrust and torque is more useful. Again, as can be seen, thrust is that part of the total reaction in the direction of flight, whilst torque is the component vertical to thrust and normally opposite to rotational velocity. The thrust component is therefore the propulsive force, whilst torque tends to rotate the aircraft in the opposite direction to that produced by rotational velocity. Figure 1-12 shows this effect.

312

(d) Blade Twist

The rotational velocity depends on the radius of the blade at which it is measured. Therefore, in order to maintain an efficient angle of attack along the length of the blade it is necessary to reduce the blade angle towards the tip. This is the reason for the helical twist of a blade as shown in Figure 1-13. In effect, it can also be viewed as allowing for change of angle of advance, to keep the thrust constant along the blade length.

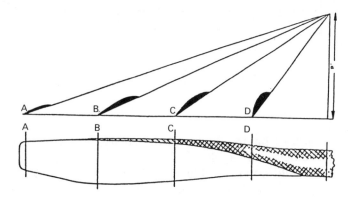

Figure 1–13 Blade twist.

(e) Centrifugal Forces

Centrifugal, bending and twisting forces act on a propeller during flight, and can be very severe at high rotational speeds. Propellers must be both strong enough to resist these forces, and rigid enough to prevent flutter. The main forces experienced are as follows:

(a) Centrifugal forces which induce radial stress in the blades and hub, and, when acting on material which is not on the blade axis, also induce a twisting moment. Centrifugal force can be resolved into two components in the plane of rotation; one is a radial force parallel to the blade axis, and the other a force at 90 degrees to the blade axis. The former produces radial stress and the latter tends to turn the blade to a finer pitch. The turning effect is referred to as centrifugal twisting moment, and is illustrated in Figure 1-14. The wider the blade, the greater will be the twisting moment.

(b) Thrust forces which tend to bend the blades forward in the direction of flight.

313

(c) Torque forces which tend to bend the blades against the direction of rotation.

(d) Air loads which normally tend to oppose the centrifugal twisting moment and coarsen blade pitch.

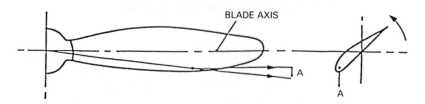

Figure 1–14 Centrifugal Twisting Moment.

(f) Blade Angle

With aircraft having no forward velocity, and a blade having rotational velocity, the angle of advance would be zero, and the angle of attack would equal the blade angle. Once the aircraft has forward velocity, the angle of advance increases and the angle of attack decreases. As with a wing aerofoil, the optimum angle of attack is achieved at 3° to 4°. Therefore, the angle at which the blade is set (on the hub) must take into account the recommended cruise speed and operating rpm.

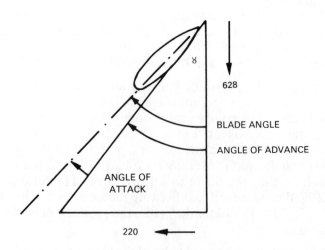

Figure 1–15 Blade angle.

The following example, based on Figure 1-15, will illustrate this point.

Blade rotating at 2000 rpm, therefore at a point along the blade at 3 ft radius, velocity = 628 ft/sec.

For an aircraft moving at 150 mph, the vector is 220 ft/sec.

Angle of advance = $\text{Tan } \gamma = \dfrac{220}{628} = 19.3$

Allowing for 4° angle of attack, therefore, blade angle is required to be set at 23.3°, ie the blade must be set at a large blade angle to allow for the angle of advance.

(g) Propeller Efficiency
The efficiency of any system can be measured from the ratio
$$\frac{\text{Power Out}}{\text{Power In}}$$
The power extracted from this system is the product of Force × Velocity, or Thrust × TAS. The power input required to overcome the rotational drag force is therefore the product of Propeller Torque (Force) × Rotational Velocity. Propeller efficiency can therefore be expressed as the ratio:

$$\frac{\text{THRUST} \times \text{TAS}}{\text{TORQUE} \times 2\,N} \qquad \text{Where } N = \text{angular velocity}$$

The power put into the system is supplied by the engine, and is therefore the BHP at the propeller shaft. Thus

$$\text{Propeller} = \frac{\text{Thrust Horsepower}}{\text{Brake Horsepower}}$$

With an aircraft stationary on the ground, propeller efficiency must be nil, for although considerable thrust may be developed, no useful work is done. Efficiency will increase with forward speed and may reach a peak of 80%. The most efficient part of a blade is approximately between $^2/_3$ and $^3/_4$ of its radius. There will be losses due to:
(a) Lack of aerodynamic shape at the boss, and poor airflow past the propeller due to the engine.
(b) Vortices and induced drag at the tips.
(c) Compressibility effects.

(h) Variation of Propeller Efficiency with Speed

Figure 1-16 illustrates the effect of speed on a fixed pitch propeller, travelling at different flight speeds at a constant rpm. If blade angle is fixed, the angle of attack will change with variation of speed, ie as speed increases, angle of attack decreases and with it the thrust. The effect on propeller efficiency is as follows:

(a) At a high speed the angle of attack of the blade will be close to zero-lift incidence and thrust will fall to zero, therefore propeller efficiency will be zero.

(b) There will only be one speed at which the blade is operating at its most efficient angle of attack and thus efficiency will be maximum.

(c) At low speeds, thrust increases with angle of attack and, provided the blade is not stalled, the thrust is large; however the speed is low and efficiency is low.

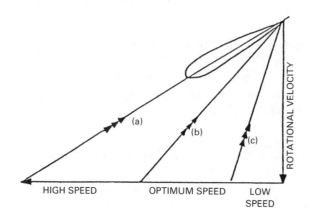

Figure 1–16 Variation of propeller efficiency.

(i) Propeller Slip

When converting engine power into thrust, losses are inevitable due to friction and 'propeller slip'. Propeller slip is the difference between the geometric pitch of the blade, and its effective pitch. Geometric pitch is the distance a propeller should advance in one complete revolution. An analogy would be the distance a screw would move into a solid during one complete turn. The effective pitch is the distance it actually advances in one 360° revolution. The effective pitch will be less because of the slippage inevitably occurring when working in the thin medium of air. See Figure 1-17.

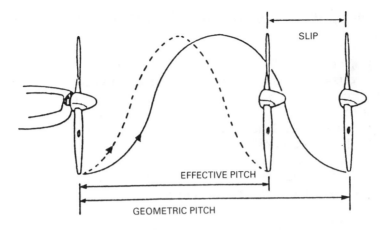

Figure 1–17 Propeller slip.

(j) Power Absorption

The propeller must be able to absorb the power imparted to it by the engine. If engine BHP exceeds propeller torque the propeller will overspeed, and both engine and propeller become inefficient. This problem is most noticeable when climbing with high power and low forward speed.

The critical factor in matching propeller to engine power is the tip velocity. Compressibility effects decrease thrust and increase the rotational drag, thereby reducing the efficiency of the blade(s).

This consideration imposes limitations on propeller diameter, rpm and TAS at which it can be used.

Factors which may improve the ability of a propeller to absorb power are:

(a) Increase blade angle and thus angle of attack
(b) Increase diameter of the propeller
(c) Increase camber of the blade aerofoil section
(d) Increase the chord of the blades
(e) Increase the number of blades

The usual method used to absorb engine power is to increase the 'solidity' of the propeller, ie the ratio between that part of the propeller disc covered by the blades relative to the total area of the disc. It can be seen that an increase in solidity can be achieved by:

(i) Increasing the number of blades, eg Contra-rotating propellers.
(ii) Increasing the chord of each blade, eg paddle blades.

317

Although the latter is easier, the low aspect ratio of the blades makes it less efficient.

(k) Swing on Take-Off

There is a tendency for propeller-driven aircraft, with tail wheel undercarriage, to 'swing' to one side on take-off. The causes of this tendency are:

(a) Asymmetric blade effect
(b) Torque reaction
(c) Slipstream effect
(d) Gyroscopic effect
(e) Cross-wind (weathercock) effect

Since (e) is not a purely propeller-generated cause, it will not be considered.

In propeller-driven aircraft with tail wheel, with the propeller turning anti-clockwise when viewed from the rear, all the causes listed above will act in the same direction (assuming cross-wind from the right). However, some aircraft configurations compensate for some of the factors, eg nose wheel type undercarriage, contra-rotating propellers, biased directional trim, etc.

(a) **Asymmetric Blade Effect** This effect arises from the axis of rotation being inclined in relation to the horizontal path of the aircraft when the tail wheel is town.

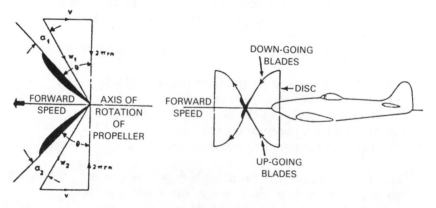

Figure 1–18 Asymmetric blade effect.

Figure 1-19 now shows how the angles of attack and resultant velocities are changed when the axis of rotation is inclined. The down-going blade has a higher angle of attack, and therefore

318

produces more thrust than the up-going blade. Also, distance travelled in unit time by the down-going blade is greater than by the up-going blade, thus the down-going blade has a higher speed relative to airflow, and for a given angle of attack produces more thrust. When the propeller is turning anti-clockwise (from rear), the left-hand half of the propeller disc produces greater thrust and will yaw the aircraft to the right. Similar lift variations are produced if the propeller is yawed and not pitched.

(b) **Torque Effect** If the propeller rotates anti-clockwise (from rear) torque reaction will tend to rotate the aircraft in the opposite direction, ie roll to starboard. One method of counteracting this involves the use of 'wash-out' (wing incidence decrease) on the lifting wing, the difference in lift causing a rolling moment opposing torque reaction.

The rolling motion caused by torque is also counteracted by the main undercarriage in contact with the ground, resulting in more weight being supported on the starboard undercarriage than the port; this increases the rolling resistance of the starboard undercarriage, causing the aircraft to swing to the right until the wings take the weight off the undercarriage.

(c) **Slipstream Effect** A propeller rotating anti-clockwise will impart a rotation to the slipstream in the same sense. This rotation causes an asymmetric flow on the fin and rudder so as to induce an aerodynamic force to the left, causing the aircraft to yaw to the right. This may be overcome by off-setting the fin, or applying bias to the rudder.

(d) **Gyroscopic Effect** As the tail wheel leaves the ground, a torque is applied to the rotating propeller in a nose-down sense. The effect of this torque on the angular moment of the disc is like that of a precessing gyroscope, ie the torque appears 90° removed from the point of application, in the direction of rotation, again producing a yaw to the right. Figure 1-20 illustrates the gyroscopic effect.

Figure 1-18 shows the condition where the propeller axis is in the line of flight. It can be seen that the speeds of each blade will be equal since angles of attack and relative air-flow on both propeller sections are equal; also, distances travelled in unit time by both up-going and down-going blade are equal.

319

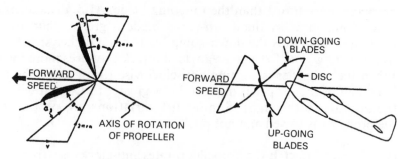

Figure 1–19 Asymmetric blade effect.

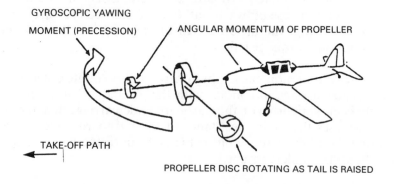

Figure 1–20 Gyroscopic effect.

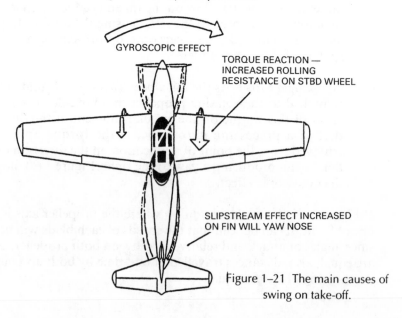

Figure 1–21 The main causes of
swing on take-off.

Section 1 Test Yourself

1. A propeller that is mounted at the front of the engine is termed:

   (a) a drag propeller.

   (b) a pusher propeller.

   (c) a thrust propeller.

   (d) a tractor propeller.

Ref. 1.8

2. The blade angle is:

   (a) equal to angle of attack plus angle of advance.

   (b) equal to angle of advance plus the helix angle.

   (c) equal to angle of attack plus blade incidence angle.

   (d) equal to angle of helix plus blade incidence angle.

Ref. 1.8

3. Ground clearance is the distance between the:

   (a) centre axis of the propeller and the ground.

   (b) blade tip and the ground with the aircraft in normal flying attitude.

   (c) blade tip and the ground with the aircraft in normal ground attitude.

   (d) blade tip and the fuselage when the aircraft is on the ground.

Ref. 1.8

4. The helix angle is:

   (a) equal to the angle of attack plus the angle of advance.

   (b) equal to the angle of advance plus the incidence angle.

   (c) the angle of advance.

   (d) equal to the angle of attack plus the slip angle.

Ref. 1.8

5. Power absorbtion may be improved in a propeller by:

(a) reducing the number of blades.

(b) increasing the diameter of the propeller.

(c) reducing the chord of each blade.

(d) reducing the camber of the blade section.

Ref. 1.8

2

Types of Propeller

2.1 Introduction

Firstly a reminder of the basic functions of the propeller. The propeller is designed to convert the turning effort of the engine into a direct push or pull along the line of flight. This push or pull is called the thrust. The propeller produces this thrust by screwing its way through the air, in much the same way as a ship's propeller does through water. The propeller blades are generally two, three or four in number. However, on some modern advanced designs many blades may be used. The blades are mounted in a hub which in turn is mounted on the engine propeller drive shaft. Figure 2-1 shows a single propeller and engine assembly.

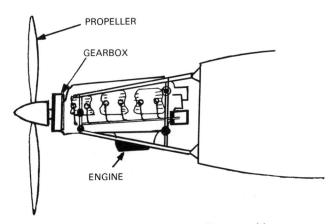

Figure 2–1 Engine and propeller assembly.

The blades are set at an angle to the plane of rotation. The distance the blades would move forward during one complete revolution if the air were solid is called the pitch. This is shown in Figure 2-2. The angle of the blade giving this forward movement is known as the blade angle. As the air is not solid, in practice the propeller always has a certain amount of slip, which means the actual distance moved forward is less than the pitch.

Because the blade tips travel round a far longer path than the root ends, yet at the same time move forward the same distance, the angle at which these two portions of the blade are set will vary. The nearer the tip the less the angle, and vice-versa. The resulting twist of the blades is shown in Figure 2-3.

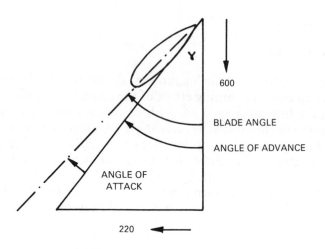

Figure 2–2 Blade angle.

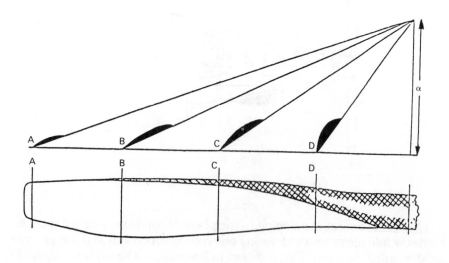

Figure 2–3 Blade twist.

2.2   Fixed Pitch Propellers

A fixed pitch propeller is one which has its blades fitted to the hub at a fixed, or set, angle which cannot be changed in flight or on the ground. Fixed pitch propellers in modern times tend to be used only on light aircraft. The optimum efficiency of such a propeller is confined to a small section of the aircraft's speed range.

2.3   Variable Pitch Propellers

This type of propeller has the ability to change the pitch of its blades in flight, or on the ground. There are various types of variable pitch propeller and in general they are designed to provide greater flexibility and efficiency over a much wider aircraft speed range than that of the fixed pitch propeller. Details of the construction and operation of the variable pitch propeller and its operating and control mechanism is discussed later. However, a basic general description is as follows:

2.4   Basic Operation of a Variable Pitch Propeller

The primary cockpit controls to consider are those of the engine throttle, which controls the engine power setting, and the RPM Control Lever. The RPM (revolutions per minute) Control Lever enables the pilot to select the required engine speed within the pitch range of the propeller. The RPM Control Lever is connected to a control unit, known as the Constant Speed Unit (CSU), that is mounted on and driven by the engine.

Once a particular engine speed has been selected, the CSU acts as a governor and maintains the selected engine speed within the power available.

For example:

Engine speed increases; through the propeller drive shaft, the propeller rpm will also increase. The propeller rpm increase will be sensed by the CSU which will move the propeller blade to a coarser angle which, in turn, will make the propeller do more work, increasing the load on the engine and so causing engine rpm to fall, thereby maintaining the rpm selected on the RPM Control Lever. In the event of engine speed reducing, the opposite will happen.

It can be seen from the above that engine speed can be controlled automatically, releasing the pilot from constantly adjusting engine rpm. This will also reduce the wear rate on the engine.

2.5   Single-Acting Variable Pitch Propeller (Constant speed)

There are two basic types of constant speed propeller operating mechanisms. They are referred to as the Single-acting propeller and the Double-acting propeller. The term single-acting essentially refers to the pitch change system utilizing engine oil pressure to operate the pitch change cylinder and move the propeller blades to fine pitch; normally a combination of centrifugal force and spring pressure moves the propeller blades to coarse pitch. The following chapter explains the operation of the constant speed unit in conjunction with this type of system.

2.6   Double-Acting Variable Pitch Propeller (Constant speed)

As this is the most common type of constant speed propeller used on larger commercial aircraft, a separate chapter has been devoted to its operation and also the operation of its associated constant speed unit.

Section 2 Test Yourself

1. The blade angle:

   (a)   is constant throughout the propeller blade length.

   (b)   is greatest at the blade root.

   (c)   is equal to the angle of advance.

   (d)   is greatest at the blade tip.

Ref. 2.1

2. A variable pitch constant speed propeller is designed primarily to:

   (a)   maintain the propeller at constant thrust.

   (b)   maintain the propeller at constant rpm

   (c)   maintain the propeller at constant pitch.

   (d)   maintain the engine at constant rpm

Ref. 2.4

3. In a single-acting propeller of the variable pitch type:

   (a)   the pitch change is limited to a specific range and not totally variable.

   (b)   the pitch change is activated hydraulically in both directions.

   (c)   the pitch change is activated hydraulically in one direction.

   (d)   the pitch change mechanism is manually operated.

Ref. 2.5

4. A variable pitch constant speed propeller:

   (a)   eliminates the need for constant adjustment to angle rpm

   (b)   eliminates the need for constant adjustment to propeller pitch.

   (c)   eliminates the need for constant changes to mixture setting.

   (d)   eliminates the need for constant boost adjustment.

Ref. 2.4

5. The pitch is controlled on a constant speed variable pitch propeller:

   (a)   by the rpm lever.

   (b)   by the throttle.

   (c)   by the CSU

   (d)   by the governor spring.   Ref. 2.4

3

Basic Variable Pitch Requirements

3.1 Introduction

Variable pitch propellers fall primarily into two basic types, those which have a limited ability to vary their pitch, eg perhaps only two or three basic positions to satisfy certain requirements such as engine starting, where minimum propeller drag is required; and take-off where high engine rpm is required together with a compromise pitch position, coupling high power with propeller drag kept as low as possible; and finally a cruise position.

Generally it is only the larger and more complex propellers which have a 'feathering' facility.

The second type of variable pitch propeller is the constant speed type which is designed to minimize the adjustments the pilot would otherwise have to make to the engine throttle in flight to maintain constant rpm on the engine to optimize fuel consumption and reduce wear on the engine.

The advantages of the fully variable pitch constant speed propeller are many and varied. Different manufacturers achieve the several functions in different ways so the following paragraphs give a generalised description of the primary functions.

3.2 Extra Fine or Fully Fine Pitch

In order to ease the task of engine starting it is useful to reduce the drag of the propeller blades as much as possible. This can be achieved by turning the blades to the finest pitch possible. This pitch setting is 'ground fine', also known as 'extra fine'. In this position not only is the load on the engine reduced to an absolute minimum, the load on the electrical starting system is also reduced.

Whilst this position is suitable for engine starting, once the engine is running there is a serious danger of the engine overheating as the propeller in this position will be generating minimum airflow over the engine for cooling purposes. To obviate this, once the engine has started and the throttle is opened the blades will automatically increase pitch into normal fine. A set of stops then immediately spring into place, preventing the propeller accidentally moving back into the extra fine pitch. In flight the stops also prevent the propeller moving into extra fine as in such a position, with reduced blade drag, engine overspeeding is likely to occur. These stops are called fine pitch stops or flight fine pitch stops and their primary function is to prevent the propeller moving into extra fine in flight, ie they are withdrawn for engine starting, allowing the propeller to move into extra fine.

3.3   Constant Speed Range

As the throttle is opened above a certain rpm, the fine pitch stops are withdrawn to permit the propeller blades to move out of the extra fine position and into the constant speed range.

Prior to moving into the constant speed range, the throttle must be set to the required power, and the rpm lever set for the desired engine speed.

The rpm lever controls the setting on the governor of the constant speed unit. Details of the operation of the constant speed unit are given later, at this point a brief description suffices.

To maintain the engine at constant rpm, virtually eliminating the pilot's need constantly to adjust the throttle to maintain constant engine rpm, the propeller will adjust its pitch to increase or decrease the load on the propeller and hence the load on the engine. If the engine rpm start to fall, propeller pitch will decrease, reducing load on the engine, allowing the engine to speed up and return to its original rpm.

If the engine rpm start to increase (overspeed), propeller pitch will increase and therefore increase the load on the engine, thus reducing engine rpm. When the propeller is in the constant speed range it is prevented not only from moving into the extra fine pitch by stops, but also prevented from moving into the feathered position by feathering stops.

Figure 3-1 shows a simple diagram of stop sequence.

3.4   Feathered Position

The propeller may have to be feathered in the event of an engine or propeller drive malfunction. This is essentially an emergency function where the engine is stopped and the blade pitch moved beyond the coarse stops into the feathered position to stop the windmilling action and any further damage to the engine. It is equally important that the propeller must not come out of the feathered position by accident as this may result in serious damage to the engine and also create asymmetric problems in controlling the aircraft.

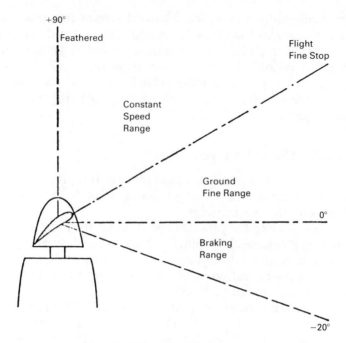

Figure 3–1 Propeller blade positions.

Section 3 Test Yourself

1. Prior to engine starting:

   (a) coarse pitch is selected to give maximum cooling airflow.

   (b) extra fine pitch is selected to reduce the load on the engine.

   (c) extra fine pitch is selected to increase cooling airflow over the engine.

   (d) fine pitch is selected to reduce the load on the engine.

   Ref. 3.2

2. After the engine has started, the propeller:

   (a) remains in its selected position until take-off.

   (b) moves into fine pitch to increase airflow.

   (c) moves into coarse pitch to increase cooling airflow.

   (d) moves into the feathered position until engine operating temperature has been attained.

   Ref. 3.2

3. The constant speed range is normally between:

   (a) extra fine and fully coarse pitch.

   (b) fine and coarse pitch.

   (c) fine and feathered positions.

   (d) extra fine and feathered positions.

   Ref. 3.3

4. In the feathered position:

   (a) the leading edge of the blade faces forward.

   (b) the trailing edge of the blade faces forward.

   (c) the thrust face faces forward.

   (d) the pressure face faces forward.

   Ref. 3.3 diag. 3.2

5. In flight:

   (a) the blades may move to extra fine.

   (b) the blades may move into feathered if the engine overspeeds.

   (c) the blades cannot move into extra fine.

   (d) the blades cannot be selected out of the constant speed range.

   Ref. 3.2

4

Single-Acting Variable Pitch Propeller (Piston Engines)

4.1 Introduction

The basic construction of a variable pitch propeller has already been discussed; however, functional differences can now be reviewed to provide a clear understanding of the single and double-acting propeller types. The double-acting type is discussed in detail in Chapter 6.

4.2 Principle of Operation

An example of a single-acting propeller is shown in Figure 4-1 and is a constant speed, feathering type that is commonly fitted to small and medium-size (usually twin-engine) aircraft.

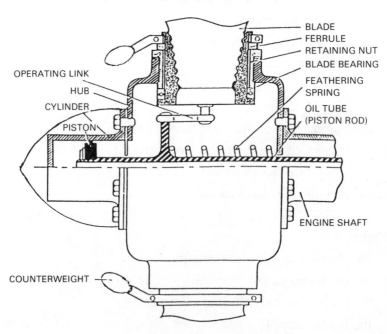

Figure 4–1 Single-acting propeller.

332

On some types of propeller the pitch change operating mechanism directs oil under pressure to the front of a piston through a hollow piston rod, which moves the piston rearward to turn the blades to a finer pitch. On other propeller types the reverse applies: with the propeller held in fine pitch by the oil pressure, the counterweights and feathering spring move the piston forward, when the oil pressure is reduced, so turning the blades to coarser pitch. The counterweights produce a centrifugal twisting moment, but because they are positioned at 90° to the chord line, they tend to move the blades to coarse pitch. The counterweights must be located far enough from the blade axis, and must be heavy enough, to overcome the natural twisting moment of the blades. However, since weight and space are limiting factors, this method tends only to be used with blades of narrow chord.

4.3   Propeller Blade Control

The blade angle is controlled by a constant speed unit which comprises a centrifugal governor, a governor valve assembly, and an oil pump which boosts oil pressure from the engine lubrication system sufficiently for the operation of the propeller pitch change mechanism. The governor is driven by the engine via an ancillary drive, and movement of the governor weights under centrifugal force is opposed by a control spring. The loading on the control spring is set by movement of the pilot's RPM Lever. Figure 4-2 shows the RPM Lever and its selection positions.

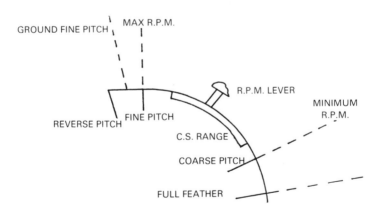

Figure 4–2 RPM control positions.

The position of the governor valve is determined, therefore, by engine speed and the force exerted by the spring; when these forces balance, the oil line to the propeller is closed, and oil is trapped in the cylinder of the pitch change mechanism.

4.4   Operation

When the pilot's RPM Control Lever is set to the maximum rpm position, and the throttle is at a low power setting, the governor valve will be in the fully down position. Oil from the pump will be directed through the hollow piston rod to turn the propeller blades to fully fine pitch. As the throttle is opened and rpm increases, centrifugal force on the governor weights will cause the valve to rise until a position is reached where maximum rpm is reached and the oil line to the propeller is closed. Any further increase in power will tend to increase rpm and result in the governor valve being lifted to allow oil to drain from the propeller and cause the blades to move to a coarser pitch and so maintain the set rpm by placing a greater load on the propeller.

During flight, rearward movement of the pilot's RPM Lever will reduce spring loading, and allow the governor weights to lift the valve. This will result in a coarser blade angle, resulting in a greater load on the propeller and hence on the engine, which will reduce engine speed until the spring force is balanced by centrifugal force on the governor weights. Forward movement of the pilot's control lever will increase spring loading and result in a finer propeller pitch and higher engine speed.

If the propeller load decreases in flight, or power is increased, the engine will begin to speed up, the governor weights will lift the valve and the propeller pitch will move to coarse to maintain the set engine speed. Conversely, an increase in propeller load, or a decrease in engine power, will result in a finer propeller pitch to maintain the set engine speed. Remember, the objective of the constant speed unit is to maintain constant engine speed, not constant propeller speed.

4.5   Feathering

On smaller aircraft, such as those fitted with a single-acting propeller, feathering is accomplished by moving the pilot's control lever to the appropriate position, which is normally obtained by moving the lever through a gate in the quadrant. This action raises the governor valve fully, allowing oil to drain from the propeller, and the blades will turn to the fully coarse position (feathered) under the action of the counterweights and spring.

In order to unfeather the propeller, a separate source of oil under pressure is required. On light aircraft this is usually provided by an accumulator, which is charged during normal flight. To unfeather, the pilot's control lever is moved into the constant speed range, thus lowering the governor valve, and the unfeathering button is pressed, releasing oil from the accumulator and allowing it to flow to the propeller. The blades begin unfeathering, and once the propeller starts to windmill the normal oil supply completes the operation.

When the engine is stopped on the ground, oil pressure in the cylinder is gradually relieved by leakage through the constant speed unit, and this would enable the propeller blades to turn to the feathered position under action of the feathering springs. This would result in unacceptable loads on the propeller for engine starting, and so a centrifugal latch is fitted to prevent forward movement of the propeller piston when the engine is stopped. The basic operation of the centrifugal latch is shown in Figure 4-3.

4.6 Centrifugal Latch

The centrifugal latch is fitted to some types of constant speed propeller to prevent the propeller blades moving into the feathered position when the aircraft is on the ground and the engine is switched off.

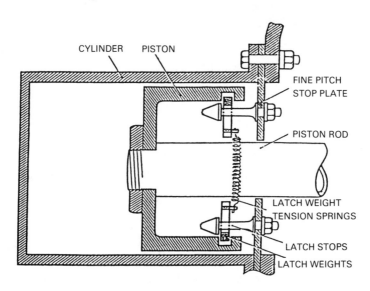

Figure 4–3 Centrifugal latch.

Centrifugal force disengages the latch at all speeds above ground idle therefore enabling the propeller to function normally during flight. Below this speed, however, centrifugal force is overcome by return springs and the piston can only move a short distance, normally equivalent to approximately five degrees of blade angle. When the engine is started, oil pressure builds up to move the blades to fully fine pitch and centrifugal force disengages the latch.

Section 4 Test Yourself

1. On a single-acting variable pitch propeller:
   (a) spring pressure changes the pitch in both directions.
   (b) oil pressure changes the pitch in both directions.
   (c) the blades have no fixed constant speed range.
   (d) the blades are operated by the piston assembly.

Ref. 4.2

2. Centrifugal latches are fitted to some types of variable pitch propellers to:
   (a) permit the blades to move into the fully fine position in flight.
   (b) prevent the blades moving into the feathered position when the engine is switched off.
   (c) prevent the blades moving into the feathered position in flight.
   (d) permit the blades going into reverse pitch in flight.

Ref. 4.6

3. On engine start-up:
   (a) the blades are already in fully fine pitch.
   (b) the oil pressure builds up and moves the blades to fully fine.
   (c) the oil pressure builds up and moves the blades to coarse pitch.
   (d) the blades will remain locked in their previous position.

Ref. 4.6

4. Normally on a single-acting propeller, feathering is accomplished by:
   (a) moving the RPM lever fully forward.
   (b) moving the RPM lever to the feather position.
   (c) pushing the feathering button.
   (d) selecting the booster pump 'ON'.

Ref. 4.5

5. On a single acting variable pitch propeller:

   (a)   the counterweights create a centrifugal twisting moment.

   (b)   the counterweights compensate for a centrifugal twisting moment.

   (c)   the counterweights assist in moving the blades to a finer pitch.

   (d)   the counterweights prevent blade flutter.

Ref. 4.2

5

Piston Engine Constant Speed Unit
As used with a Single-Acting Propeller

5.1 Introduction

A variable pitch propeller theoretically permits the pitch to be so adjusted
that the engine is running at the rpm best suited for the particular conditions of flight. For any given pitch, altered conditions of flight affect the
propeller efficiency and hence the engine rpm, thus calling for constant
adjustment. The constant speed unit effects this automatically and so
relieves the pilot of the need to continually alter propeller pitch to maintain the rpm at the desired figure.

It should be noted that the primary function of the constant speed unit
is to maintain the engine rpm at the figure selected on the RPM Control
Lever in the cockpit. It does this by altering the pitch of the propeller
blades, but the particular pitch required for any given rpm will vary with
the flight conditions. The constant speed unit maintains rpm constant,
not pitch constant.

Figure 5-1 shows the construction and operation of a constant speed
unit.

5.2 Description

A hollow shaft driven by the engine, drives a plate on which are pivoted
two flyweights that are restrained against centrifugal force by a governor
spring. A cup mounted on the driving plate prevents the weights flying
out too far. The weights act on a piston valve which fits inside the hollow
drive shaft and serves to control the flow of oil to the propeller.

Also driven by the shaft is a gear type oil pump, sometimes referred to
as a booster pump, which receives oil from the engine lubrication system
oil pump and increases its pressure to the required value; a relief valve
prevents excessive pressure.

The pilot-operated RPM Control Lever varies the load on the upper
end of the governor spring through a rack and pinion mechanism, or a
bell crank lever.

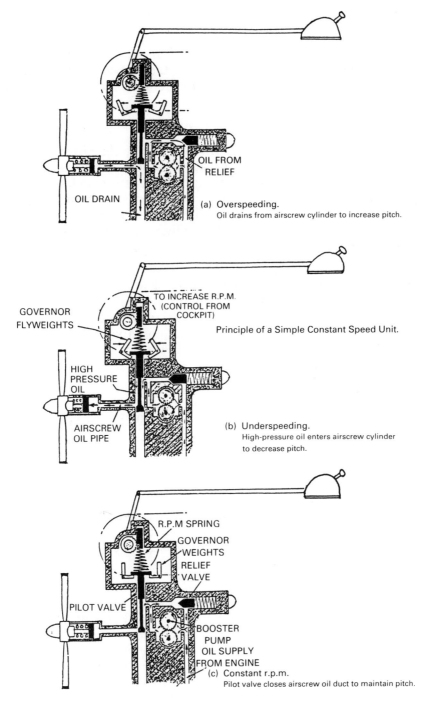

(a) Overspeeding.
Oil drains from airscrew cylinder to increase pitch.

OIL FROM RELIEF

OIL DRAIN

GOVERNOR FLYWEIGHTS

TO INCREASE R.P.M.
(CONTROL FROM COCKPIT)

Principle of a Simple Constant Speed Unit.

HIGH PRESSURE OIL

AIRSCREW OIL PIPE

(b) Underspeeding.
High-pressure oil enters airscrew cylinder to decrease pitch.

R.P.M SPRING

GOVERNOR WEIGHTS

RELIEF VALVE

PILOT VALVE

BOOSTER PUMP OIL SUPPLY FROM ENGINE

(c) Constant r.p.m.
Pilot valve closes airscrew oil duct to maintain pitch.

Figure 5–1 Principle of a Simple Constant Speed Unit.

5.3 Operation

While the engine is running at the desired rpm the piston valve will be in the neutral position, closing all oil ports to the propeller. The centrifugal force of the flyweights just balances the compression of the governor spring in this position.

(a) If the engine rpm rises:
   The flyweights will fly outwards, raising the piston valve and opening the ports. This will allow oil flow to cause the propeller blades to move to a coarser pitch. The coarser pitch will increase the load on the engine, the engine rpm will decrease, and the piston valve will return to the neutral position as the spring pushes it down against the reduced centrifugal force of the flyweights.

(b) If the engine rpm falls:
   The spring pressure will be greater than the reduced centrifugal force of the flyweights and will force the piston valve down. The oil flow will now be in the direction of making the propeller blade pitch finer. The engine will speed up and the increased centrifugal force will cause the flyweights to return the piston valve to neutral.

(c) Increasing rpm in flight:
   Should the pilot wish to increase rpm, he will move the RPM Control Lever forward. This action will compress the governor spring through the rack and pinion mechanism, the centrifugal force of the flyweights no longer balances the increased spring pressure, and the piston valve is forced down. The propeller blade pitch is made finer and so reduces the load on the engine and the engine rpm will rise until the centrifugal force of the flyweights can balance the spring pressure and return the piston to neutral. The rpm is now maintained automatically at the new selected value. When the pilot wishes to reduce rpm, then the reverse operation will take place.

(d) Feathering.
   On some constant speed systems, the last portion of movement on the cockpit mounted RPM Control Lever in the decrease speed direction causes the spring control to engage with a stop on the upper end of the piston valve and thus raise the valve positively. The governor is now out of action and the piston becomes coarser until the propeller blades are fully feathered.

6

Double-Acting Propellers

6.1   Introduction

In general, apart from the operating mechanism, these propellers are similar in design to the single-acting type. The primary difference between the single-acting type, in which the pitch change action is by hydraulic pressure to move the propeller blades from coarse pitch to fine pitch and spring and centrifugal force to move the blades into coarse pitch from fine, is that in the double-acting type hydraulic pressure is used to operate the pitch change in both directions. In the double-acting type the cylinder remains stationary and the piston moves, provision is also sometimes made for feathering. Figure 6-1 shows the mechanism of a double-acting propeller.

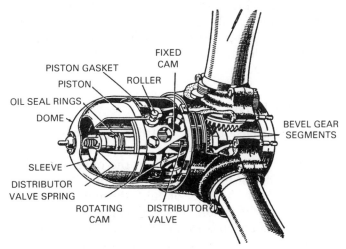

Figure 6–1 Double-acting propeller.

6.2   Construction and Operation

The blades and hub are similar in design to the single acting propeller. The brackets on the root end of the blades, however, are replaced in this type by bevel gear segments which are coupled to the blades by leaf springs that pre-load the gear teeth. The hub is retained on the engine

341

drive shaft by a separate nut. The piston slides in the dome which is attached to the hub by dowels and a retaining nut. Passing through its centre is the distributor valve which is attached to the propeller shaft. An oil seal round the circumference of the piston, and oil seal rings on the distributor valve which bear on the sleeve attached to the piston, prevent oil from passing from one side of the piston to the other. The piston is guided by four sets of rollers, which slide in the right hand helical slots in a fixed cam ring which is attached to the dome. Inside and concentric with the fixed cam is a rotating cam, which has a bevel gear formed at its rear end that meshes with the bevel gear segments on the blade. This cam has four left-handed helical slots in it in which the rollers attached to the piston also work. Ball races support the rotating cam and take the end thrust; stops are fitted to limit the blade movement.

Note:
(a) The helical slots are as shown for a left-handed propeller. However, for a right-handed propeller they are reversed in hand.

(b) For Feathering propellers, the helical slots are extended beyond the normal coarse pitch position, but at a reduced pitch. This reduction of angularity decreases the effectiveness of the cam mechanism and requires a higher pressure than normal to operate the rotating cam. This arrangement will allow the blades to be feathered only by applying this higher pressure, which is provided by a separate pump. Accidental feathering due to a defect in the constant speed unit is thereby prevented.

6.3   Distributor Valve

The inner oil tube extension of the distributor valve housing screws into the engine propeller shaft and retains the valve in position. When fully home, the base of the housing seats on the outer oil tube inside the propeller shaft, a washer making an oil tight joint. Normally, engine oil pressure passes through the inner oil tube, through the distributor valve, and so to the front of the piston. 'Boosted oil pressure' from the oil pump in the constant speed unit passes through the annular space between the outer and inner oil tubes, through the distributor valve, and so to the back of the piston.

The spring loaded piston type valves housed in the distributor valve housing operates only during the unfeathering operation.

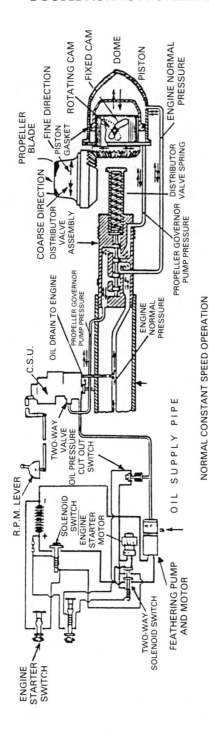

PROPELLER BLADE

FINE DIRECTION

ROTATING CAM

FIXED CAM

DOME

PISTON

ENGINE NORMAL PRESSURE

PISTON GASKET

COARSE DIRECTION

DISTRIBUTOR VALVE ASSEMBLY

DISTRIBUTOR VALVE SPRING

PROPELLER GOVERNOR PUMP PRESSURE

OIL DRAIN TO ENGINE

PROPELLER GOVERNOR PUMP PRESSURE

ENGINE NORMAL PRESSURE

C.S.U.

NORMAL CONSTANT SPEED OPERATION

R.P.M. LEVER

TWO-WAY VALVE

OIL PRESSURE CUT OUT SWITCH

SOLENOID SWITCH

ENGINE STARTER MOTOR

OIL SUPPLY PIPE

ENGINE STARTER SWITCH

TWO-WAY SOLENOID SWITCH

FEATHERING PUMP AND MOTOR

Figure 6–2.

6.4 Operation

(a) Movement to Coarse Pitch
In order to move the propeller blades to coarse pitch, 'boosted' oil pressure from the constant speed unit oil pump, sometimes called the booster pump, is admitted to the back of the piston. The piston is forced forwards and its guide rollers acting in the slots of the fixed cam cause it to rotate. At the same time the forward movement of the rollers in the slots in the rotating cam force that cam to rotate. As the slots in the fixed and rotating cam are of opposite 'hand', the rotation of the piston causes the rotating cam to turn further in the same direction: the blades are turned in their sockets by means of the bevel gears. See Figure 6-2.

(b) Movement to Fine Pitch
To turn the blades to fine pitch, the 'boosted' oil pressure is cut off, the oil behind the piston is allowed to drain to the engine sump, and the engine oil pressure acting on the front of the piston forces the piston backwards, then turns the blades through the medium of the rollers, cams and bevel gears. The inherent tendency of the blades to turn to fine pitch under the influence of centrifugal force assists this operation.

(c) Feathering the Propeller on the Ground
To feather the propeller when testing it on the ground, the cockpit control lever is pushed fully forward, with a low throttle setting, and the feathering switch pressed. This starts an electric motor which drives a separate oil pump supplying oil at extra high pressure to the constant speed unit through a two-way valve. This is automatically pushed over to close the normal oil passage to and from the piston valve and to admit the extra high pressure to the passage leading to the back of the piston. The extra high pressure passes to the back of the piston and feathers the blades. At the fully feathered position, the oil pressure builds up and operates the oil pressure cut-out switch to break the circuit and switch off the motor. See Figure 6-3.

(d) Unfeathering the Propeller
To unfeather the propeller, the cockpit control lever is pulled back, the feathering switch is pressed and held in. This prevents the high oil pressure switching off the motor. The pressure acting on this distributor valve forces it forward against the spring. This reverses the oil circuit through the distributor valve, the high pressure oil is directed to the front of the piston, and the blades are unfeathered. When the desired speed is obtained by the propeller 'windmilling' the engine, the feathering switch is released. See Figure 6-4.

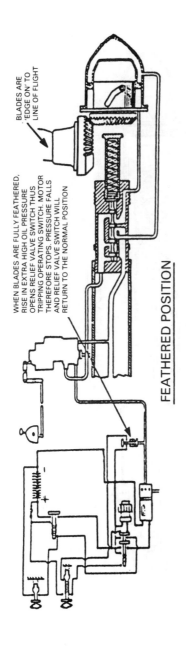

BLADES ARE 'EDGE ON' TO LINE OF FLIGHT

WHEN BLADES ARE FULLY FEATHERED, RISE IN EXTRA HIGH OIL PRESSURE OPENS RELIEF VALVE SWITCH THUS TRIPPING OPERATING SWITCH. MOTOR THEREFORE STOPS. PRESSURE FALLS AND RELIEF VALVE SWITCH WILL RETURN TO THE NORMAL POSITION

FEATHERED POSITION

Figure 6–3.

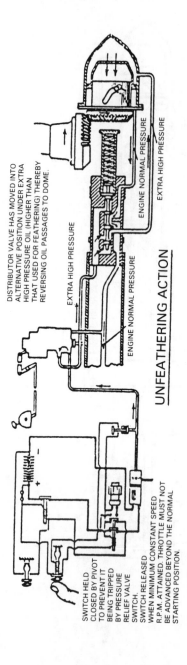

DISTRIBUTOR VALVE HAS MOVED INTO
ALTERNATIVE POSITION UNDER EXTRA
HIGH PRESSURE OIL (HIGHER THAN
THAT USED FOR FEATHERING) THEREBY
REVERSING OIL PASSAGES TO DOME.

EXTRA HIGH PRESSURE

ENGINE NORMAL PRESSURE

EXTRA HIGH PRESSURE

ENGINE NORMAL PRESSURE

UNFEATHERING ACTION

SWITCH HELD
CLOSED BY PIVOT
TO PREVENT IT
BEING TRIPPED
BY PRESSURE
RELIEF VALVE
SWITCH.
SWITCH RELEASED
WHEN MINIMUM CONSTANT SPEED
R.P.M. ATTAINED. THROTTLE MUST NOT
BE ADVANCED BEYOND THE NORMAL
STARTING POSITION.

Figure 6–4.

Notes:

(a) When testing on the ground, it is unnecessary to stop the engine, but it should not be run for more than a few seconds with the propeller feathered.

(b) The feathering motor requires a very large current and, to avoid running the aircraft battery down, a ground starter battery should be coupled up to the aircraft for ground testing.

Section 6 Test Yourself

1. A double-acting propeller utilizes:

(a) oil pressure to change the pitch angle in one direction only.

(b) oil pressure to change the pitch angle in both direction.

(c) oil pressure to operate in one direction and spring pressure in the other.

(d) a double piston assembly to provide an emergency back-up should one piston fail.

Ref. 6.1

2. Normally when feathering a double-acting variable pitch propeller:

(a) the extra high oil pressure required is provided by the booster pump in the C.S.U.

(b) the extra high oil pressure required is provided by an electrically operated pump.

(c) the oil pressure required is provided by the engine lubrication system.

(d) the oil pressure will dissipate and the spring will move the blades to the feathered position.

Ref. 6.4

3. The inherent tendency of the blades of a propeller is:

(a) to remain in their selected position until hydraulic force is applied.

(b) to move towards coarse pitch.

(c) to hunt.

(d) to move towards fine pitch.

Ref. 6.4

4. Hydraulic oil flow control is directed by:

   (a)   the rpm selector.

   (b)   the throttle valve.

   (c)   the distributor valve.

   (d)   the two-way valve.

Ref. 6.3

5. Movement of the blades to coarse pitch requires an oil supply from:

   (a)   the engine-driven pump only.

   (b)   the electrically-operated pump.

   (c)   the booster pump.

   (d)   the spring return side of the piston.

Ref. 6.4

7

Feathering Propellers (Piston-Engined Aircraft)

7.1 Introduction

In the event of engine failure, or an unserviceability which requires the engine to be shut down, the feathering of the propeller is likely to be required. Not all propellers have the ability to be feathered. However, in the event that such a facility is available, an example procedure is given below.

7.2 Typical Feathering Procedure

Feathering is the procedure by which the propeller blades are turned until, with the blade chord lines almost parallel to the line of flight, there are no rotating forces acting on the propeller blades as a whole. Figure 7-1 shows the position of the propeller blade relative to the hub.

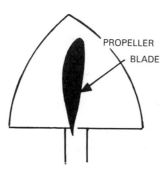

Figure 7–1 Feathered position.

In the event of engine failure and the engine ignition being switched off, the airflow passing through the propeller will continue to turn the engine over, that is rotate the engine, and such action may cause considerable damage. If the propeller is feathered it can be seen the propeller will be stationary and therefore no further damage will be inflicted on the engine.

7.3   Reduction of Drag

By feathering the propeller on a failed engine, considerable drag that would otherwise be created can be avoided.

7.4   Feathering Action

On hydraulically-operated propellers, feathering may in an emergency be carried out by an electrically-driven high pressure oil pump. This pump is independent of the engine and can be used whether the engine is running or not. The pump is normally operated by pressing a push button in the cockpit. On electrically-operated propellers the feathering motor is activated by a feathering switch in the cockpit.

7.5   Feathering Operation (Piston-engined Aircraft)

All feathering mechanisms obtain their motive power for feathering from the electrical services of the aircraft. The propeller blades are moved through a large angle at a much greater rate than in normal constant speed operation. The process of feathering and unfeathering imposes a severe drain on aircraft batteries unless the generators are charging satisfactorily.

Example Feathering Procedure:
(a)   Close the throttle on the engine of the propeller which is to be feathered.
(b)   Push the appropriate feathering switch or button.
(c)   Turn off the fuel supply to that engine and switch off the booster pump to that engine.
(d)   If the failed engine is on fire, operate the correct fire extinguisher but only after the propeller has stopped rotating.
(e)   Switch off the ignition of the dead engine.

Note: Operation of the fire extinguisher before the propeller has stopped rotating will normally result in the extinguishant being blown out of the engine bay by the engine cooling air, so preventing the extinguishant from doing its job of putting out the fire.

7.6   General Variations

The basic feathering drill given above is standard practice. The feathering operation of piston engine driven propellers will, however, vary according to the type of propeller fitted to the aircraft.
The most important differences are as follows:

(a) With some types the propeller is feathered by operating the push button only, while with other types it is necessary to move the rpm control lever through a feathering gate to the feathering position before the push button is depressed.

(b) Some push buttons must be held in manually during the feathering operation; others are operated by a solenoid, and after pressure is released they will remain in until feathering is completed. If this type is fitted, the pilot must ensure that the push button springs out when feathering is complete. If it does not, it must be pulled out by hand.

(c) Electrically-operated propellers feather at a slower rate than hydraulic propellers. When the blades reach the feathered position the current to the electric motor is automatically switched off.

Feathering is an emergency action and should be practiced until it is instinctive and automatic.

7.7 Unfeathering

Other than practice and test feathering, a propeller is only feathered after engine failure or as a safeguard when low engine oil pressure or excessive engine temperature is indicated, which may lead to a possible defect. In such circumstances an engine should not be restarted in flight. When unfeathering for practice or if, having regard to the reason for which the propeller was feathered in the first place, the pilot considers that the circumstances nevertheless justify restarting the engine, this should be done at a safe speed and/or height. If this is not done, difficulty may be experienced owing to the increased critical speed resulting from the additional drag of the windmilling propeller while under conditions of asymmetric power.

7.8 Unfeathering in Flight

An example unfeathering sequence in flight is as follows:
(a) Set the throttle in the fully closed position. The throttle should not be moved from this position until the propeller reaches its peak windmilling rpm. If the throttle is opened before peak windmilling rpm, a fire can result from a blowback through the carburettor.
(b) Set the RPM Control Lever just forward of the minimum rpm position, or just out of the feathering gate.
(c) Switch on the ignition.
(d) Operate the feathering push button or switch. When the correct rpm is reached, the pilot should check that the feathering push button is fully out; it must be pulled out by hand if it has not come out automatically.

(e) Turn on the fuel supply and switch on the booster pump if fitted.

(f) Warm up the engine and then return to the normal constant speed conditions.

7.9 Unfeathering on the ground

The following is a procedure which is normally used when unfeathering a propeller on the ground after a practiced feathered landing:

(a) The stopped engine should be restarted with its propeller still in the feathered position. This avoids discharging oil from the unfeathering propeller into the engine sump while the scavenge pump is not working.

(b) The controls should be set and the engine started in the normal manner. When the engine is running steadily, and the propeller has not started to unfeather, the feathering push button should be pushed in. When the propeller has moved from its feathered position, the push button should be released, if applicable.

In many cases the propeller will start to unfeather without the push buttons being pressed, but on some installations when this occurs pressing the push button will first cause the propeller to refeather before it finally unfeathers. If difficulty is found in starting certain engines due to the high drag of the fully feathered propeller, it may be partially unfeathered first. This should not be done if there is any evidence that flooding of the crankcase may result. This will be indicated by oil being ejected through the crankcase breathers immediately after starting. With radial engines there is a danger of hydraulic locking when starting in this manner, and these engines should be started as soon as the propeller is partially unfeathered. If for any reason an immediate attempt cannot be made to start the engine, or an attempt is made to start and the engine fails to turn over through one complete revolution of the propeller when the starter is operated, no further attempt to start should be made until a check for hydraulic locking, by hand turning, has been carried out.

7.10 Practice and Test Feathering

Feathering should not be practiced or tested if the air temperature is below minus 15deg C. Most aircraft are limited to a specific number of practice feathering and unfeathering cycles in a given flight. A typical example would be twelve in a training situation.

Care should be taken on multi-engined aircraft that are fitted with one generator on one engine that limited practice feathering is carried out on the engine with the generator or a severe drain could be made on the batteries. It is also advisable to switch off all unnecessary electrical loads to reduce the loads on the batteries when practice feathering.

A watch should be kept on the oil temperature of the engine with the propeller feathered to ensure the temperature is not allowed to fall too low before the engine is unfeathered.

Section 7 Test Yourself

1. Prior to feathering the propeller:

(a)   firstly turn off the fuel supply to the engine.

(b)   close the throttle to the engine of the propeller which is to be feathered.

(c)   in the event of an engine fire, operate the extinguisher.

(d)   in the event of fire, push the appropriate feathering button.

Ref. 7.5

2. When unfeathering a propeller, the:

(a)   unfeathering button should be pressed first.

(b)   feathering button should be pressed first.

(c)   ignition should be switched on first.

(d)   fuel supply should be turned on first.

Ref. 7.7

3. When unfeathering a propeller, normally:

(a)   the throttle should be fully closed.

(b)   the throttle should be fully open.

(c)   the throttle should be set at cruise setting.

(d)   the throttle should be set at flight idle.

Ref. 7.8

4. When unfeathering a propeller in flight:

(a)   the rpm lever is set to cruise rpm.

(b)   the rpm lever is set to minimum position.

(c)   the rpm lever is set to maximum position.

(d)   the rpm lever is set to flight idle position.

Ref. 7.8

5. When unfeathering a propeller in flight:

(a)   select constant speed range prior to selecting unfeather.

(b)   select constant speed range as soon as the engine has fired.

(c)   select constant speed range when the engine has warmed up.

(d)   select constant speed range after selecting unfeather.

Ref. 7.8

8

Electrically-Operated Variable Pitch Propellers

8.1 Introduction

In some cases, variable pitch propellers are operated electrically instead of hydraulically, a reversible electric motor being bevel geared to the root ends of the blades. Such propellers are otherwise similar to the hydraulically-operated types.

8.2 Description

Normally the electric motor is situated in the front of the hub and is fitted with a 'no voltage' brake, spring loaded to hold the motor armature from turning except when current is applied.

A reduction gear of very high ratio is interposed between the motor and the blade root ends. It is of the epicyclic type and drives a large bevel gear at the rear end.

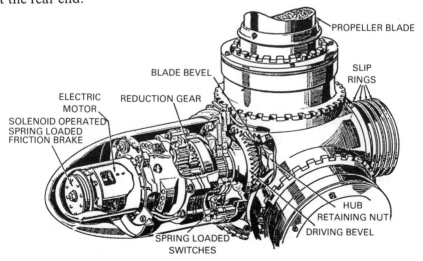

Figure 8–1 Electrically-operated propeller.

355

Figure 8-1 shows an example of an electrically operated variable pitch propeller hub.

The electric current is picked up by four brushes and slip rings at the rear of the hub; the four slip rings are respectively the 'feathering', 'common return', 'fine pitch' and 'coarse pitch' connections.

At the forward ends of the internal connections between slip rings and motor are spring loaded switches which are cut out by cams on the driving wheel, thus acting as pitch range stops. There is also a mechanical fine pitch stop fitted in the reduction gear housing.

8.3 Operation

Electric propellers are usually controlled by an electric governor unit which operates in a similar manner to that used on hydraulically-operated propellers. Instead of the oil pressure passing to the propeller it passes to one side or other of a servo piston, the movement of which causes current to flow one way or the other to the motor, thereby altering the pitch as required. The variation of pitch is an automatic function when in normal flight in the same way as with the hydraulically-operated types discussed in previous chapters. However, with an electrically-operated propeller often a hand-operated control is fitted for emergency use.

8.4 Emergency Hand Operation

A master switch in the cockpit controls all the propeller electric circuits; a three-way switch is used for hand control and an example of its positions and effects are as follows:
(a) Knob to bottom left – blades move to coarser pitch, rpm decreases.
(b) Knob to bottom right – blades go to finer pitch, rpm increases.
(c) Knob upwards – blade pitch automatically controlled by the governor.

In the neutral position the propeller is locked in the pitch it happens to be in. By using (a) or (b) it is possible to select any pitch desired, and lock the propeller in that pitch by returning the knob to neutral or the central position. For feathering purposes a separate switch is fitted.

8.5 Electric Governor Unit

The unit uses flyweights, mounted in a cup, to operate a piston valve in a similar way to a normal constant speed unit. There is also a small pressure booster pump and a pressure relief valve. The controlled oil from the piston valve operates a servo piston which is loaded to the downward position by a spring and engine oil pressure. The servo piston rod carries the positive electrical contact. A cam, driven from the oil pump idler gear, operates a spring loaded rod which carries the fine and coarse pitch contacts. These contacts are arranged above and below the positive contact and are usually referred to as the jogging contacts.

8.6   Operation

When the engine is on speed the controlled oil pressure will hold the servo piston at roughly the centre of its travel, and the jogging contacts will not quite touch the positive contact on either side.

If the engine is overspeeding more high pressure oil will be allowed past the piston valve and the servo piston will rise against its spring. This will cause the positive contacts to touch the coarse pitch contact of the jogging contacts once per revolution of the cam, so coarsening the pitch of the propeller progressively until the engine is again on speed.

Figure 8-2 shows an example electric governor unit.

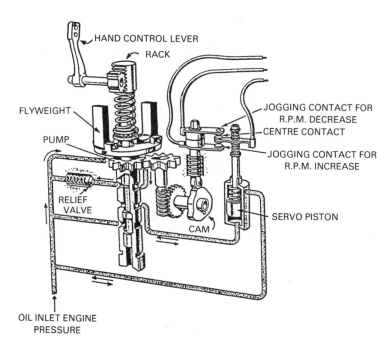

Figure 8-2 Electric propeller governor unit.

If the engine revolutions are too low, the piston valve will cut off the high pressure oil and subject both sides of the servo piston to engine oil pressure. The spring will now force the servo piston to fall. This will now

357

cause the positive contact to touch the fine pitch contact of the jogging contacts once per revolution of the cam until the engine is again on speed.

Note the term 'on speed' in propeller terms means the propeller is rotating at the selected rpm and therefore the engine is rotating at the selected rpm.

Section 8 Test Yourself

1. An electrically-operated variable pitch propeller is operated by:

   (a)   an electrically-operated hydraulic pump.

   (b)   an electric motor connected to each blade to change pitch.

   (c)   a single electric motor to collectively change the pitch.

   (d)   an electrically-signalled hydraulic pitch change mechanism.

Ref. 8.1

2. The selected pitch of an electrically-operated propeller is held in its selected pitch by:

   (a)   the pitch change stops.

   (b)   a hydraulic brake.

   (c)   a spring loaded no voltage brake.

   (d)   a mechanical geometric lock.

Ref. 8.2

3. In the event the electric governor unit fails:

   (a)   the propeller will be fixed in the last selected pitch.

   (b)   the pitch change may be operated by a manually operated emergency pitch change master switch.

   (c)   the propeller will automatically go to fully coarse pitch.

   (d)   the propeller will go to flight fine pitch.

Ref. 8.4

4. The servo piston is:

   (a)   hydraulically actuated.

   (b)   electrically actuated.

   (c)   mechanically actuated.

   (d)   actuated by centrifugal force.

Ref. 8.3

5. The no voltage brake:

   (a)   applies a disc brake to the pitch change mechanism.

   (b)   applies a mechanical lock to the blade change mechanism.

   (c)   is a centrifugal lock.

   (d)   holds the armature of the motor.

Ref. 8.2

9

Turbopropellers

9.1 Introduction

A turbopropeller is a propeller which is driven by a gas turbine engine and
although the basic propeller theory is the same as for piston engine-driven
propellers, there are a number of differences in how constant speed and
control are achieved.

9.2 Basic Construction and Operation

Normally the power control lever is connected to both the fuel control
unit and the propeller control unit (PCU) in a turbopropeller
installation.

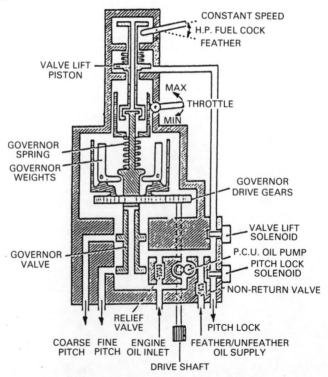

Figure 9–1 Propeller control unit.

Essentially, the pitch change control mechanism is similar to that of the double-acting type propeller mechanism in that the constant speed operation is controlled by governor weights opposing the control spring force to raise or lower the governor valve, and to supply oil to the appropriate side of the pitch change piston whenever engine speed varies from the speed selected.

Figure 9-1 illustrates the propeller control unit.

In the on speed condition, centrifugal force on the flyweights balances the force of the control spring, and the governor valve traps oil in both sides of the piston in the pitch change cylinder.

In the underspeed condition, control spring force is greater than the centrifugal force on the flyweights, and the governor valve is lowered, supplying oil to the rear of the pitch change cylinder and providing a drain for oil from the front of the cylinder. Blade angle decreases, and the engine speeds up until centrifugal force on the flyweights balances the force of the control spring, and the governor valve returns to the on speed condition.

In the overspeed condition, control spring force is less than the centrifugal force on the flyweights, and the governor valve is raised, directing oil to the front of the pitch change cylinder and providing a drain for oil in the rear of the cylinder. Blade angle increases, and the engine speed decreases because of the added load, until the flyweights and control spring are again in balance.

Figure 9-2 shows a double-acting pitch change mechanism.

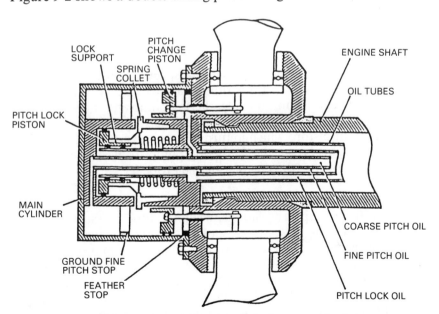

Figure 9-2 Double-acting pitch change mechanism.

9.3 Feathering

Facilities for the manual feathering of most large propellers are provided both on piston engine and turboprop installations. With some types of turboprop engine installation, however, the drag from a windmilling propeller in fine pitch could be dangerous, in particular with twin-engined aircraft, and to avoid such dangers automatic feathering is also provided.

(a) **Manual Feathering**

Manual feathering of a piston engine propeller is normally carried out by movement of the rpm control lever to the feather position, and operation of the feathering pump. These actions raise the governor valve, and supply oil under pressure to the appropriate side of pitch change piston. On a turboprop installation, manual feathering is carried out by an interconnection between the propeller control unit and the high pressure fuel cock. When the fuel cock is moved to the feather position, linkage to the propeller control unit lifts the governor valve independently of the governor control, and oil is directed to the front of the pitch change piston to turn the blades to fully coarse. Since the oil pump in the propeller control unit is driven by the engine, oil supply pressure may be insufficient to feather the propeller completely, and operation of the electric-driven pump is required to boost the pressure.

(b) **Automatic Feathering**

Automatic feathering is initiated by a torque switch which becomes operational whenever the power levers are set above the idling range.

If engine torque falls below a specific value with the power levers set above idling range, the torque switch closes and completes a circuit to the feathering pump and the valve lift sole-noid in the propeller control unit. The solenoid directs oil to the valve lift piston, which in turn lifts the governor valve and opens the oil ports from the feathering pump to the front of the pitch change piston, thus feathering the propeller.

(c) **Unfeathering**

On turboprop installations, when the high pressure fuel cock is open and the power levers closed, the governor valve is in a suit-able position to direct oil from the feathering pump to the rear of the pitch change piston. Selection of the feathering pump switch supplies oil to the propeller control unit and then to the propeller, and activates the engine ignition system. When the propeller blades have turned from the feathered position, the airstream starts to rotate the propeller (windmill) and rotate the engine. As the engine is rotated, the oil pumps will again be driven and so the oil pressure starts to build up to complete the unfeathering operation.

(d)   Fine Pitch Stops

When starting a turboprop engine, as with a piston engine, to ease the load on the powerplant it is necessary to reduce the load on the propeller. This is best achieved by provision by the selection of a very fine pitch on the propeller blades. Whilst this is desired when engine starting, to move into such a fine pitch in flight would be very dangerous, because it could lead to engine over-speeding and excessive drag if the propeller control unit were to fail. To cater for these requirements, the pitch change mechanism for most propellers is provided with two fine pitch stops. The flight fine pitch stop is withdrawn for engine starting and ground operations. The flight fine pitch stop takes the form of a spring collet, the prongs of which are designed to spring inwards. When the collet is operating as a stop, the pitch lock piston is held in the forward position by a spring, forcing the spring collet open, and preventing the pitch change piston from moving forward farther than the flight fine pitch position. When ground fine pitch is required, a solenoid in the propeller control unit is energised and oil pressure is ducted through a third oil line to the front of the pitch lock piston; as the piston moves rearward, support for the collet is withdrawn and the prongs spring inward, allowing the pitch change piston to move fully forward to the ground fine pitch position.

9.4   Reverse Pitch

Reverse pitch is normally used during the landing run to create additional braking force. This is achieved by turning the blades of the propeller from the constant speed range, through ground fine pitch into reverse pitch.

To achieve reverse pitch, the propeller mechanism includes a removable ground fine pitch stop which enables the propeller to fine off to a negative pitch when certain actions have been taken and certain conditions fulfilled.

Various safeguards are incorporated to prevent selection of reverse pitch during flight. The means of achieving negative pitch vary considerably. However, a typical example of a hydraulically-operated propeller is as follows:

(a)   Electrical control is exercised by throttle mounted switches, weight contact switches that are mounted on the undercarriage, and a master switch or lever to arm the circuit. With the throttle levers closed beyond normal idling to a datum position (that is, reverse selected) and the weight of the aircraft on its wheels, electrical power is supplied to a pitch stop withdrawal solenoid, and oil pressure is directed to withdraw the fine pitch stop and move the pitch change piston forward to the reverse stop, where it is held by hydraulic pressure. Operation of the reverse lever also changes the sense of operation of the throttle levers, which are pulled further back to increase power in reverse pitch.

(b)   Indication of stop withdrawal, and movement of the blades to negative pitch, is provided by hub mounted switches which illuminate appropriate warning lights in the cockpit.

(c)   Re-selection of positive blade angle is achieved by moving the throttle into the normal idling range, and by moving the master lever out of the reverse position. Oil is ducted to the front of the pitch change piston, and the blades move to a positive angle; the stop returns to normal operation once the blades have moved past the ground fine pitch angle.

9.5   Beta Control

On some turboprops, a form of control, known as 'Beta', or blade angle control, is used for ground operations, and may be applied equally to single acting or double acting propellers. With this system, the throttles, usually termed the power levers, operate in a gated quadrant. During flight these levers cannot be closed below the flight idle gate, and the constant speed unit operates normally to maintain the pre-selected propeller speed. In the ground idling and reverse range, the power levers control propeller pitch to vary power at both positive and negative blade angles, at constant propeller speed, and the governor mechanism is overridden. An overspeed sensor and a mechanical pitch stop prevent operation in the ground (fine pitch) range during flight. In the Beta range, the pitch stop is withdrawn, and movement of a power lever rotates a setting cam in the associated constant speed unit, which raises or lowers the governor valve according to whether a coarser or finer pitch is required. A mechanical feed-back mechanism, operated by linkage from the propeller blades, resets the governor valve via a follow-up cam, and pitch change ceases when the angle selected through the power lever is achieved.

Section 9 Test Yourself

1. On turboprop pitch change mechanisms, the increased oil pressure required to feather the propeller is normally provided by:

(a) an engine-driven booster pump.

(b) an electrically-driven booster pump.

(c) an accumulator.

(d) the second stage of the normal oil pump.

Ref. 9.3

2. Automatic feathering of a turboprop is normally available:

(a) throughout the full pitch range.

(b) throughout the full 'Beta' range.

(c) below flight idle only.

(d) above the idling range.

Ref. 9.3

3. Automatic feathering of a turboprop is initiated by:

(a) push button control.

(b) the 'Beta' controller.

(c) the torque switches.

(d) the CSU

Ref. 9.3

4. When unfeathering a turboprop:

(a) the power lever should be in the cruise position.

(b) the power lever should be in the flight idle position.

(c) the rpm lever should be in the closed position.

(d) the power lever should be in the closed position.

Ref. 9.3

5. On a turboprop engine:

(a) the propeller is feathered by spring pressure.

(b) the propeller is feathered by counterbalance weights.

(c) the manual feathering is carried out by an interconnection between the PCU and the HP cock.

(d) the manual feathering is completed by manual force.

Ref. 9.3

10

Propeller Inspection and Limitations

10.1 Introduction

Whilst it is the engineer's responsibility to maintain and repair the propellers of an aircraft, any damage that may occur to the propeller assembly in normal operational use will first be observed by the pilot. In such circumstances the aircraft may be away from base and the pilot needs to know if the propeller is safe for flight or what limitations may be applied as a result of such damage.

10.2 Limitations of Damage to Blades

The propeller blades are the most likely part of a propeller assembly to sustain damage during ground operations, such as taxying or ground running, and in flight by being struck by foreign objects such as birds, etc.

The following are some of the more common faults that are found on propeller blades:

(a)   **Tracking**

While no visible sign of damage to a propeller blade may be observed, if it has been struck by a foreign object the blade may be bent slightly out of true. This will normally be indicated by vibration from the propeller assembly. In such cases the tracking check of the propeller will show if the blades are out of true.

The track of the blades is the path followed by the blades when the propeller is turned with the aircraft stationary. It is important that each blade shall follow exactly the same track within narrow limits. Correct track may be checked by fixing a pointer just clear of any one blade tip, measuring from this blade, and then turning the propeller until the next blade tip occupies the same position; the measurement should be the same.

Some larger propellers are fitted with a strobe system and tracking should be carried out in accordance with the aircraft manuals.

(b)   **Hub Retaining Nut**

Should the propeller hub retaining nut be disturbed in any way the pilot must note that when it is replaced the correct tightening procedure is used. The correct procedure will be given in the aircraft manuals and different types will vary in the correct procedure. Some details to note:

(i)   The propeller retaining nut should not be tightened if the main propeller shaft is warm. Normally after operational use the propeller shaft will become warm and this heat must be allowed to dissipate before the nut is tightened or a tightness check carried out.

(ii)   Propeller retaining nuts are normally torque loaded and the degree of loading is very important and must be carried out strictly in accordance with the aircraft manual.

(c)   **Blade Damage Limitations**

The propeller blades should be inspected for damage in the form of abrasions, cuts, nicks, and/or corrosion. Minor erosion or dents may usually be left until the propeller is removed for overhaul. However, cuts or gouges which may lead to cracks, known as stress raisers, should be brought to the notice of the engineer, who will then blend out such damage and repaint the damaged area. This type of damage is usually on the blade leading edge.

Limitations regarding the area and extent of acceptable damage are laid down by the propeller manufacturer and must be strictly adhered to.

Blades that are bent, twisted outside the normal blade twist profile, are cracked, or have severe surface damage must be considered unserviceable.

(d)   **Oil Leaks**

All connections and joints must be examined for any sign of leaks. Leakage of oil is not acceptable.

(d)   **Vibration**

After the engine has been started and warmed up to normal operating temperature the engine and propeller assemblies should be checked for any sign of excessive vibration. Vibration in a propeller assembly is a clear indication of damage or unserviceability.

Section 10 Test Yourself

1. The track of the propeller blades is the:

(a) path followed by the blades when the aircraft is in flight.

(b) path followed by the blades when the engine is at reference revolutions.

(c) path followed by the blades when the aircraft is stationary and the propeller turned by hand.

(d) path followed by the blades when the aircraft is on the ground and the engine at idle rpm.

Ref. 10.2

2. Tracking checks are carried out by measuring relative points at the:

(a) roots of the blades.

(b) tips of the blades.

(c) span of each blade.

(d) hub of each blade.

Ref. 10.2

3. Dents to the leading edge of a propeller blade:

(a) are not acceptable.

(b) are usually acceptable until the next propeller overhaul.

(c) may be ignored.

(d) may be repaired immediately by painting over them.

Ref. 10.2

4. Propeller retaining nuts:

(a) must only be hand tightened to allow for expansion.

(b) must be tightened when the shaft is heated.

(c) must not be tightened when the shaft is warm.

(d) must be tightened before each flight.

Ref. 10.2

5. Propeller assemblies:

(a)   are checked for vibration before flight.

(b)   must be continually monitored for vibration in flight.

(c)   must be continually monitored for vibration when in operation.

(d)   are checked for vibration before and after flight.

Ref. 10.2

11

Propeller De-icing

11.1   Introduction

Ice in the atmosphere is caused by coldness acting on moisture in the air. Icing consists of crystals, their size and density being dependent on the temperature and the type of water from which they form. Ice formation on propellers can be classified under three main headings: Glaze Ice, Rime Ice and Hoar Frost.

11.2   Glaze Ice

Ice forms when the aircraft propeller encounters large water drops, in cloud or in rain, and both the air and the propeller are below freezing point. The liquid flows over the propeller blade surfaces before freezing and so the ice formed is dense, tough and adheres closely to the surface of the blade material. Glaze ice is the most severe and dangerous form of ice formation.

11.3   Rime Ice

The type of ice formation is a light, porous, opaque, rough deposit and results from small water drops freezing as individual particles with little or no spreading, when the air and propeller are below freezing point.

11.4   Hoar Frost

This type of ice is formed in clear air when water vapour is converted directly into ice and builds up a white feathery semi-crystalline coating, when the propeller is below freezing point.

11.5   Effects of Ice

Ice formation on propellers is a danger to propeller performance and safety, in that:
(a)   Changes of blade section resulting in reduced thrust.
(b)   Roughening of the blade surfaces resulting in increased drag.
(c)   Weight of the ice will increase loading and upset stability.

(d)   Ice formation may upset pitch change movement of the propeller blades.

(e)   Ice formation on propellers may cause vibration, loss of efficiency, and if dislodged can cause severe damage or be ingested by the engine.

11.6   De-icing System Types

There are two basic types of de-icing system used on propellers. They are fluid systems and electrical systems.

11.7   Fluid De-icing

The system provides a film of de-icing fluid to the propeller blade surface during flight, which mixes with the water, or moisture, on the propeller blades, reducing the freezing point of the mixture. Where ice has already formed on the blades, the fluid penetrates under the ice, which is then loosened, and the ice there upon thrown off by centrifugal force.

Ice tends to form more readily at the root end of the propeller blades and it is at this point that the de-icing fluid is fed on to the blades surfaces by what are termed 'Slinger Rings'. The slinger rings are fed with de-icing fluid from a reservoir tank and on leaving the tank passes through a filter and is then delivered under pressure to the slinger rings, mounted in the hub of the propeller. The de-icing fluid is pumped to the slinger rings by an electrically-driven pump. The pump is controlled from the cockpit by a three-position switch to select any of the three modes: 'Automatic', 'Manual' or 'Emergency'.

(a)   **Manual Selection**
        Low flow rate pump runs intermittently at a ratio of one period 'ON' to four 'OFF'.

(b)   **Automatic**
        Flow as manual selection but operation is controlled by ice detectors.

(c)   **Emergency**
        This switch is gated to prevent inadvertent operation. High flow rate with pump running continuously to combat severe icing conditions.

        Two indicator lights are normally provided: a green light to indicate the pump is running and a red light to indicate emergency is selected.

11.8 Overshoes

At the root end of the propeller blades on some aircraft types, and particularly those fitted to larger types of aircraft, are devices known as overshoes. The overshoe is bonded to the leading edge of the blade and extends for about twenty-five per cent of the blade length towards the tip. Its purpose is to provide a guide to produce an even spread of de-icing fluid across the propeller blade.

11.9 Electrical De-icing

The principle of electrical de-icing is to provide effective de-icing by heat. The heat is generated within elements constructed from resistance wire to form a mat type structure which is in turn bonded to the leading edge of the propeller. The heater element is supplied with ac or dc electrical power, depending on type. Most modern systems utilize single phase ac electricity. On many modern turboprop aircraft, the propeller de-icing system is integrated with the powerplant de-icing system.

The power required for the heating elements is conveyed via cables, slip rings, and by brushes contained within a brush block housing. The slip rings are mounted at the rear of the propeller hub, or on a starter ring gear, and the brush housing on the engine front case. In some systems, however, the method of mounting may be the reverse way round. The cables are of sufficient length and are so positioned as to allow for movement of the blades through their complete pitch range.

11.10 Heating Control

Efficient operation of these types of electrical de-icing requires a relatively high consumption of electrical power. This is, however, modulated by employing a cyclic de-icing technique whereby a short unheated period allows a thin film of ice to build up on the leading edges of the propeller blades. Before this film of ice builds up sufficiently to interfere appreciably with the aerodynamic characteristics of the blades, the cyclic control applies heating power. The ice already deposited then acts as a thermal insulation, and as the ice in contact with the blade melts, the main ice catch is carried away under the action of centrifugal and aerodynamic forces.

12

Performance and Design

12.1 Introduction

This chapter deals with some of the variations and specialist features in propeller design and the general handling and performance of propeller driven aircraft. Each aircraft type has its own handling features and must be learned on type. The following paragraphs discuss some general aspects of the behaviour of propeller-driven aircraft.

12.2 Counter-rotating Propellers

This type of propeller is sometimes used on high powered engines to transform more efficiently the power of the engine into useful thrust; this is effected by mounting two separate propellers in tandem on two shafts, one inside the other which rotate the propellers in opposite directions, one clockwise the other anti-clockwise. The two propellers rotating in opposite directions will cancel out the torque effects and, therefore, improve some handling characteristics of the aircraft. A further improvement is obtained because the slipstream is straighter than that behind a single propeller.

Usually the front propeller contains the pitch change mechanism and alterations to the rear propeller pitch are transmitted by a translation unit. The propeller has normal constant speed operation and is handled in a similar manner to single propellers.

Note: The term Counter-rotating Propellers is normally used when each propeller shaft is driven by a separate engine. This term may also be used to describe the rotational action on a twin engined aircraft where the engines are mounted one in each wing, one with a left-handed propeller the other with a right-handed propeller. Such aircraft are said to have handed propellers.

12.3 Contra-rotating Propellers

At first sight the contra-rotating propeller appears to be the same as a counter-rotating propeller. However, the accepted definition of the contra-rotating propeller is the mounting of two propellers in tandem, driven by a single engine and caused to rotate in opposite directions by a gearbox mounted at the front of the engine. It has similar advantages to the counter-rotating arrangement. With this type, however, it is not possible to feather just one element of a twin propeller.

12.4 Braking Propellers

Some propellers, in addition to their constant speed variable pitch capabilities, have reversible pitch. The propeller pitch can be reversed quickly through zero pitch so enabling the propeller to exert a reverse thrust, or braking force. These propellers are used to produce reverse thrust immediately after touch-down as an aid to reducing the length of the landing run and to assist in manoeuvring during taxying.

Full throttle, in most cases, can be applied when the angle of the blade is in reverse pitch, allowing maximum power to be available for braking purposes. The constant speed unit is inoperative when reverse pitch is engaged and rpm will therefore be controlled by throttle movement.

12.5 Handling

(a) Failure of the Constant Speed Unit.

If the CSU fails in flight, the pitch may lock at the setting which was being maintained at the time of the failure. If failure occurs during a climb, the rpm at the time of the failure may be high for continuous flight. The rpm should be kept as low as possible by restricting the throttle openings and by flying at a suitably reduced airspeed.

(b) Failure of CSU in Level Flight

If failure occurs in level flight in the cruise, the rpm will normally be low and the propeller pitch at a fairly coarse setting. These conditions will be suitable for level flight. However, any manoeuvre requiring high power should be avoided.

(c) Probable Cause of CSU Failure

Dirt or grit in the oil is the most likely cause of CSU failure. Whilst every effort is taken to avoid contamination of the oil, particles worn from the components in the system will cause possible problems and failure of CSU operation. When a problem is indicated, the first action that should be taken is to exercise the CSU in an attempt to dislodge any foreign matter by allowing the oil to circulate through the CSU. The oil will be caused to flow by operating the rpm indicator. Complete failure may be caused through loss of oil pressure due to a fractured pipeline or leaking seal. This could eventually lead to a complete loss of engine oil and so, under such circumstances, the propeller should if possible be feathered immediately.

(d) Flying at Low Temperatures

Under cold weather conditions, the oil in the CSU may congeal and make CSU operation very sluggish. In such circumstances the RPM lever should be operated from time to time to circulate the oil in the CSU and maintain a free flow.

(e) Electric Propellers

Electric propellers are equipped with an alternative manual control. In the event of a CSU failure, pitch change can still be maintained through manual selection.

(f) Overspeeding

Overspeeding is often caused by a complete loss of oil pressure, or possibly the failure of the CSU. In either situation, the following actions should be taken immediately to prevent serious damage to the engine:
(i)   Reduce the airspeed.
(ii) Close the throttle.
(iii) If the propeller cannot be returned to constant speed conditions, attempt to feather.

If the propeller will not feather and the aircraft will not maintain height due to the high drag caused by the propeller, the throttle may be opened slightly, with caution, in an attempt to obtain a small amount of power and so reduce the drag. Rpm must not exceed normal take-off maximum.

12.6   Failure to Feather

If the propeller fails to feather when selected (using the correct procedure) with electric and certain hydraulic types an alternative method may be used. Normally this will cause the propeller to feather, but at a greatly reduced rate:

(a) Electric Variable Pitch Propeller

The switch should be held to the 'decrease' rpm position until the propeller stops.

(b) Hydraulically-Operated Variable Pitch Propellers

On types which the rpm control lever has a feathering gate, the lever should be moved back through the gate.

It should be noted that the drag on a windmilling propeller in fine pitch is much greater than the drag on a feathered propeller. Flight with asymmetric power will be adversely affected and critical speeds will be higher.

12.7 Turboprop Engine Handling

The following is related to the effects on the propeller and not specifically to the gas turbine element of the powerplant.

(a) Take-off

When the aircraft is correctly aligned on the runway, the brakes should be applied and the rpm increased to the recommended value for the particular aircraft type. When any increase or decrease of rpm is required, throttle lever movement should be made as smoothly and as slowly as possible. On releasing brakes for take-off, smoothly increase the power. If careful operation of the throttle or power lever is not exercised, overspeeding of the propeller can occur. The maximum torque may be reduced as altitude or air temperature increases.

(b) Flight

In normal flight conditions the throttle should not be closed below the flight idle position except in a re-light situation. When the engine is operating within the constant speed range, all movements of the throttle between the flight idle gate and the take-off gate should be made smoothly. There is a possibility of a flame-out if the throttle is closed too quickly. The rpm should not be allowed to fall below the constant speed range. If, however, this does happen, the propeller fines off until it reaches the flight fine pitch stops. If this occurs, the stops should be disengaged otherwise the propeller will behave as a fixed pitch propeller, that is to say, any further reduction in power will result in a reduction in rpm and any rapid opening of the throttle may stall the engine. Normal rpm can be maintained by observing the indicated airspeed and power combinations for the particular aircraft. When it is not practical to meet these conditions, the flight fine pitch stops should be withdrawn manually or by lowering the undercarriage.

(c) Engine Failure

When a piston engine fails in flight, or on the ground when taxying, taking-off or landing, the CSU moves the propeller pitch to fully fine, usually an angle of about 25 degrees, in an attempt to maintain the set rpm, after which the propeller windmills until it is feathered.

With turboprop engines, however, an engine failure would result in the propeller pitch reducing to a much smaller or finer angle, sometimes as low as 12 to 8 degrees, a suitable angle for engine starting. The much smaller pitch angle causes the blades to present the maximum frontal area to the airflow, resulting in very high drag and a steep gliding angle. The airflow over the tailplane, fin and rudder will be disrupted to such an extent that rudder and elevator control will be seriously impaired. The propeller is said to be 'Discing' when this occurs. To prevent this undesirable situation developing, a Reverse Torque Switch is fitted to many aircraft which, when activated by an overspeeding propeller, ie torque conditions are reversed, the switch overrides the CSU and causes the feathering motor to feather the propeller. Sometimes a momentary period of reverse torque may be encountered, which may occur when throttling back too quickly, which will be indicated by the flashing of the reverse torque warning light. However, when pitch adjusts itself after a matter of seconds the feathering action is halted and the propeller reverts to normal operation.

Note: On turboprop powered aircraft it is usual for the flight fine pitch stops to be withdrawn automatically when the undercarriage is selected down, to enable the pitch to operate below flight fine for taxying and engine starting purposes.

(d) **Approach and Landing**
Turboprop engines, in comparison with turbojet engines, have poor response to inputs when on approach. As a result, early corrective action must be taken when undershooting. When an increase of power is selected, for example, there is no immediate impression of an increase of power from the engine, and so reference should be made to the torque meter to gauge the engine response. The throttle should never be closed behind the flight idle gate until the aircraft has touched down on the runway. After touchdown, deceleration is very poor if the throttle is left at the flight idle position or gate. This is primarily due to the high residual thrust that will still be produced. Throttles should be moved to the ground idle position on touchdown. Rapid closing of the throttle to the ground idle position should be avoided as this will cause a rapid fining off of the propeller with a sudden large increase of drag. Whilst this will produce rapid deceleration in the initial stages of the landing run, the discing effect of the very fine pitch is to blank the rudder and elevator, greatly reducing their effectiveness. As a result, any drift or yaw at this stage will be accentuated and any swing which may develop will require very careful and early use of the brakes. The throttle should therefore be closed smoothly, thereby avoiding such situations. The use of power

to check swings is not particularly effective due to the poor response of the turboprop.

(e) Stopping Turboprop Engines
The engine should be run down at the specified rpm to ensure even cooling and the throttle closed to the ground idle position. The engine is stopped by closing the HP fuel cock fully. Some engines require the start pitch button to be pressed to speed up the feathering of the propeller to slow it down more quickly and, where fitted, the propeller brake applied. Most turboprops are feathered when parked and a brake is also provided to prevent the propeller windmilling.

12.8 Turboprop Synchronizing of Propellers

The primary purpose of synchronizing propellers, both in flight and where possible on the ground, is to reduce noise levels. Synchronizing ensures that the propeller speeds, on multi-engined aircraft, are all the same. The synchronizing system compares electrical signals from engine mounted generators. One engine is designated as the master engine and any out of balance signals from the other engines are automatically corrected by electrically trimming the engine speed until all signals are in phase.

12.9 Turboprop Synchrophasing of Propellers

The synchrophasing system also assists in reducing noise levels and in principle ensures that any given propeller blade of a propeller is in the same relative position as the corresponding blade of the propeller on the master engine. This is achieved automatically by very fine trimming of the engine speeds as a result of signals transmitted from the engine's synchrophasing generators.

12.10 Propeller Slipstream Effect

In the same way as the aircraft's wing and tailplane provide their lift by deflecting the air downwards, the propeller through a similar action produces thrust by forcing air backwards. The result of this action is a stream of air which flows over the fuselage, wings or mainplanes, tailplane and fin; this stream of air is called the slipstream. The slipstream generally maintains a flow of air behind the propeller approximately equal to the diameter of the propeller, and with the exception of an area a short distance behind the propeller itself, where the diameter of the slipstream contracts slightly, the same diameter is maintained for some considerable distance, usually well in excess of the length of the aircraft. (Figure 12-1.)

Figure 12–1 Propeller slipstream.

The slipstream velocity is usually greater than that of the aircraft airspeed. Under some conditions the slipstream velocity may be as much as 100 per cent to 120 per cent higher at the aircraft's stalling speed. It should be noted therefore, that the slipstream flowing over various parts of the aircraft may be at twice the velocity of the airflow flowing over other parts of the aircraft effectively outside the slipstream effect.

Within the slipstream effect, the drag will be four times as great as the drag outside the slipstream. As forward speed is increased the difference is not so great, being only about fifty per cent at normal speeds, and as little as ten per cent at high speeds.

The extra velocity generated by the slipstream may be advantageous in providing more effective control for rudder and elevators, especially when the aircraft is moving at low airspeeds. This is basically the same as the wing-blowing and jet-flap principles by maintaining laminar flow over the surfaces and thereby minimizing boundary layer separation. This is normally available only with propeller-driven aircraft. As well as increasing the effective control over the rudder and elevators, the slipstream will provide increased effectiveness of flaps by blowing air over the wing and flap surfaces and therefore similarly reducing the boundary layer separation problem.

In addition to the increased velocity of the propeller slipstream, the propeller also imparts a swirl, or rotary motion to the flow of the slipstream which rotates in the same direction as the propeller. This creates a tendency for the airflow to strike one side of the keel surface and/or fin more effectively than the other, and so may have a considerable effect on the directional and lateral balance of the aircraft. (See Figure 12-2.)

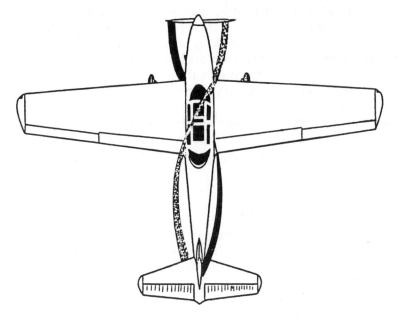

Figure 12–2 Airflow pattern due to rotational effect of the propeller.

If these effects are compensated for in normal flight, by offsetting the fin so that it does not lie directly for and aft, then the balance will be upset when the engine/propeller reduces rpm, or stops, and the slipstream ceases to exert its influences.

It is virtually impossible to remove all such disadvantageous problems from an aircraft and so a design compromise is settled upon, which generally satisfies most conditions.

12.11   Gyroscopic Effect

In addition to that discussed in previous chapters the gyroscopic effect is dealt with here as an operational, or performance problem. The modern propeller assembly constitutes a considerable rotating mass which causes a gyroscopic effect. Whilst every effort is made to reduce the weight of the propeller assembly some degree of gyroscopic effect cannot be avoided. A rotating body tends to resist any change in its plane of rotation, and if such a change does take place there is a superimposed tendency for the plane of rotation to change also in a direction at right angles to that in which it is forced. This can be illustrated with a wheel mounted on a shaft. If the wheel is rapidly rotated and is held by the horizontal shaft and the holder attempts to keep the shaft horizontal while he turns, the shaft will either tilt upwards or downwards, depending on whether the holder turns with the direction of rotation of the wheel, or in the opposite direction. An aircraft will behave in much the same way in that, if the aircraft has a right-handed propeller, that is a propeller which rotates clockwise when viewed from the cockpit, the nose will tend to drop, or if the aircraft is equipped with a left-handed propeller the tail will drop, ie the nose will tend to pitch up.

This tendency is normally only appreciable in exceptional cases: eg on aircraft fitted with very large propellers or on some very old aircraft designs which used rotary engines where the rotating mass is much greater.

12.12   Swing on Take-off

Many aircraft designs have a tendency to swing to one side on take-off, ie a yawing action to port or starboard. There are many possible reasons for this tendency, some of the basic principles of which have been discussed earlier.

There are a number of possibilities that should be examined. First, the main probable cause is the propeller, in that the torque reaction of the propeller on a right-handed type will cause the reaction to be anti-clockwise, this in turn will cause the left-hand wheel to be forced more firmly on the ground creating greater friction which in turn should cause the aircraft to yaw to port.

The second point that should be considered is the effect of the slipstream.

Assuming the same right-handed propeller (rotating clockwise as viewed from the cockpit) it will also create a clockwise rotating slipstream which will strike the fin and rudder on the left hand, or port side. This will cause the aircraft to yaw to the left as the fin and rudder will be forced to the right so causing the aircraft to move about the normal or vertical axis.

A further problem that must be considered by the pilot when handling tail wheeled aircraft is that when the tail wheel is on the ground and the propeller axis is inclined upwards with the aircraft travelling along the ground, or runway, the down-going propeller blade will strike the air at a larger angle of attack than the up-going blade, the result of which is an increase of thrust on the down-going blade and therefore in the case of a right-handed propeller again will cause the aircraft to yaw to the left, as there is more thrust produced to the right of the centre line than the left.

By fitting contra-rotating propellers virtually all the problems of asymmetrical slipstream, propeller torque, and gyroscopic action are removed. Such propeller assemblies increase cost, are heavier than normal or single propeller assemblies, and tend to be far more complex. The contra-rotating propeller delivers a straight high speed flow over the wings and tailplane providing improved control and stability.

Figure 12-3 illustrates a contra-rotating propeller assembly.

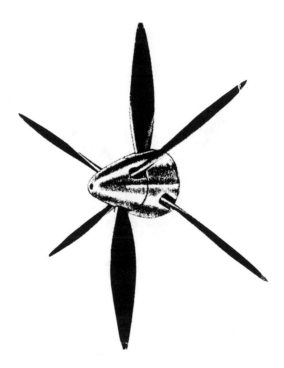

Figure 12–3 Contra-rotating propeller.

12.13 Propeller Effects on Nose Wheeled Aircraft

On aircraft equipped with a nose wheeled undercarriage there is inherent directional stability when in motion on the ground due to the fact the CG is ahead of the main wheels, unlike the tailwheel configuration which suffers from divergent tendencies.

A nose wheeled aircraft is virtually in its normal flying attitude throughout its take-off run. Asymmetric blade effect and gyroscopic effect can be almost ignored. The nosewheel configuration is however, still subject to torque reaction, slipstream effect, and cross-winds; the swing on take-off is, nevertheless, more easily controlled.

12.14   The Modern Propeller

At subsonic speeds the propeller offers greater efficiency than the turbojet engine when operating at low and medium altitudes. This efficiency can be used to produce more thrust from a given engine size, or fuel economy by using a small engine with a lower fuel consumption.

To extend the use of the turboprop engine into the higher speed and altitude ranges, that is speeds of up to Mach 0.8 and a cruise capability at 30,000 ft, requires the development of advanced propeller designs.

Figure 12–4 Modern turboprop propeller.

By applying existing high speed flight techniques to the design of the propeller blade, it is possible to delay the onset of compressibility effects at the outboard sections of the propeller blades, ie to delay the Critical Mach Number (M_{crit}). Such techniques involve the use of reduced blade thickness, using improved aerofoil sections and propeller blade tip sweep. Figure 12-4 shows an example of such a modern propeller.

The development of the modern propeller can be attributed to two main basic requirements: the first being to produce a more economic use of the gas turbine engine, and the second to reduce the noise generated by the complete powerplant.

Economy is an essential requirement for today's civil aircraft operator and so engine manufacturers have spent large sums of money on research to achieve more economic standards. This has lead to the development of two distinct types of engine, the first being the widely used Turbo-Fan. The Turbo-Fan engine is essentially a High By-pass gas turbine producing a by-pass ratio in the order of 5:1 leading to a very high by-pass ratio of 15:1. During the 1980s it became clear that in order to reduce the fuel fills and reduce the size of the engine required for a given task a greater use of improved propellers was essential. This has led in certain areas to the use of the Prop-Fan engine, that is a later development of the Turboprop engine. At the same time increased efficiency was being obtained from Turbo-Fan development and so the High By-Pass engine was a natural progression evolved by shrouding the Front Fan, or low pressure compressor. This produced a more economic engine and one which makes far less noise due to reduced blade tip turbulence. A further progression is the development of the Unducted Fan which is only possible because of the great strides which have been made in propeller technology. (Figure 12-5.)

Figure 12–5 Prop-fan.

12.15   Summary of Propeller Development Types

(a) Modern Prop-Fan Engine.
Engines on which this type of propeller are used are developing more than 12,000 hp and providing high thrust with low noise and increased economy. In order to provide high thrust at low velocity to minimize noise, at least eight blades are normally fitted. Sweeping of the blades delays M_{crit} and reduces the noise from the tips of the blades. The sweep also alters the phase of the noise generated by each radial section along the blade causing a certain amount of interference which results in noise reduction.

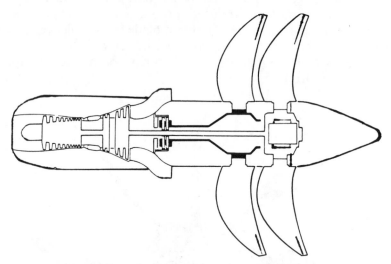

Figure 12–6 Prop-fan engine.

(b) Low and High By-Pass Engines.
The development of this engine type has taken two forms: by having the fan either at the front or at the rear. In both cases the fan element by-passes air around the engine core. For a low by-pass type, in the order of 1:1 that is equal parts of air enter the engine core and an equal amount of air by-passes the engine. The air that by-passes the engine core may be ducted the full length of the engine, or partially ducted for only part of the length of the engine. The high by-pass engine produces a by-pass ratio of 5:1, that is for every part of air entering the engine core, five parts by-pass the engine core.

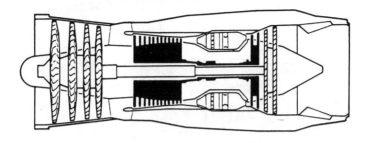

Figure 12–7 Low by-pass ducted
fan engine.

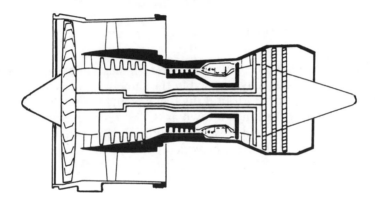

Figure 12–8 High by-pass partially ducted fan
(front fan engine)

It must be noted that the examples given are just examples; almost any combination of the arrangements of these engines can, and have been used.

(c) Very High By-Pass Engines.
The by-pass ratio of this category of engine is in the region of 15:1 (Figure 12-9).

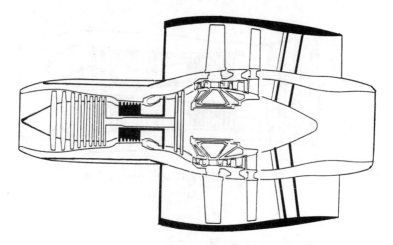

Figure 12–9 Very high by-pass engine.

As can be seen the fan element of these engines can be considered as a form of propeller and may be used in the same way as earlier propellers to provide reverse thrust for braking by reversing the pitch of the blades. This type of configuration is known as 'Cold' reverse thrust as opposed to 'Hot' reverse thrust which is provided by the hot exhaust gases of the engine. Cold reverse thrust is provided by reversing the pitch of the fan element only.

12.16 Advanced Propellers or Ultra High By-Pass

A further advance of the propeller is the total replacement of the 'Fan' concept by a propeller assembly. Unlike the turboprop design where a turbine drives a propeller via a gearbox, in this type the propeller forms an extension of the turbine assembly itself. This can be seen in Figures 12-10 and 12-11. By-pass ratios in the order of 30:1 and higher have been achieved. It is proving to be very economical and is much quieter. It may take the form of a single or contra-rotating propeller assembly.

12.17 Propeller Spinners

The performance of the propeller is not only to provide thrust to drive the aircraft in forward flight. The airflow produced by the propeller assembly must be as turbulence-free as possible, not only to ensure a smooth slip-stream but also to provide, in the case of piston-engined aircraft, a smooth flow of air to cool the engine. Similarly, in the case of the turboprop engine a smooth airflow to the engine intake is desirable to supply the compressor with air. To assist in smoothing the airflow a spinner is

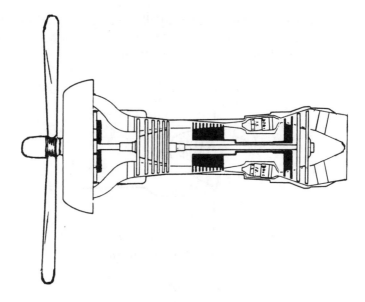

Figure 12–10 Turboprop with propeller
driven by rear turbine.

Figure 12–11 Advanced propeller concept.

normally fitted over the hub of the propeller; the spinner reduces drag and assists in directing the slipstream to the compressor, or cooling intake.
An example of a spinner is shown in Figure 12-12.

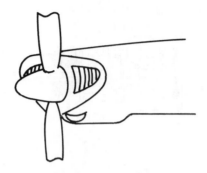

Figure 12–12 The spinner.

12.18 Propeller Contamination

It is of the utmost importance that the propeller is carefully examined before every flight. It should be checked for security of attachment, including the spinner, signs of excessive erosion, cracking, stone damage, and contamination. On some types of wooden propeller checks should also be made for any signs of delamination, to ensure the layers of wood from which the propeller is manufactured, are not separating in any way. It is also very important with this type of construction that contamination is avoided. Contamination from oil in the atmosphere may attack the adhesive material which is used to bond the layers of wood together, causing delamination. To prevent this, the propeller blades should be cleaned at regular intervals to remove any build-up of contaminants.

Note: DO NOT HANDLE PROPELLERS as they may be 'LIVE'. Before carrying out cleaning, ensure the propeller and engine ignition system are made safe.

Section 12 Test Yourself

1. When flying in low temperature conditions:

   (a) the CSU is heated to prevent congealing of the oil.

   (b) the CSU operation should be kept to a minimum.

   (c) the CSU should be exercised periodically to prevent the oil congealing.

   (d) the CSU rpm lever should be set to a higher value.

   Ref. 12.5

2. Overspeeding of the propeller in flight may be the result of:

   (a) excessive oil pressure in the CSU.

   (b) loss of oil pressure in the CSU.

   (c) faulty latches.

   (d) rpm lever set too high.

   Ref. 12.5

3. On turboprop aircraft it is normal for:

   (a) the flight fine pitch stops to withdraw when the undercarriage is selected down.

   (b) the flight fine pitch stops to withdraw when the weight on switches are activated.

   (c) the flight fine pitch stops to engage when the weight is on the undercarriage.

   (d) the flight fine pitch stops to be unaffected by undercarriage operation.

   Ref. 12.7

4. Operation of the reverse torque switch:

   (a) feathers the propeller.

   (b) overrides the CSU.

   (c) overrides the throttle.

   (d) unfeathers the propeller.

   Ref. 12.7

5. Synchronizing of propellers is based on:

(a)   all propellers being set at the same pitch angle.

(b)   all propellers rotating at the same speed.

(c)   all propellers developing the same thrust.

(d)   all propellers developing the same shaft horsepower.

Ref. 12.8

Final Practice Questions

Propellers

1. When unfeathering some types of turboprop, this is achieved by:

   (a) pushing the rpm lever fully forward.

   (b) pulling the rpm lever fully back.

   (c) pulling the throttle fully back.

   (d) moving the HP fuel cock to the feather position.

   Ref. 9.3

2. When unfeathering a turboprop:

   (a) the power levers are closed.

   (b) the rpm levers are closed.

   (c) the HP fuel cock is closed.

   (d) the throttle must be set to cruise.

   Ref. 9.3

3. Automatic feathering of a turboprop is initiated by:

   (a) a torque switch.

   (b) the power levers being set at idling rpm.

   (c) the centrifugal clutch.

   (d) the manual feathering override switch.

   Ref. 9.3

4. When a turboprop moves into negative pitch:

   (a) hub mounted switches operate warning lights in the cockpit.

   (b) the blade thrust face is facing forward.

   (c) the stops will engage.

   (d) the blade pressure face will face aft.

   Ref. 9.3

5. Beta control:

(a) will automatically feather the blades in flight, when selected.

(b) will operate on the ground only by manual selection.

(c) will operate only below flight idle.

(d) can be operated under any conditions of flight.

Ref. 9.3

6. When a piston-engined VP propeller is to be feathered:

(a) the ignition of the engine should be switched off first.

(b) the throttle of the engine should be fully closed first.

(c) the feathering switch should be first operated.

(d) the fuel supply should be turned off first.

Ref. 7.5

7. The geometric pitch of a propeller in flight is:

(a) equal to the blade angle plus slip.

(b) greater than the slip plus effective pitch.

(c) greater than effective pitch.

(d) less than effective pitch.

Ref. 1.3

8. In flight, the propeller total reaction is:

(a) aft of the pitch change axis.

(b) acts through the pitch change axis.

(c) acts through the blade CG.

(d) forward of the pitch change axis.

Ref. 1.4

9. A left-handed propeller will:

(a) rotate clockwise when viewed from the cockpit.

(b) rotate clockwise when viewed from the front of the aircraft.

(c) rotate anti-clockwise when viewed from the front of the aircraft.

(d) be fitted to the port engine.

Ref: Para 1.7

10. The angle of advance of a propeller is:

(a) the same as the helix angle.

(b) the same as the blade angle.

(c) the angle of attack plus the helix angle.

(d) the same as the angle of attack.

Ref. 1.8

11. A propeller's ability to absorb power may be improved by:

(a) decreasing the solidity.

(b) increasing the solidity.

(c) decreasing the diameter.

(d) decreasing the blade chord.

Ref. 1.8

12. A constant speed propeller:

(a) is controlled by controlling engine rpm.

(b) maintains the engine at constant rpm.

(c) maintains constant speed by adjusting the engine CSU.

(d) maintains constant propeller thrust.

Ref. 2.4

13. Selection of a specific engine rpm, with a constant speed propeller fitted, is achieved by:

(a) the engine throttle adjustment.

(b) the engine rpm lever adjustment.

(c) the propeller rpm adjustment.

(d) the propeller thrust adjustment.

Ref. 5.1

14. Engine rpm is adjusted in flight on a piston-engined aircraft with a constant speed propeller by:

(a) adjustment of the engine throttle.

(b) adjustment of the rpm lever which adjusts the governor spring.

(c) adjustment of the rpm lever which directly adjusts blade pitch.

(d) adjustment of the throttle which adjusts the CSH spring.

Ref. 5.3

15. A double-acting propeller:

(a) utilizes oil to operate the pitch change piston in both directions.

(b) utilizes oil to operate the pitch change piston in one direction.

(c) is a propeller which has a two-position pitch variation capability.

(d) is a propeller which has an aerodynamic braking capabiltiy.

Ref. 6.1

16. Normally an electrically-operated variable pitch propeller assembly is controlled by:

(a) a hydraulically controlled mechanism.

(b) an electrically controlled mechanism.

(c) a hydro/mechanical mechanism.

(d) an electrical/mechanically operated mechanism.

Ref. 8.3

17. The governor of an electrically-operated variable pitch propeller is:

(a) similar to a normal CSU governor.

(b) purely electrically controlled.

(c) hydraulically controlled.

(d) a hydro/electrical device.

Ref. 8.5

18. On an electrically-operated variable pitch propeller, when a specific blade pitch has been reached, the blade is locked in that position by:

(a) a hydraulic brake.

(b) a mechanical friction brake.

(c) a no voltage brake.

(d) an electrically actuated piston.

Ref. 8.2

19. The tracking of a propeller is carried out:

(a) measuring the distance between each blade tip.

(b) by measuring relative points at the blade tip against a fixed point when slowly rotating the propeller.

(c) by measuring relative points at the blade root against a fixed point when slowly rotating the propeller.

(d) by measuring the span of each blade.

Ref. 10.2

20. Propeller assemblies:

(a) are checked for vibration before and after flight.

(b) most be continually monitored for vibration when in operation.

(c) must be only tightened to grip the hub, so allowing for expansion.

(d) are lifed to a certain number of calendar days.

Ref. 10.2

21. On some single-acting propellers, the blades are:

(a) assisted in moving into coarse pitch by counterweights.

(b) assisted in moving into the feathered position by counterweights.

(c) assisted in moving out of coarse pitch by counterweights.

(d) assisted in moving into fully fine pitch by counterweights.

Ref. 4.2

22. Reverse pitch:

(a) rpm is controlled by the CSU.

(b) selection should be made with the throttle closed.

(c) selection places the CSU inoperative.

(d) is achieved by the blades passing through the feathered position.

Ref. 12.4

23. In the event the propeller overspeeds, constant speed type:

(a) close the throttle.

(b) increase overspeed.

(c) select fully fine.

(d) increase engine rpm.

Ref. 12.5

24. On most large double-acting propellers, feathering is accomplished by:

(a) additional oil pressure provided by the engine-driven booster pump.

(b) additional oil pressure provided by an electrically-driven booster pump.

(c) assistance from counterweights.

(d) assistance from the feathering spring.

Ref. 6.2

25. On most double acting propellers, the feather position will not be achieved unless:

(a) high boost pressure is selected.

(b) the engine has stopped.

(c) the latches are withdrawn.

(d) the stops are withdrawn.

Ref. 6.2

26. Within the propeller slipstream, drag will be:

  (a) the same as the drag within the free stream airflow.

  (b) less than the drag in the free stream airflow.

  (c) twice the value of drag in the free stream airflow.

  (d) four times the value of drag in the free stream airflow.

Ref. 12.10

27. The slipstream of a propeller will:

  (a) rotate in the opposite direction as the propeller.

  (b) reduce the effectiveness of the flaps when they are lowered.

  (c) increase the effectiveness of the flaps when they are lowered.

  (d) create a turbulent boundary layer within the slipstream.

Ref. 12.10

28. On a single-engined aircraft, directional stability may be:

  (a) reduced due to the slipstream swirl effect.

  (b) increased by the propeller torque.

  (c) increased by the slipstream swirl effect.

  (d) reduced by the increase of engine rpm.

Ref. 12.10

29. On an aircraft fitted with a left-handed propeller and a tail undercarriage, on take-off:

  (a) the nose will not be affected in pitch.

  (b) the nose will pitch down.

  (c) the aircraft will yaw to starboard.

  (d) the nose will pitch up.

Ref. 12.11

30. A right-handed propeller rotates:

  (a) clockwise when viewed from the front.

  (b) clockwise when viewed from the rear.

  (c) anti-clockwise when viewed from the rear.

  (d) to the left when viewed from the cockpit.

Ref. 12.11

31. With a clockwise rotating propeller, as viewed from the cockpit, the slipstream will:

(a) rotate anti-clockwise when viewed from the cockpit.

(b) strike the port side of the fin causing a yaw to port.

(c) strike the right side of the fin causing a yaw to port.

(d) strike the left-hand side of the fin causing a yaw to starboard.

Ref. 12.12

32. A propeller is normally more efficient at:

(a) high speeds and high altitudes.

(b) low speeds and high altitude.

(c) low to medium sub-sonic speeds at medium altitudes.

(d) low to medium speeds at low altitudes.

Ref. 12.14

33. A low by-pass fan engine has a ratio of:

(a) 1:1.

(b) 5:1.

(c) 15:1.

(d) 30:1.

Ref. 12.15

34. A very high by-pass fan engine has a by-pass ratio of:

(a) 5:1.

(b) 15:1.

(c) 30:1.

(d) 60:1.

Ref. 12.15

35. Reverse thrust in most Ducted Fan engines is achieved by:

(a) exhaust gases aft of the turbines.

(b) cold reverse thrust from the low pressure compressor.

(c) cold reverse thrust from the high pressure compressor.

(d) hot reverse thrust from the low pressure compressor.

Ref. 12.15

36. Advanced turbopropellers achieve a by-pass ratio in the order of:

(a) 5:1.

(b) 15:1.

(c) 30:1.

(d) 60:1.

Ref. 12.16

37. The advanced propeller concept drives the propeller through:

(a) a gearbox driven from the compressor shaft.

(b) a gearbox driven from a turbine shaft.

(c) a gearbox driven from an auxiliary drive.

(d) an extension of the turbine assembly.

Ref. 12.16

38. The spinner:

(a) provides a safety lock for the propellers.

(b) minimises turbulence at the root, or hub, of the propeller.

(c) minimises turbulence at the tip of the blades.

(d) reduces the swirl effect of the propeller.

Ref. 12.17

39. A laminated wooden propeller is one which:

(a) is made from a solid section of wood.

(b) is made of layers of wood.

(c) is made of alternate layers of metal and wood.,

(d) is made from plywood layers.

Ref. 12.18

40. A laminated propeller is:

(a) bonded together with adhesive.

(b) screwed together.

(c) bolted together.

(d) made from a single section of wood.

Ref. 12.18

41. When flight practice of feathering and unfeathering propellers is carried out:

(a) the oil should be allowed to cool before unfeathering is carried out.

(b) maximum boost should be selected before unfeathering.

(c) the oil must not be allowed to cool too low before unfeathering.

(d) boost must be de-selected before unfeathering.

Ref. 7.10

42. If the propeller is feathered with the engine stopped on the ground:

(a) the propeller should be unfeathered before the engine is started.

(b) the propeller should be unfeathered manually before restarting the engine.

(c) the propeller should be left in the feathered position until the engine is started.

(d) it will have no effect on the engine start procedure.

Ref. 7.9

43. When unfeathering a propeller in flight, the throttle should be set:

(a) to max rpm.

(b) to the same rpm as the other engine.

(c) to minimum rpm.

(d) to just above minimum rpm.

Ref. 7.8

44. When unfeathering a propeller in flight, the RPM lever must be set:

(a) to max rpm.

(b) to peak rpm.

(c) just above minimum rpm.

(d) to minimum rpm.

Ref. 7.8

45. When unfeathering a propeller in flight, the propeller rpm lever should be moved into the constant speed range:

(a) before the engine is started.

(b) after the engine has started.

(c) after the engine has warmed up.

(d) before the propeller is unfeathered.

Ref. 7.8

46. When unfeathering a propeller in flight:

(a) the fuel should be switched on before unfeathering.

(b) the fuel should be switched on immediately after unfeathering.

(c) the fuel should be switched on when the engine reaches max rpm.

(d) the fuel should be switched on when peak windmilling speed is reached.

Ref. 7.8

47. When feathering an electric propeller:

(a) current should be switched off when feathered position is reached.

(b) current will automatically switch off when feathered position is reached.

(c) the propeller will feather much quicker than a hydraulic propeller.

(d) the propeller will feather at about the same speed as a hydraulic propeller.

Ref. 7.6

48. Prior to feathering most piston engine propellers:

(a) the engine must be stationary.

(b) the throttle must first be fully closed.

(c) the throttle must be set at flight idle.

(d) the throttle must be set at ground idle.

Ref. 7.5

49. When feathering a propeller because of an engine fire:

   (a) operate the fire extinguisher as soon as the fire is detected.

   (b) operate the extinguisher when the engine has been switched off.

   (c) operate the extinguisher when the propeller has stopped.

   (d) operate the extinguisher when ignition has been switched off.

Ref. 7.5

50. To unfeather a variable pitch propeller:

   (a) move the RPM lever to zero setting.

   (b) push the unfeathering button.

   (c) push the feathering button.

   (d) move the RPM lever to feather.

Ref. 7.4